PENGUIN BOOKS

1207

TAKE THESE MEN

CYRIL JOLY

D1484334

CYRIL JOLY

TAKE THESE MEN

Take these men for your example.
Like them remember that prosperity can only be for the free,
that freedom is the sure possession of those alone
who have the courage to defend it.

PERICLES

PENGUIN BOOKS

Penguin Books Ltd, Harmondsworth, Middlesex

CANADA: Penguin Books (Canada) Ltd, 178 Norseman Street,
Toronto 18, Ontario

AUSTRALIA: Penguin Books Pty Ltd, 762 Whitehorse Road,
Mitcham, Victoria

SOUTH AFRICA: Penguin Books (S.A.) Pty Ltd, Gibraltar House,
Regent Road, Sea Point, Cape Town

—

First published 1955
Published in Penguin Books 1956

TO MY WIFE

*without whose patience and encouragement the
book would never have been finished*

Made and printed in Great Britain
by The Whitefriars Press Ltd
London and Tonbridge

Contents

Acknowledgements

I should like to acknowledge the help given me by Major-General G. P. B. Roberts, C.B., D.S.O., M.C.

The Order of the Day quoted on p. 245 is taken from *Rommel* by Desmond Young. My thanks are due to the author and his publishers, Messrs Collins, for their kindness in allowing me to print it.

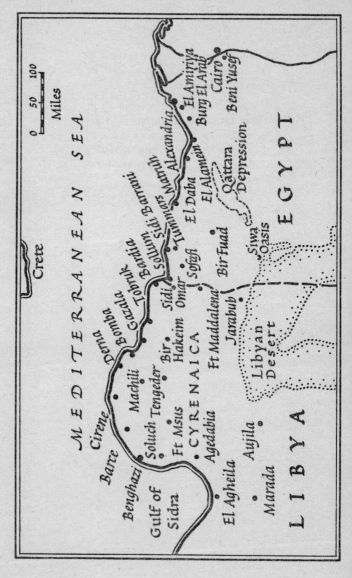

Crete

MEDITERRANEAN SEA

0 50 100
Miles

Benghazi
Barce
Cirene
Derna
Bomba
Gazala
Machili
Soluch Tengeder
Ft Msus
Gulf of Sidra
Agedabia
CYRENAICA
El Agheila
Aujila
Marada

Tobruk
Bardia
Sidi Barrani
Sollum
Sidi Omar
Bir Hakeim
Ft Maddalena
Jarabub

Tummars
Matruh
Sofafi
Bir Fuad
Libyan Desert

Alexandria
El Daba
El Alamein
Qattara Depression
Siwa Oasis

El Amiriya
Burg El Arab
Cairo
Beni Yusef

EGYPT

LIBYA

8

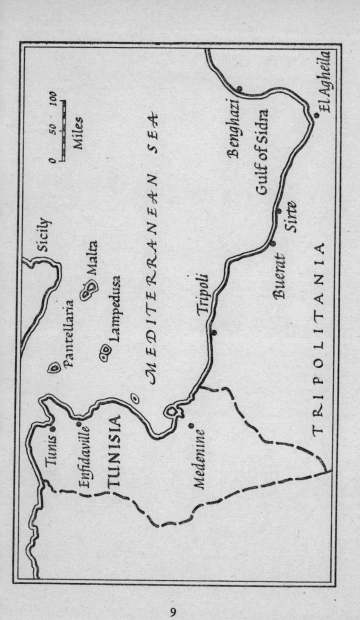

MEDITERRANEAN SEA

Sicily

Malta

Pantellaria

Lampedusa

Tunis

Enfidaville

TUNISIA

Medenine

Tripoli

Buerat

Sirte

Gulf of Sidra

Benghazi

El Agheila

TRIPOLITANIA

0   50   100

Miles

Preface

BECAUSE of the nature of the battlefield, the main actions in the Western Desert were fought by tanks. The story of the Desert Army is therefore in essentials that of its armoured formations. Of these 7th Armoured Division was the one with the longest association with the desert. Throughout the long battles they were usually in the van in victory, often the rearguard in retreat, frequently the sentinels in the months of vigilance.

All the characters depicted in this story are fictitious. If the names I have used and the characters I have drawn bear any resemblance to those of any of the men who served in Africa, it is pure chance. Where I have mentioned the senior commanders, whose names are household words, I have done so impersonally, and only to show the influence they had on those serving under them and on the events of the campaign.

The main incidents of the story are factual. The minor actions, the tank battles, the many pictures I have tried to paint of life in the desert, are based on fact, knowledge and experience. They did not all occur exactly as described nor take place exactly at the time I have put them in the story. Nevertheless I hope that some sort of picture emerges of the life we led.

There are two main reasons why I have attempted to tell this tale. First, because we have heard and read so much of Rommel and the Germans that we may perhaps forget that they originally learnt the foundations of their armoured doctrine from us and that we beat them soundly in the end.

Second, because what has been written so far has in the main dealt with the movements of armies, corps and divisions, and not with the actions and reactions of the men who fought. There were so many fine and gallant actions fought by all arms of the Desert Army that there should be some record, however inadequate, of their doings.

I have tried to show how some of these men, the men in tanks, lived and fought and in some cases died.

If I have succeeded, at least in some measure, I will have justified my claim to the right of fellowship with the gallant dead, and to the friendship of those who saw these battles to the end so that the ideals for which they fought and their friends died would be the pattern of the future.

I have not tried to glory in war and have not hidden its horror and futility. But we should say with Pericles:

The whole earth is the sepulchre of heroes, monuments may rise and tablets be set up to them in their own land, but on far-flung shores there is an abiding memorial that no pen or chisel has traced; it is graven not on stone or brass, but on the living heart of humanity. Take these men for your example. Like them remember that prosperity can only be for the free, that freedom is the sure possession of those alone who have the courage to defend it.

PART ONE

1940: EARLY SKIRMISHES

1

I Journey to the Desert

I SAT in the cramped confines of the back of an Army truck and watched the deserted streets of Cairo slip past and vanish behind me. It was early morning of a day in August 1940.

There were four of us in the truck: Alan Egerton and myself, Tony Stannard; the driver, and an officer called Templeton, who had come down from the desert to fetch his regiment's share of a batch of officers newly arrived from England. Egerton and I were the regiment's share. He and I had first met at the Royal Armoured Corps Base Depot at Abbassia. Tall and squarely built, with fair, unruly hair and irregular features, he had a friendly, reckless air that made him an easy person to like, and in the lonely strangeness of my new surroundings I had taken to him instantly. He was, I soon discovered, a reserve officer whose civilian job had been in the world of publicity, and the self-confidence and ready wit he had developed there were his chief characteristics. He was also determined to take nothing seriously, particularly nothing to do with the Army, and his irreverence on a subject which for me, since I was a Regular officer, was important and serious, had occasionally caused words between us during our brief acquaintance.

We had both been in the fighting in France, had escaped by various routes to England, had been re-kitted and sent as reinforcements to the Army of the Nile, and here we were, after less than forty-eight hours in the country, on our way up to the desert and the war with the Italians.

Neither of us had taken an immediate liking for Templeton. He was a small, dark man, with a thin, almost meagre frame and a bitter, shut-in expression. 'I'd say he's what the psychologists call maladjusted,' Egerton remarked after our first meeting with him, and we were agreed that his high opinion of himself (I told the O.C. that was the wrong thing to do, and he now agrees with me) was but a cloak to a crashing inferiority complex. But we were too new to everything to analyse our first impressions very deeply, and for the present we accepted Templeton at his own valuation.

Egerton and I had left the Royal Armoured Corps Base Depot, on the outskirts of Cairo, as the first rays of the morning sun had lit the sky. We had called for Templeton at a hotel in Cairo, where he was to spend his leave, and then we were away. Past the University and the Zoo and the close streets on the outskirts of the city and on to the Mena causeway we went. This was a route we were all to know well later on, when we were stationed, while refitting, in the camps near Cairo.

We drove along the causeway past the ornate, ugly roadside villas, past the gardens and mango groves, turned right at the end of it and drove past Mena Camp and so up the long slope leading to the open desert beyond. It was here that we got our last view of the Nile and Cairo, a view to hold in the mind's eye as a picture of the oasis of comfort and pleasure to which we could look forward to returning. On the right were the Pyramids, with Mena House Hotel nestling below them. On the left was the green streak of the rich vegetation on the banks of the Nile. Beyond this, the tall houses of Cairo stood out above the huddled hovels of the native quarters, with Saladin's Citadel high over them all, and filling the edge of the horizon the jagged outlines of the Moquattam Hills. At this time of the day the buildings and the hills behind were studded and cut with shadows and all the land was thrown into relief by the slanting rays of the low-lying sun. This was the hour when it all looked at its best and made the most vivid picture to remember.

We drove for the next six hours along the thin strip of tarmac which was the road from Cairo to Alexandria. At the end of every two hours we halted for ten minutes to stretch our legs and relieve ourselves. As the day progressed the heat grew more and more intense. In the enclosed cab and tarpaulin-covered body of the truck the temperature rose until it was almost unbearable.

Egerton and I lay in a dazed stupor, too lethargic to converse. The breeze stirred by the movement of the vehicle was no relief, as it was merely a disturbance of the oven-hot air around us. The metal-work of the truck body was toasted to a temperature which made it painful to touch. By eleven o'clock the discomfort was such that Templeton decided to halt and rest.

'We'll have a bit of a break and a siesta,' he said, when we had scrambled out of the truck. 'It's bloody hot and we're well up to schedule. Unless we're unlucky we should reach Amiriya by early afternoon. It's at Amiriya that we turn west along the coast road to Mersa Matruh.'

We drove the truck off the road on to a patch of good, hard sand at the side and made a shelter at the front with a spare tarpaulin sheet. Under this we clustered in the welcome shade away from the heat and ate our lunch.

After eating we lay or sat for a time and slept or talked intermittently. The driver slept. Egerton tried to sleep. Templeton dozed, absorbed with his own thoughts and memories. I sat and looked out on to the burning view of endless sunbaked sand and let my thoughts wander over the recent past and brood on all that lay before me.

Through my mind, as I sat under the tarpaulin, there passed in review the scenes of all that had happened to me in the last month: the brief, hectic leave at home, followed by the long, hot railway journey to Liverpool; the fuss and excitement of embarkation; the departure on a grey, misty morning from a deserted dockside; the assembly of the convoy, guarded by the lean grey shapes of the escort vessels. Then there was the slow progress westwards far into the Atlantic, later veering slowly farther and farther south and east until on a hot morning we saw the great battlements of Gibraltar to the north. Here we were joined by the ships of the redoubtable Force 'H' for our passage through the Mediterranean. Bombed and harassed though we were by Italian aircraft, we at length reached Alexandria late in the evening of a day during which the heat was a grim foretaste of what we would suffer without the fresh sea-breeze. Overnight we travelled by train to Cairo. And now here I was really on my way to the desert.

At about one o'clock we started off again, and soon reached

15

the point near Amiriya where the road forked west to the desert and east to Alexandria.

It was difficult for those of us who were new to the desert to imagine what it was going to be like. No pictures or photos showed it with any accuracy. They all tended to make the landscape look too flat and featureless. Egerton perhaps best summarized our silent thoughts when he remarked, 'It's like Salisbury Plain with the knobs off.' And that was it. The land rose and fell and undulated; there were ridges, hillocks, valleys; there were stones and rocks. But all the features directly attributable to rain were absent: there were no streams nor lakes; no hedges, trees, woods, nor crops. Nor were there, at least away from the coastal belt, any of the other signs of civilization, such as roads, railways, canals, houses, villages, towns. It was as if some great hand had wiped clean from, say, southern England, all greenery and signs of life.

Some hours later, as we drew near to Mersa Matruh, there appeared on each side of the road the first signs of the Army. Here and there were notice-boards pointing into the empty spaces of the desert saying that such and such a unit was hidden somewhere behind the ridges. At this distance behind the lines the units were mainly those essential to the lines of communications: ordnance depots and workshops; the supply columns who fetched the rations from Alexandria, and somewhere a little farther forward handed them over to those of the divisions who had come back and who would later, in their turn, go forward to hand over the supplies to the units; the main engineer stores, dumps of wire and mines and other paraphernalia of defence – all the sinews of war without which the fighting units in the front line would have been powerless.

Matruh itself, when we came to it, was in comparison almost deserted. The few troops who were there lived in the subterranean caverns and galleries hewn in the rock by the Romans.

In Matruh we turned south with the road which led to the edge of the plateau. Here the main coastal road turned west and on to Sidi Barrani. So we left the road and went on south into the desert, where the majority of 7th Armoured Division was now concentrated.

16

On the day Italy had entered the war the Armoured Car Regiment and the Support Group had moved up to the frontier areas, and the rest of the Division had followed the next day.

The Italian fort at Sidi Omar was captured before the occupants even knew they were at war. The capture of Fort Capuzzo soon followed, and from then on for the next six weeks patrol activity and forays of all kinds kept the Italians on the alert.

But although the armoured cars and tanks and the patrols of infantry completely dominated the open country by day and by night, the Italians were able gradually to reinforce their troops in the frontier areas, and by the end of July had about four divisions manning the small triangle of country between Bardia, Capuzzo and the sea.

By this time the vehicles of all kinds in the 7th Armoured Division were beginning to bear traces of the strain and hard work to which they had been subjected since their war had started. Repairs and replacements were urgently needed, and since it was clear that it was only a matter of time before the Italians eventually attacked, the bulk of the Division withdrew to refit and overhaul, to be ready to deal with the expected advance when it came. Early in August the Armoured Brigades were withdrawn and the frontier defence was left to the Support Group, made up of three infantry battalions, a regiment of guns, the armoured-car regiment and one squadron of tanks. It was to this squadron that Templeton belonged and from which he had gone for his turn of leave. It was to this squadron, too, so he told us, that we would almost certainly go to release other officers for their leave.

It was after we had left the coastal road that Templeton stopped the truck and said, 'Now, if you two are going to learn to drive in the desert, you might as well start now. You'll find it's not so easy as you may think. Stannard, you take first crack.'

He allowed each of us a turn and, being novices at what we later recognized as something of an art, our efforts were exhausting. It was not so much that we lacked practice in driving, but that with unfailing regularity each of us managed to pick just those soft patches of sand into which the truck sank axle deep each time. Then followed the business of digging out the wheels, placing the sand channels and driving forward or backward to

17

the limit of the channels, so that, repeating the process time after time until firm ground was reached again, we could drive on until we struck the next patch of soft sand. It was after yet another of these incidents that Egerton, his normal cheerfulness somewhat subdued, was heard to remark, 'If the whole — desert's like this, it's going to be a bloody long war.'

This was almost despair from Egerton, for nothing in our so far brief association had ever seemed to worry him unduly. But we were all feeling tired and irritable by now and were thankful when Templeton decided on a meal halt.

We now made our first attempt at the recognized Desert Army method of a 'brew-up' of tea. We cut in half one of the thin sheet-metal four-gallon petrol tins used at that time, punched it with holes and filled it with sand and gravel. We then poured on a generous splash of petrol and set it alight. The tea we brewed in the other half of the tin. When the water was boiling, tea, sugar, and milk were all added and the whole potion was vigorously stirred. The resulting brew was strong and sweet, like no other tea that I had tasted before.

Templeton explained, too, the simple method of navigation using a sun compass. It depended on knowing the exact sun time, from which we could determine the sun's bearing throughout the day. I found it easiest to remember that at midday, when the sun was due south, the shadow falling due north, the direction of movement at right angles to the shadow would obviously be either due east or west. From this conclusion I found I could work out the other simple problems which Templeton set us. For the rest it was a question of noting the distances travelled in any direction and carefully plotting them on to the bare spaces of the map, so that we could determine to within a few hundred yards the position, in relation to the starting point or any other, of the few definite landmarks on the route.

It was late in the evening when we reached the regiment and joined the squadron to which we had been temporarily allotted. As it was summer and the chance of rain was slight, the majority of the men slept in the open. It was the work of a few moments only to select a suitable patch not too far from the mess, to erect my camp-bed and unroll my bedroll, and then to go over to the tent to meet the other officers and to have a meal. We were tired after our long day and, since the mess tent was lit by only one hurricane lamp, when darkness fell there was no incentive to stay there long, and we went to our beds early.

2

I Join an Armoured Regiment

THERE was now a pause in our progress, easy to endure with patience because there was so much to learn and it was all so directly associated with our future desert operations. We were another seven days with the regiment. Some of them we spent in the leaguer, checking and counting tools and kit and equipment and sorting out the men's pay accounts and pay problems; others we devoted to trials of tanks which had been repaired or had been returned from complete overhaul in the main base workshops in Alexandria. Some we devoted to gun trials and shooting practice, to navigation tests and night exercises. We saw something of most of the aspects of life in an armoured squadron in the desert and learnt something of the new techniques on which life and survival would depend in the future. Gradually we prepared ourselves for the time when we were to be sent to join our squadron. We were waiting for a total of four tanks to be returned from overhaul, and these we were to take to the forward squadron to fill the gaps caused by breakdowns of the older tanks.

We had no great amount of time for leisure nor any great inclination for relaxation either. We found our time fully occupied with our duties and our minds intent on becoming useful members of a well-working and efficient team. It was surprising how, dispersed as they were over a large area, the regiment still managed to retain a sense of corporate living, to foster, and indeed to strengthen, the unseen bonds of friendship and mutual esteem and to keep the sense of urgency of a job to do, and to do well, which had held them earlier in the more exacting conditions in contact with the enemy. The old members had had, of course, the inestimable advantage of successful action to weld them together and had not suffered more than a few casualties to be replaced with new faces.

Being new officers in an established unit, Egerton and I tended to stick together, but we were soon absorbed into the pervading friendly atmosphere. Templeton we did not see much of, but we found no cause to revise our earlier impressions of him. We soon discovered he was not much liked. When we mentioned that we had been taught this or that by him on the way up, the usual response was, 'Oh, Templeton told you that, did he? He would, of course.'

But Templeton was not the only problem in the regiment. There was more than one officer who would not settle down, who was unpleasant or unpopular: here and there was an N.C.O. too weak or with too heavy a hand to deal successfully with men who were battle seasoned and trained to a high pitch; some men who were unwilling or incapable of 'mucking in', as the soldier's phrase put it, of pulling their weight, doing their share. These blemishes were in the main ignored by the rest of the regiment and time was allowed to work its own solution. In the end such officers were usually found an appointment elsewhere at Brigade, or Division, or even farther back; often this diplomatic removal was accompanied by promotion, which came to be known in fighting units as 'promotion by rejection'. The N.C.O.s were usually baulked and frustrated by sullen, unco-operative men and settled their own futures by either striking one of them, going absent or getting drunk, being court-martialled as a result and reduced to the ranks. The men – well, there were always demands for men for this, that, and the other; and who could blame a regiment, faced with the possibility that its future and fortunes might at some time depend on one of these men, for getting rid of its misfits?

I was made particularly conscious of the feeling that I was a member of a good team when I was put in command of one of the tanks which had been overhauled and which we were to take up to join the forward squadron. I worked each day with my crew at the many tasks. We cleaned and greased the tank, checking the engine, the transmission, the suspension and the tracks. We cleaned the guns and fired them and adjusted the telescopic sights to coincide with the actual strike of the shots. We tested and fitted the wireless. Finally we stowed the tank with the ammunition for the two-pounder gun, the machine-gun and the light-machine-gun, with cartridges for the Very-light pistol, with food, water, and our kit. My crew were all old soldiers with a keenness and sense of humour which amused and encouraged me. They reminded me of my father's workers at home: men who knew their jobs and who were as capable of deciding what was to be done as my father was himself, but who nevertheless never resented the show of authority inherent in each instruction that was given. Orders were never necessary. A daily cataloguing of the tasks to be done was sufficient to ensure that each would be done during the day. So it was with my crew, and I welcomed the chance that had given me such men, as I was reluctant at that time to wield authority too obviously.

Not that the use of naked authority was ever the best way to control a tank crew. Nowhere else did such a small body of men with such diverse backgrounds, interests and education live so much together for so long in such close contact with the enemy.

In such conditions no man could hide his fears and weaknesses for long. As I had learnt in the fighting in France, in moments of stress in battle, in the periods of release from tension, something of the fundamental qualities of each member of the crew was revealed to the others. No shield of rank or education was of any avail behind which to hide any faults. Each drew some strength and courage from the qualities of the others. Each gave something of himself to build the spirit of the whole crew. Where there was a man who could not or would not adjust himself to these conditions, the whole crew suffered as a result.

Among the crews with whom I was to serve in the years to come there were men of all races, religions, and ranks. We each had our moments of despair and distress, but nearly always some chance remark, some spark of humour, some small thoughtful act of one of the others, revived and restored our spirits.

The tanks we had at that time were the cruiser tank A9, the first of the new range of tanks developed in peace time and just beginning to come off the production lines at the outbreak of war. It was armed with a high-velocity armour-piercing gun, firing a two-pound solid-steel shot, with a Vickers machine-gun mounted co-axially with the two-pounder, and with two further Vickers guns in two sub-turrets, one on each side of the driver, who was located forward and below the centre of the main turret. These latter sub-turrets were cramped and of only limited value.

Due to a shortage of crews, they were seldom manned, the space thus freed being used to stow extra ammunition and the hundred and one other things needed on a tank. The armour thickness, though not great, was proof against any other tank-mounted guns at that time, though not against some of the higher velocity ground-mounted anti-tank guns. The main fault of these tanks, and of the A10, which gradually replaced them, was that their transmissions and tracks were unreliable. The engine, being similar to those of the London buses, was admirable, but the drive from the engine to the sprockets, which transferred the power to the tracks, was weak. The tracks themselves, and particularly the pins joining the track-plates, were also not robust enough for the hard, stony ground normally met in the desert. The A10 was basically the same vehicle, but with a Beza machine-gun in place of the Vickers, and only one of these mounted next to the driver, instead of the two sub-turrets in the A9. It entailed hard work and not a little expert knowledge to keep these tanks running for months on end and over long distances.

On the day before we were due to move forward I gave my tanks a final inspection. I inspected the outside first. I walked slowly round, checking the tracks and road-wheels. I opened the bins which were fixed on the track-guards and made sure that the spares, the tools, and the food were stowed neatly and correctly. Grasping the track-guards at the front of the tank, I climbed on to the frontal armour-plate and so on to the hull above the driver's compartment. I opened the driver's hatch and looked down on to the seat, the gear lever and the steering levers, and beyond these, on the forward bulkhead, to the mass of dials – the speedometer, the revolution counter, the pressure-gauges. All seemed to be in order.

I opened the hatch to the cupola and climbed down into the turret and sat on the small, hard leather seat provided for the commander. From here, on the right of the turret, I could survey all I wanted to see. Immediately in front of me was the gunner's seat, so close that when the gunner was there my knees would be pressing against his back. In front of the gunner, at head height, was the rubber pad guarding the eyepiece of the telescope, flanked on one side by the brass quadrant of the range-drum. On the turret wall, at the gunner's right hand, was the hand-wheel for the mechanical traverse of the turret, and next to it the lever for the hydraulic power traverse. On his left were the firing triggers for the two-pounder and the machine-gun on the elevating handle for the mounting.

Behind me, in the bulge at the back of the turret, was the wireless set, flanked on one side by a fixed bin in which I kept my head-phones and wireless microphone and the Tannoy microphone with which I gave orders to the crew. On the far side of the wireless set was another bin in which the operator kept his spares and tools and where we also kept the Very pistol and cartridges.

In the centre of the turret, jutting back from the gun trunnions on the inside of the frontal armour-plate, was the main mass of the two-pounder gun, the buffers, the breech-block and, behind that, stretching almost to the back of the turret ring, the metal deflector guard, to protect the crew from the recoil of the gun, and from which hung the large canvas bag into which the empty cartridge cases were automatically ejected from the breech which opened when the gun ran out again after recoil.

Beyond the gun, on the left side of the turret, was the position for the gun-loader, who was also the wireless operator. Hinged from the turret ring was the small seat which had to be fixed back out of the way when the gun was firing so that the operator could have all the space possible in which to handle the ammunition and load the gun. Under the revolving floor of the turret, round the edge of this floor and beyond it on the inside surfaces of the walls of the tank hull, were clipped and stacked the two-pounder rounds and the boxes containing the machine-gun ammunition.

I sat in silent contemplation of all I saw, my mind only partly occupied by the inspection. Mainly I was thinking of all that a return to battle meant to me – preparing myself to meet the exhaustion and the fear.

3

We Move to the Frontier

FOUR officers went forward with the tanks next day – Templeton, Egerton, myself, and another called Ryan whom I did not know – and on our way west to Sidi Suleiman, Egerton and I had our first experience of the desert under active service conditions.

We had had an uneventful day. When we moved off from the regimental leaguer area soon after first light there had been a cool ground-mist blanketing the desert, making it difficult for us to see each other. But there was the advantage that the surface had been dampened, and therefore little dust was thrown up by the tracks. An hour later the sun had dried the desert, so that behind each tank there was a plume of sand, and behind each truck and lorry a faint cloud of dust billowing up as high as the canopies. We kept up a steady eight to ten miles an hour, strung out over the desert in open formation, with about 300 yards separating each vehicle. As the morning progressed the heat grew more intense and, to add to our discomfort, a wind sprang up from the east, behind us, blowing the heat of the engines and the dust-cloud raised by the tracks forward over the tank, so that we were enveloped, and found dust getting into our eyes and nose and caking our lips. There was nothing we could do about it. The twenty-minute halts which we took at the end of each hundred minutes' running time were all the more welcome and appreciated.

We were a small, compact body going forward to join the squadron. There were four anks, a three-tonner carrying petrol, another with ammunition, and a third with the fitters and mechanics and their tools. The doctor in his 15-cwt truck was accompanying us to pay a visit to the squadron, though they were being looked after by the medical officer of the Armoured Car Regiment. It was really an excuse for him to get away on a 'swan', as any journey into the desert which was not entirely necessary was known.

At midday we halted for our meal and a brew-up of tea. Each vehicle crew cooked for themselves and planned and prepared their day's ration in the manner to suit their own tastes. My crew had already developed a well-tried routine. Sykes, the driver, prepared the fire and the cooking utensils, opened the tins and afterwards was responsible for stowing all the necessary articles in the proper places. Holton, the gunner, cooked and generally directed operations. Tilden, the operator, produced and cleaned the plates and mugs and eating utensils, and helped Holton to dole out so that each had a fair share, afterwards cleaning all the utensils. I was firmly told that I could be allotted no definite job, as at any moment I might be needed on the wireless or be called away to receive orders. However, I managed to look busy, and if any of the other crew members were not available I was ready to take their places: when Sykes had to adjust something which was giving him cause to worry or when Tilden was busy on the wireless set, and later, in the intervals of action, when Holton was busy stowing new supplies of ammunition.

We halted to have our evening meal two hours before last light, so that the petrol fires would not be as conspicuous as they would be later on against the darkening shadows of the setting sun. This gave us ample time to complete the meal in comfort and for the petrol lorry to do the round of the four tanks to refill them again after their day's run. The drivers, apprehensive of any faults which may have come to light during the first long march, gave the engines and suspensions a specially close inspection. We were moving forward in wireless silence, so there were no calls or reports to give, and our progress would, we knew, be reported by an east-bound convoy of vehicles which we had passed in the early afternoon, among which were two vehicles of our own squadron returning for supplies.

As the sun set and dusk began to close in – when, in fact, it was dark enough for us to be sure that no last Italian reconnaissance plane would see us and mark us down for attention by the bombers later that night – we moved the tanks and vehicles together into close leaguer, the tanks taking up positions two on each side of the centre column of soft vehicles, about ten paces dividing the vehicles in each column and the same distance between each column. It was in this or some similar fashion, though on a larger scale, that each regiment formed itself into close leaguer at night, the better to carry out the many details of supply, repair and reorganization and to be able to protect itself against enemy patrols.

It did not take long to make the last arrangements for the night and to detail the guard, and soon most men were asleep. The drivers of the tanks and those in each crew who had also taken a turn were relieved of any guard duties, and the night's watches were shared between the remainder of us, so that the leaguer was watched throughout the hours of darkness by two men who were on guard for an hour. We officers took our turn with the rest.

Templeton, who was in command, arranged that he was on guard during the first hour, so that he could cope with any unforeseen incidents before all were asleep, and that I, the next senior, was on during the last hour of the night, so that at dawn I could ensure that all were awake and ready for the day.

Before going to bed I went to the M.O.'s truck for a drink, at his invitation. It was here that I met Sid Ryan for the first time. A small, round, red-faced man with twinkling eyes and a flashing smile, he was an ex-N.C.O. who had been commissioned about six months earlier. He was to teach me many things in the future, not least how to accept with composure the rough with the smooth. The toast he offered us before we turned in was typical.

'Let's drink,' he said, 'to all the parties we'll miss while we're away and all the girls we'll kiss when we get back.'

To the usual morning salutation of 'Wakey, wakey' the leaguer was soon astir, bedrolls were stowed, engines started and warmed up and within ten minutes we were all ready to move. As the sky lightened to the east each vehicle moved off into open formation, so that when the full light of day reached us we were already so dispersed that we were unlikely to attract the attention of any searching plane. There was now a delay of about half an hour while we waited for the sun to rise high enough to light the desert sufficiently so that our petrol fires would not be conspicuous. As the sky imperceptibly paled, so the desert round us gradually took on different hues. It turned from black to grey, from grey to a golden red, matching the first rays of the rising sun, from red to the pale glistening yellow tinge which was to burn and dazzle our eyes for the rest of the day until the sun again set. The muffled figures, huddled against each vehicle in what was still the cool dampness of dawn, gradually stirred to life and busied themselves with breakfast. Afterwards we moved off again.

We halted late in the morning for our main meal, and towards noon came near to Sidi Suleiman, where the Support Group was concentrated – a relative term – with each vehicle 300 yards apart. I was keenly on the look-out for any signs pointing to the squadron, but even though I knew we were close I failed to see the dispersed vehicles, and was only aware that we had arrived when

I saw a truck moving towards us. It turned round when it was still some way ahead and led us into our positions in the leaguer.

4

The Weary Vigil

GUIDED by the sergeant-major, the tanks and lorries were soon dispersed to their allotted places in the leaguer. There were willing hands to help us unload and many inquiries about Cairo and Alexandria.

While Templeton and Ryan busied themselves with various details, Egerton and I, with our kit, were driven to the officers' mess tent. Here we met our squadron commander, Peter Kinnaird.

A stranger might have been justified in being surprised at finding Kinnaird in this situation, for he did not look anything like the conventional picture of a Regular soldier. His face was clean shaven, lean and rather long, with the finely chiselled features, imposing brow and firm eyes of a barrister or a man of letters. His manner, too, was unusual in its restraint and stern aloofness. By those who knew him his honesty was admired, his integrity respected. A stranger might also be forgiven for wondering what there was of humour and humanity in his make-up to relieve the clear evidence of apparent austerity. There was not much, at first sight, which could be taken as a sign of a lighter touch, but for those who knew him well, and for the officers in his squadron, there were from day to day many indications of a not insignificant sense of humour. His friends and subordinates found that he had an abiding interest in their welfare, touched with a perceptive compassion which surprised some of them.

In the summer of 1940 he was thirty-six years old, had served for fifteen years in the Army and had been promoted a major on the outbreak of war.

As Egerton and I, loaded with our kit, ducked into the tent, Kinnaird rose to meet us with hand outstretched.

'I'm Kinnaird. What are your names?' he said.

Dropping what we held on to the floor of the tent, we drew ourselves stiffly to attention and saluted, saying our names as we did so.

'Don't do that in here,' he remarked, shaking each of us by the hand. 'It may not look much, but we regard this as our mess and have no formality in here. Leave your things there and have a drink.'

As he handed each of us our drinks he added, 'I hope you'll enjoy yourselves with us here. I expect the doctor has told you how bloody it can be if you're in the desert for any length of time.'

Despite Kinnaird's efforts at friendliness, the conversation did not flow very easily. Even Egerton, tainted by the influence of other more formal messes, was somewhat awed by Kinnaird's outward appearance of sternness. When Kinnaird left, saying to the doctor, 'John, I've got one or two things to see to. Look after these two till I get back, will you?' – there was a moment's silence, and then Egerton remarked:

'He's a cold, hard-looking cuss, isn't he?'

We were both unprepared for the doctor's quick rejoinder:

'Don't you make a mistake about that. You can thank your stars that he's as good a man as I ever want to know, and he's probably as good a soldier as any of us will ever meet. He looks stern and aloof and unbending, but that's his armour. You get beyond that – as you will if you do your jobs well and measure up to his standards – and you'll find he's a good friend as well as being your O.C. I'm a silly old man and you'll probably laugh at me. You can be sure, though, that I didn't come all this way to look after you. I wanted a swan – that's true – but I also wanted to see Peter Kinnaird.'

We laughed at his taunt, but we were both impressed by this independent opinion expressed so forcibly.

For the next five weeks we were fully occupied. With such a wide frontage to watch and harass, and with the ever-increasing strength of the Italian forces on the frontier, our tanks were in continual demand. We were either co-operating in offensive patrols or attacks on isolated enemy positions, or standing by to move at a moment's notice to help outlying infantry positions being menaced by Italian tanks, or to rescue a returning patrol being closely harried by the enemy. If we were not fighting or standing-to ready to fight in our tanks, we were out on patrol with the armoured cars or joining in one of the many nightly assaults which the infantry made to keep the Italian nerves at fever pitch. The perpetual opportunities for offensive action were exhilarating, and kept us all on our toes, and at a pitch of eagerness and enthusiasm which served to mask the long hours, the hard work and the chances we were taking.

At times, though, we were tired and dispirited, worn out by the heat and the lack of water and the monotony of the food. Fresh meat, milk, bread and vegetables were out of the question; they would never have lasted the four- or five-day journey from Alexandria or Cairo without adequate refrigeration facilities. The ration consisted of a variety of tinned foods, some more popular than others. Bully beef there was at all times and in the main it was our favourite, since we could make it quickly into a satisfying and palatable meal, either hot or cold. Tinned bacon was invariably all fat and was rolled in revolting lengths of paper which we took to be bacon, only discovering our error when we could chew the solid lump no longer. Tinned sausages we liked until they were replaced by a substitute variety made, it was alleged, from soya beans which were promptly named 'Soya links' and reviled at all times, except when they came as a novelty to any other diet which had begun to pall. There was a tinned stew of meat and vegetables, known shortly as M & V. Biscuits there were in unlimited quantities, thick or thin, hard or soft, some of which tasted of sawdust, others of mud, but always there by the boxful when all else ran out, to be eaten by themselves, with tinned margarine, or with tinned jams or marmalade. Tea, of course, was the main standby, thick and sweet and strong as only the Army made it – a 'brew' as it was known to all and sundry. Mixed with a dash of rum on a cold night or in any depressing circumstances it was a life-saver and reviver.

Water, too, was always a problem and, except for those troops who were near the supply points, was limited to never more than three-quarters of a gallon per man per day. Separated as we were from the main water-points at Matruh by so great a distance, we were limited to a mere half-gallon per man per day. This four pints was all that each man could expect, though in the spring and autumn, after the small amount of rain that fell, we might hope to have the ration augmented a little from the nearest 'bir' which might have filled up. In the course of time we all evolved a method

29

of allocating the usual four pints in a satisfactory way. One pint we heated and used for washing and shaving. After use it was poured into a crude filter, made of a four-gallon petrol tin with holes punched in the bottom and filled with alternate layers of stones and sand. Each day's supply was caught and kept in another petrol tin, which by the end of a week or ten days was sufficiently full to provide a bath of sorts. After the bath, the water was again filtered and used for washing clothes. Finally after another filtering it was used in the radiators of the lorries and trucks.

Another pint we kept in a water-bottle as an emergency supply which we could consume each day, though the whole pint was not normally drunk, as most of us preferred to wet the material covering the outside of the bottle, which, when left in the shade, was then cooled by the evaporation of the water.

The two remaining pints were issued to mess or cook-house, one pint to be used for making tea, the other to be used for cooking.

Meagre though this supply was we soon learned to manage on it and to work out a system of private rationing which satisfied our wants. Some drank little and often, others a lot at certain fixed times. Some men preferred the water by itself, others mixed with fruit-juices or lemonade tablets. We were always affected by the quality of the water, which was often the greatest tribulation which had to be endured. Usually it was fairly good and tasted reasonably sweet despite the disinfectant prescribed by the doctors. Sometimes, however, it was brackish, salty and discoloured. At these times life was made distinctly more unpleasant. The milk curdled in the tea, the sugar seemed to have no effect; the water was loathsome by itself and equally vile when mixed with anything else.

I gradually settled down to the new conditions and soon felt that I had been there months instead of weeks. I had been allowed to keep the tank and crew I had already got to know so well, and to this were added another two tanks, one commanded by a sergeant, the other by a corporal. Sergeant Wharton had been with the regiment for over five years, all the time in Egypt, and had served without interruption in the desert since the previous May, when the regiment had moved to Gerawla near Matruh before moving up to the frontier when war with Italy broke out. He was a competent, intelligent, firm N.C.O. who knew his job well and was not afraid to tell all and sundry, including the officers, when they were doing wrong. His manner of doing so with the officers was that acquired by the majority of the good N.C.O.s of the Regular Army – a mixture of respect, directness and honesty, laced with a touch of humour and ribaldry. His advice or criticism could only be accepted in the spirit in which it was meant. I found that Sergeant Wharton was a staunch support, and in the course of the next few months had discussed most things, military and otherwise, with him and gained a lot of worldly advice and opinion as reward.

At the first few attempts to command my troop of tanks I had little success. My ability was rusty after even so short a time, my mind stagnant and slow from lack of practice. The great handicap which we all had to overcome was that there were too many things to think about at the same time. A course had to be set either by the troop commander or, more usually, by his conforming to the movements of the squadron or regimental navigator. The enemy had to be found and identified. The other two tanks had to be instructed about their formation or chivvied if they failed to keep in place. The driver had to be given his orders about his direction and speed, the gunner warned about the target and which gun to use, the loader-operator told to load the gun. The correct information had to be passed over the wireless to the squadron commander. If these things were not done properly, or if they were done at the wrong time, the whole manœuvre or battle was liable to fail at the crucial moment, with men's lives lost and valuable tanks destroyed. It was a matter of practice and more practice and practice whenever possible. It was a question of lengthy discussion about the action that each tank would take in certain eventualities, of careful planning of the use of ground or the mutual support that might be given by other troops or even other arms, such as the infantry and guns.

Gradually I gained more confidence. Navigation or map-reading became less of a problem. We evolved certain simple drills which covered most of the troop's tactics. I learnt where to look for the enemy and quick methods of identifying him. Orders and information, which earlier I had hesitated in passing, I now gave out almost unconsciously. I soon had no difficulty in remembering the correct wireless procedure and, in fact, learnt also new, abbreviated and simplified methods. We all acquired a great deal of confidence in each other, and so made ourselves into a really effective fighting machine.

At the same time the training within the crew improved. Though the tank broke down just as frequently, we mended it more quickly. As my ability to judge the distance to each target – always difficult in the peculiar condition of light and ground in the desert – improved, so, with the improvement of the gunner's shooting, we were able to hit our targets sooner in each action.

5

A Skirmish with the Italians

TOWARDS the end of the first week we took part in an action which was the pattern of many others at the time.

Armoured-car and infantry patrols ranged far and wide each day and night, keeping watch on most of the outlying posts which the Italians were continually extending farther and farther towards the escarpment overlooking Sollum. In each position they assembled the force which was to reach out and seize the next piece of vital ground dominating the area of desert which they were intent on controlling. By careful observation of each of their forward positions, this building-up process could be discovered and a fairly accurate estimate could be made on each occasion as to the next piece of ground which was to be taken.

During the first few days of the week the armoured-car patrols noted the gradual increase in the garrison of a particular post. When at last it was reinforced by some twenty tanks and was visited by some person who was obviously of fairly high rank, judging by the preparations and precautions taken before and during his visit, it was clear that an advance was impending, and fairly soon. Towards midday of the same day, Kinnaird got a warning order detailing a small force of all arms – a battalion of infantry, a battery of guns and all of C Squadron's tanks – to stand by for a move that night. Later in the afternoon the armoured-car patrols reported that no further troops had arrived that day and that all the signs indicated that final preparations were being made for an advance next day.

In C Squadron we completed our preparations during the late afternoon. We gave the tanks a final overhaul; we tested the guns, checked the ammunition and loaded food, water and fuel. Half an hour before the time at which we were due to move each operator manned his wireless set for a final 'netting' to check that they were all exactly tuned to the frequency of the controlling set, the squadron commander's.

At the appointed time we moved off in open formation, in a wide crescent with some 300 yards between each tank and about 400 yards between each troop, so that the squadron covered some 4,000 yards of front and could observe, with the good visibility at that hour of the day, over some 6,000 to 7,000 yards in all. Kinnaird, with his squadron headquarters, moved in the centre and about 500 yards behind the two centre troops. By dint of very hard work we had managed to make every tank fit for the operation, so we were up to the full strength of four troops each of three tanks and a squadron headquarters of four tanks, making a grand total of sixteen. With us, too, just behind Kinnaird's four tanks, came the fitter's lorry, two lorries with reserve ammunition, two with petrol, and Kinnaird's own truck, in which he could confer with us later that night if there were any last orders to be issued.

The rest of the force took station about us. There were three troops of armoured cars ahead of us, ranging and watching over an even wider frontage than we covered. The infantry battalion moved in two long, widely dispersed columns, extending the ends of our crescent to the rear. The battalion headquarters and the guns were in the centre, about 1,000 yards behind Kinnaird's tank. It was a compact arrangement, similar but on a smaller scale to that adopted by each brigade when it moved, so that we could halt at an instant's notice and be in a good formation to give battle if attacked or threatened.

We had some twenty miles to go to place ourselves in a position about five miles due east of the ground which we were going to contest with the Italians the next day. Our night leaguer area had been picked with two things in mind. First that, in case the Italians were to reconnoitre their objective during the night, they would not have any warning of our presence. And second, that when we moved the next morning we would go due west, and so have the sun directly behind us, blinding the Italians and making it difficult for them to see us and impossible to measure our numbers and our composition. We could have moved to occupy the vital ground that night, but to do so might have caused us to fail in our main object, which was to inflict casualties on the Italians, who, if they knew the ground was already occupied, might not have advanced.

As it grew darker the vehicles closed in towards one another. When we could be sure of not being observed, Kinnaird moved us in to two close columns of vehicles, the infantry and the guns taking up positions on our flanks. Though we had all been listening on the wireless in case of emergency, we had moved in wireless silence. By day this had caused little difficulty, as we had been able to transmit what orders were necessary by visual signals, but by night it was a much greater problem to control so large a number of vehicles without wireless. The task was made more difficult still by the clouds of dust which enveloped us, choking and blinding us as we tried to watch the vehicle in front or for any light signals which might have been used.

It was a great relief when this most trying part of the advance eventually came to an end. In the last mile we swung through a wide arc from our original course due north to one which brought us facing due west, ready for the next morning's advance. We went into leaguer with ourselves on the forward face, the infantry guarding the sides and rear and the remainder, including the guns, in the middle.

We were astir early the following morning. By first light we were mounted in our vehicles and ready to move. Preceded by the armoured cars, we advanced in the same formation as that of the previous evening. We were soon on to the objective. The infantry quickly began digging what pits and trenches they could in the hard ground and the guns got into position. While this went on we and the armoured cars moved farther west to make contact with the Italians.

About two miles west of the main position Kinnaird found an ideal ridge which flanked, on the south, the direct route which the Italians were expected to take. Here we disposed ourselves in 'turret-down' positions, so that to anyone on the other side of the ridge only the barest minimum of the turret was visible, but we were still able to see the ground before us.

Meanwhile the armoured cars moved a further three miles west before making their first contact. The Italians were preceded as usual by a thin screen of motor-cyclists, spectacular but useless advance-guards. These the armoured cars allowed to within 250 yards of their positions before they moved up on to the ridge behind which they had been hiding. The first thin chatter of their machine-guns told us that the battle had begun.

. A moment or two later Bolton, the squadron second-in-command, reported:

'Hello, COMO; COMO Ack calling. Friends in front say that they are engaging about three zero motor-cyclists and that they have destroyed six. The remainder have now withdrawn to the main body. Off.'

Bolton's job was to act as a link between Kinnaird and the force commander, on whose control net the armoured cars were reporting. To do this Bolton, who was in one of the squadron headquarter tanks, placed it next to the one of which the set was on the force-control net. He was then able to pass our news back and transmit to Kinnaird on the squadron net any orders or information, such as that from the armoured cars.

At intervals he continued his commentary:

' ... The cyclists have now joined the main body of the enemy, which has halted. Off.'

' ... Still no move by the enemy. There is a lot of to-ing and fro-ing by staff cars, but nothing else is moving. Off.'

' ... Friends now say that some figures fifteen to twenty tanks have moved forward, very slowly and very cautiously. They say they will have to pull back soon to the next position. Off.'

We knew that there was little that the armoured cars could do against tanks, since they were armed only with a machine-gun. Bolton's next report confirmed this.

' ... Enemy tanks are now pushing forward quite fast. They seem to have realized that they are only faced by armoured cars. Off.'

Kinnaird now took a hand.

'Hello, COMO Ack; COMO calling. That's good. Make sure

that friends know exactly where we are. I want them to delay turning south over our ridge until as late as they possibly can, so that the enemy tanks will be drawn on to us face to face. Over.'

'Hello, COMO; COMO Ack answering,' Bolton replied. 'Friends say they know exactly where we are and will try to do as you say. They are finding things a bit tricky at present. They want to withdraw fast enough to get the tanks away from the rest who are now moving again, but if they go too fast they think the tanks will lose heart and give up the chase. Off.'

Soon, in the distance, we could see through our binoculars the small shapes of the armoured cars and beyond them, in a wide fan, those of the pursuing tanks. When the armoured cars were almost due north of us they changed the line of their withdrawal so as to come through our positions. The tanks on the Italian right flank immediately increased speed in an attempt to cut off the armoured cars. This uncharacteristically offensive manoeuvre had not been foreseen by Kinnaird, who at once ordered Egerton:

'Hello, COMO Two; COMO calling. Withdraw immediately from your position and face west to take on those enemy tanks when they appear round the end of the ridge. Over.'

'Hello, COMO; COMO Two answering. O.K., but the end of the ridge will be a bit bare. Over.'

'COMO Two,' Kinnaird replied, 'you get on with what you have been told to do. I want someone below the ridge as soon as possible – those tanks are coming fast. Off to you.' And since the remainder of the Italian tanks had now conformed to the move of those of their right flank, and were moving to the end of the ridge which Egerton had just vacated, he ordered: 'Hello, COMO Ack. Go to the position which Two has just left. I do not want to move any of the others, and I think you can get there as soon as anybody. Off.'

Bolton immediately moved with all three of the headquarter tanks which had been in the low ground behind us, where Kinnaird had left them when he himself moved up on to the ridge into a position where he could see the whole battle.

Though Bolton only just got into position in time, this unplanned manoeuvre could not have worked out better as far as we were concerned. Since he was moving, he was the first to be seen by the enemy. Before they could warn the remainder, however, those which had moved round the ridge came face to face with Egerton at short range.

We heard the crack of his first shot, and then in a breathless rush of words:

'COMO Two calling. Three enemy tanks now five hundred yards. ...' Then in an aside to his gunner he said, 'Down two hundred and fire again,' and continued, ' ... to my front. Missed first shot. Off.'

Before me now on the other flank the enemy had closed to about 700 yards, and I gave my fire order. 'Holton – traverse right – take the outside tank – seven hundred – fire.'

As I watched the tracer of the shot flying towards the enemy tank I saw, out of the corner of my eye, the flash of Sergeant Wharton's gun and beyond him those of Ryan's troop.

As yet the Italians had not fired. They were handicapped by having to shoot uphill, and moreover had the sun in their eyes.

Ryan was the first to get a kill. He hit an enemy tank which was turning on the slope before him fairly and squarely in the engine, shattering the petrol tanks and starting a fire which spread rapidly. Mixed with the flame, clouds of billowing black smoke rolled across the desert, blocking my view of the enemy entirely. With a dull roar the ammunition then exploded, throwing a mass of debris into the air. A moment later we were horrified to see a figure with face blackened and clothes alight stumbling through the smoke. He staggered for some yards, then fell and in a frenzy of agony rolled frantically in the hard sand in a desperate effort to put out the flames. But to no avail. Gradually his flailing arms and legs moved more slowly, until at last, with a convulsive heave of his body, he lay still.

While my view was blocked, the battle still raged on the other flank. Egerton announced triumphantly:

'COMO Two calling. We have hit this tank three times now, but he won't brew. Hello! Wait a moment; there goes the crew – they're baling out. I'll let 'em go – doesn't seem right to shoot a sitting bird. That's one, anyway. Off.'

Before anyone else could get a word in he was on the air again. 'COMO Two calling. We've knocked a track off another tank, and the third one has turned and is tearing away flat out. Off.'

Ryan then reported, 'COMO Four calling. We've knocked out

another tank – at least, the crew's leaving it now. I can't see anything to my right, as the smoke is blocking the view. Over.'

Before Kinnaird could answer, Templeton called in over-precise tones, 'COMO One – I think I must claim that tank which Como Four has just reported – I distinctly saw my shot strike. Over.'

To which Kinnaird replied, 'Como Four, O.K. Off to you. COMO One – I see no point in arguing the point now, and do not call in future when I have a call to answer. Have you anything else to report? Over.'

In a clearly disgruntled voice Templeton answered, 'Hello, COMO; COMO One answering. Nothing further to report. Off.'

There was now a pause for some time. The black smoke from the burning tank gradually died away, and I could see that the Italian tanks had withdrawn out of range and were lying about half-way between us and the main Italian column, which had now caught up and was halted immediately to our north, where it had come under shell-fire from our main position to the east.

To break this deadlock and to further his later plans, Kinnaird ordered Egerton:

'COMO Two – we can do little more on this flank. I want to be able to move unobserved via our main position to the other flank. We can't do so while those enemy tanks are so close. I do not want to leave these positions either. So I want you to work your way round the end of the ridge and attack the enemy right flank. Do not get carried away – I just want you to look as aggressive as you can. We may be able to convince them that they must move back a bit for the good of their health. Is this all clear? Over.'

Egerton's enthusiastic reply was, 'COMO Two answering. Quite clear. I don't think they can see me at present, but they may hear me when I move. Can you all do some shooting to drown the noise? Over.'

'COMO Two – good idea. Yes, we will do that. Off to you,' Kinnaird answered. Then, 'Hello, COMO; COMO calling. Start shooting now. Do not waste ammo, but make enough noise. Off.'

Some ten minutes later we saw Egerton's troop emerge round the western end of the ridge, firing on the move as they closed the range to the nearest enemy tank. It must have been by sheer chance – since even on the relatively flat surface of the desert shooting on the move was never very accurate – that this flank tank was hit, and we saw the crew leap out. They tried to run away, but a warning burst of machine-gun fire from Egerton's tank stopped them and we saw them walk towards him with their hands raised.

Egerton reported, 'COMO Two calling. I hope you enjoyed that. Can I send these four prisoners back, as they are rather in the way here? Over.'

By now the remaining Italian tanks had withdrawn well out of range on to the fringe of their main body, so Kinnaird answered, 'COMO Two. Jolly good! The result has been just what we wanted. Stay where you are though until I relieve you. Off.'

During the ensuing lull we withdrew, a troop at a time, to a position some 1,000 yards south of the ridge, where we refilled the tanks with petrol and ammunition. Ryan went first, and then relieved Egerton.

At this first relaxation of tension I found, to my surprise, that it was already eight o'clock and that the battle, which had seemed to take so short a time, had in fact been waging for close on three hours. Later I was to notice again and again this same swift passage of time while we were closely engaged. The intense concentration required and the exhilaration of fear were both factors which together made us live entirely in the moment of the battle and oblivious of time.

By now I was beginning to feel very hungry and weary. Our active day had started some six hours earlier and had been full of movement and excitement. The brew of tea, despite the increasing heat of the day, was very welcome, and we ate our cold bully as if it were a feast.

At eleven o'clock, taking advantage of the haze of heat which shrouded the desert at midday, particularly in summer, reducing visibility to about 1,000 yards and distorting all shapes and movement, Kinnaird ordered:

'Hello, COMO; COMO calling. We are going to use the haze to cover our move from here behind our main position and so to the enemy's other flank. COMO One, you will stay here and try to give the impression that we have not gone. The rest of us will have to move slowly from here to avoid kicking up too much dust, which will give the game away. COMO One, are you quite clear about your task? You will have to spread yourself out along the ridge. Over.'

'COMO One answering,' we heard Templeton say with a slight note of anxiety in his voice. 'I am quite clear, but what do I do if I am attacked? Over.'

'COMO One,' Kinnaird answered briskly – 'if you do your job properly you won't be attacked. But if you are, you can withdraw when you like as far as you like. Off to you. Hello, COMO. Move now and conform to my speed and direction in the order Three, Two, Four. Off.'

We had to cover a distance of about twelve miles to reach the new position. In view of the reduced speed, we were not ready to attack until about three o'clock in the afternoon. We had apparently been unobserved, but to make surprise even more certain the main force now launched what appeared to be a determined attack on the front of the Italian column, which had made no further move. Supported by the battery of guns firing a furious bombardment on to the centre of the mass of Italian vehicles, some infantry in extended order moved forward down the slope towards the enemy. When Kinnaird saw this he ordered us to advance.

Moving at about fifteen miles an hour, with plumes of dust billowing out behind us and the sun glinting on the barrels of the guns, we pitched and rolled over the rough desert. The unsuspecting Italians were lounging round the lorries on this hitherto undisturbed flank. We closed to within 200 yards of the vehicles on the edge of the main mass, turned west and, moving in line ahead, ran down the whole length of the Italian column, machine-gunning any and every target that crossed our sights.

Here and there a man, braver or more alert than the rest, raised his rifle to fire hopelessly against our armour until he was caught in the hail of fire and fell dead or wounded; some lorries, filled with petrol or oil, caught fire; some, filled with ammunition, burned for a few moments and then exploded; others being driven frantically away from the attack had their tyres riddled with bullets and came to a lurching halt or overturned.

For some two miles we continued in this fashion, moving west all the time, on the flank of the Italian column. At the end of that distance the Italian vehicles were fewer, and warned by what they had seen, were making their escape to the south. So Kinnaird ordered us to perform a wide sweeping turn to the right which, when completed, brought us back on to the Italian flank again, but now moving in the opposite direction. Back we went, finishing the destruction we had started on the first run, until some thirty lorries were left burning or crippled.

As we reached the front of the column again we were met by the fire of some of the Italian guns which had been switched towards us, and we could see, to our right, the Italian tanks moving hurriedly through the centre of their column to intercept us. Satisfied with the damage we had done and reluctant to risk losing any of the tanks at so great a distance from support, Kinnaird now ordered us to turn left, to the north, and back to the starting position.

The Italian tanks followed us for only a short distance, but we were shelled spasmodically for the rest of the day while we stayed menacing the Italian flank. Just before the light failed we and Templeton on the other flank of the Italians made a further assault which served to cover the withdrawal of our infantry back to their original positions.

We leaguered about two and a half miles south-east of our day position, to avoid being shelled at night and to defeat any Italian offensive patrols who might have been out searching for us. We reoccupied the position again on the following day, but towards evening were forced to withdraw by the Italians, who had received considerable reinforcements of both tanks and guns. We withdrew due south, and that night the infantry launched an attack on the rear of the new Italian position. They left it in confusion and caused casualties to both men and vehicles. They had particular satisfaction in setting fire to an unusually ornate caravan belonging to the Italian commanding officer.

6

The Italians Advance

At last, on 13 September, the Italians advanced into Egypt. It was with a fanfare of triumphant threats that they launched the new campaign.

For three days before the advance actually began the indications had been so clear that we had already started to take the preliminary action before withdrawal. The track down the escarpment at Halfaya Pass had been torn up and mined, as had the coastal track from Sollum to the east. Mines had been sown, too, at various vital places in the desert and the available water supplies had been salted.

Our squadron was kept with the majority of the British force which stayed on the top of the escarpment covering the more open and better route of advance, ready to combat any wide movement into the desert south of the escarpment.

The Italian advance was, however, entirely down Hellfire Pass and along the coastal road.

The move down the pass was bombed by the R.A.F., shelled by our artillery and hampered by exploding mines, until such confusion reigned that the Italian troops were forced to dismount from their lorries and scrambled down on foot. The subsequent advance along the coast was preceded, as usual, by motor-cyclists to reconnoitre, supported by groups of tanks to execute the main thrusts and assaults, backed by guns to clear each new objective and disperse opposition, and finally reinforced by the infantry, whose task it was to occupy the ground captured and to repel any counter-attacks.

For four days, from 13 to 16 September, the slow, fumbling, hesitant advance continued until it had reached Sidi Barrani, sixty-five miles from the Italian starting positions. Each small ridge was contested. The Italian columns were bombed by day by the R.A.F. and by night were shelled by the guns, who found it easy to locate and hit the Italian night leaguers, since their positions were given away by searchlights which continually swept the surrounding desert.

At Sidi Barrani the advance halted and, to our surprise and indignation, the Italians started to dig in and prepare defended positions – surprise because till then the Italians had not had to overcome any prepared positions nor had they suffered excessive losses; indignation because a strong counter-thrust had been prepared farther east by the remainder of the 7th Armoured Division lying in wait.

From the beginning of the war in June the Italians had suffered some 3,500 killed and wounded and had lost 700 prisoners; many guns, tanks and lorries had also been destroyed. Our losses had been 150 men killed, wounded and missing and not more than fifty tanks and lorries destroyed or captured. Despite the disparity in numbers and the distance from the base, we had, for three months, not only contained a vastly superior enemy, but had also made ourselves such masters of the open desert that, even with five divisions, the Italians now felt obliged to bring their ponderous advance to a grinding halt, to secure the sixty-five miles of communications against the mere threat of action which might have cut them off from their base.

And so while days turned into weeks, weeks into months, we settled down to the interminable, monotonous process of probe and counter-probe, reconnaissances and fleeting skirmishes.

PART TWO

1940: AN ARMY DESTROYED

1

Out of Battle

WE saw little action during the withdrawal, separated from the enemy as we were by about thirty miles, with the escarpment between us and the sea. At the end of a week we rejoined our regiment and were soon absorbed into the daily routine. The majority of the squadron had come to know this part of the desert well, and settled back into the regular monotony of the waiting they had experienced before Italy declared war. To Egerton and me the situation was novel and not altogether attractive. During our short stay with the regiment on our way forward to join the squadron we had been too busy to be touched by the ennui which was then beginning to affect all and sundry. Now we began to be aware of it soon after our arrival. It was a disease to which we were more particularly susceptible, having just left the first stress and tension of contact with the enemy. We felt dispirited and deflated after the excitements and the earlier sense of purpose. It was some time before I saw that it was now as much my business to resist the insidious attack of boredom as it was earlier my duty to be ready at an instant's notice for action.

Soon, however, we began to accept and adopt the philosophical attitude of those who had become accustomed to the strain of waiting. Our days were occupied with the hundred and one tasks inseparable from the maintenance and preparation of tanks. The food was better than we had been able to get when on the frontier. Water was more plentiful. We were able to see the Cairo daily papers only a day late and our mail was more regular and less out of date. The sea being nearby, we were each able to get down for a bathe at least once a week.

The shorter, cooler days of autumn were a relief to us all. By the end of October the days were cold enough to wear battle-dress, though still at midday on some days the temperature was high. The lassitude brought on by boredom and increased by the heat of the summer began to go.

There were disadvantages, though. In the winter months our clothes were something of a problem, since they were not so easily washed as the shorts and shirts worn in summer. After even short periods the collar of the battle-dress jacket had accumulated so much sand and dust that the effect when it rubbed on the back of the neck was like sandpaper, and in a period of a few days could cause uncomfortable rawness. So we started to blossom out into a variety of coloured scarves, worn primarily to protect the neck, but also as an easy means of giving added warmth, when tightly tied, during the cold of the early mornings, and yet being easy to adjust to the warmer temperatures of midday. We also felt the sandpaper effect in the battle-dress trousers. This we found easier to endure, but nevertheless some men took to wearing corduroy or twill trousers of different shades and patterns. These and the coloured scarves gave a touch of gaiety and individuality which was wholly out of character with an army at war.

We found, all the same, that there were times when we could relax and enjoy the brief moments in the desert which were filled with enchantment. Our days by the sea were often so perfect a way of passing the time that it was difficult to realize that it was all part of the process of waging a war for our very existence. Some afternoons in the late autumn also had a beauty of their own. The hot sunshine pouring down from a cloudless, flawless sky was fanned by enough of a breeze to remove any uncomfortable heat. The desert sand was clean and cool and dry. There was nothing to do, and even the aircraft sentry allowed himself to doze, keeping only an occasional watchful eye on the sky. The men were reading or writing or sleeping. It was all warmth, and clean sand and silence, with only the occasional sound of an engine or gun to show that there were inhabitants of the wastes of the desert.

But this half-way life was difficult to endure with ease. It was neither the fever and tense watchfulness of the life when in close contact with the enemy, nor was it the pleasant, comfortable existence some had known in barracks in Cairo and Alexandria.

We could look forward to some leave, but this, when it came, would afford only passing pleasure, too brief and hectic to be fully enjoyed at the time, and afterwards acting as a perpetual irritant of discontented longing.

2

Lessons from Experience

AT various times during the day and in the long autumn evenings as we sat huddled round the single lamp in the mess tent, Kinnaird could occasionally be got to talk on matters more serious than the normal run of the conversation. At these times I felt that he talked to us and encouraged us to argue so that he could crystallize the opinions and ideas which were slowly growing in his mind. A lot of it was new to us, but each of us learnt something which was to stand us in good stead later.

A chance remark from one or other of us would start a discussion in which Kinnaird would join sooner or later if the subject interested him or was important enough.

One evening Ryan remarked, 'I reckon these cruiser tanks haven't shown up so bad – sorry, I mean too badly,' he added with a grin as he saw us prepare to correct his grammar, which he was keen to improve. 'I mean they've a bloody good gun and the power traverse is useful. Maybe they are a bit unreliable, but when old Taff Morgan 'ere 'as 'is fitters working properly we ought to be able to mend 'em in double-quick time.'

'You mind your own business, Sid,' Morgan replied. 'If you tank commanders saw the maintenance was done better, the fitters would have less work.'

Taff Morgan was the second captain of the squadron, whom Kinnaird had put in charge of all repairs which were beyond the scope of the crews. It was his job to ensure that the fitters were efficient not only as individuals but drilled and practised as a team to do the big repair tasks with speed and under all conditions.

Bolton, the second-in-command, slow, ponderous and meticulous, now joined the argument. We tended to ignore or laugh at him as a rule, but he frequently confounded us by his quiet wis-

46

dom or the detailed efficiency of his work. 'I don't agree with you, Sid, that these cruisers are what we want. They can knock out these Wop tanks, but we can't do anything about dug-in anti-tank guns, which are always just as dangerous.'

Kinnaird suddenly spoke. 'You're right, Jim. A small solid shot can't do the necessary damage, and the M.G. is useless if they have any sort of protection. Trouble is, our own artillery can't really help us, as they are an area weapon and can't hit these small targets. No, what we want in the tank is a gun which is big enough to fire our own H.E. shell. We'll want them bigger soon enough to penetrate the thicker armour the enemy will put on his tanks.'

On another day Egerton was grumbling about our continued inactivity. 'Damn me, I joined the Army to finish the war, not to stay in it for the rest of my life – which is what I will be at this rate. We kept the Wops on the hop with one squadron before, so why don't we form about ten squadron columns now and go and beat them up?' he asked, glaring at us all defiantly.

'You'll get us all finished off that way without even ending the war,' Kinnaird remarked quietly from the corner of the tent where he had been sitting reading. He went on, 'No, Alan, that's not the way we should fight. Look at the Germans in France. They've proved the truth of the lesson we were teaching years ago on Salisbury Plain. Just because tanks have been a success now, it doesn't mean to say you can do what you want with a few tanks. I remember all the years when people said no number of tanks could do anything, and now people like you think we can win a war or a campaign with penny packets of them. Don't look so miserable, Alan,' he went on, laughing. 'I'm sure you're not the only one who thinks like that now. But seriously, we must remember that, as with any other arm, to be effective we must fight at the fullest possible or necessary strength. Just because we can manoeuvre faster, or go farther with relative impunity on the battlefield, we cannot afford to neglect the rule that we should always fight concentrated – there may be exceptions to that rule, but they are jolly few.'

It was I who next raised a subject on which Kinnaird again had strong views. Some days later, when we had been out on an abortive chase in the hope of catching an Italian column which had ventured out of the camps, I remarked in exasperation, 'If our bloody tanks could only go at a decent speed we would have got that lot.'

'Nonsense, Tony,' Kinnaird replied. 'If we had gone at twice the speed we would still have missed them. Speed is not always the answer. In a tank it's an expensive luxury, as it is in a horse or a car ...'

'... or a woman,' Ryan added, grinning.

'Oh, control your one-track mind, Sid,' Egerton said, laughing.

'As I was saying,' went on Kinnaird with a smile, 'more speed beyond a certain point isn't the answer. Usually we can't overrun a line of guns merely by attacking them at speed. A charge is seldom a profitable manoeuvre, a race with the enemy leaves too much to chance, and a hurried approach march may well give away surprise and will probably result in too many broken-down tanks. I agree there is a place for speed – in manoeuvre and in thought. But – much more important – there is a vital need for clear, far-thinking before battle is ever joined.'

This was a subject on which he frequently elaborated. He felt that the habit was too often to make no plan until the order to move was received, which meant that there was then likely to be a fairly considerable pause while all the necessary detailed arrangements were completed, followed by a breakneck and hurried advance, which often resulted in an unco-ordinated arrival in face of the enemy, with a force depleted by mechanical breakdowns. To avoid this he always tried to make sure that we were continually thinking on the same lines as himself, so that in emergency only a brief word was sufficient to get done what he wanted.

Wireless at that time was used extensively and as a matter of habit only by armoured units and formations. Templeton, who remained silent on most occasions when his knowledge might be disputed by those with more experience than himself, had his views on its use. 'I can't see why, if a message can be passed for miles on a wireless set, any commander need be far forward in battle. He can plan and fight the battle just as well from farther back.'

'He'd be asking for trouble,' Kinnaird said immediately. 'Just because he can hear what is going on, doesn't mean to say that he can know enough to direct the battle. Besides, in a tank battle, moving fast, he may not even hear about something in time to take the necessary action. No, I believe that, certainly in an armoured unit or formation, the commander at every level must be far enough forward to see all he possibly can.'

But above all else he continually stressed the need to make use of ground. 'Unless we do all we can to force the enemy to fight us on ground of our own choosing, we shall be at a disadvantage. We do not want to just swan aimlessly about the battlefield attacking anything we happen to find. We should think first and as far ahead as possible, move first and at a sensible speed, and seize the ground we think the enemy wants or which he doesn't want us to have, and force him to attack us.'

The longer we all knew Kinnaird the more we admired and relied on him. He had a tireless, unrelenting energy which, allied to an infinite capacity for taking pains over every detail, meant that he was master of every aspect of his job, whether it was the detailed tactical control of a battle or the maintenance of his squadron or the welfare of his men.

So the period of reflection and preparation came gradually to an end. We grew ever more confident of our ability to match the Italians. The early skirmishes and forays had served to rub off the edges of bewildered hesitancy which inevitably mars the actions of any troops new to battle. We had changed our mode of life to such an extent that we could view the desert as home and think of its empty spaces as a friend. Warfare in its wastes had none of the complications of fighting in more civilized countries. It was a duel without external influences.

During this time neither side was idle. The Italians were busily preparing a string of fortified camps stretching from just east of Sidi Barrani in a wide arc to the south and west, guarding all the possible approaches to the coastal track which they were making into a metalled road connecting Sidi Barrani with Bardia. Maktila and a post called Point 90, both about twenty miles east of Sidi Barrani, guarded the direct coastal route from Mersa Matruh. A group of camps at Tummar guarded the routes which we would follow if we intended to pass Maktila and Point 90 to the south. The Camp at Nibeiwa guarded the track which ran down the escarpment at Bir Enba. The camps at Rabia and Sofafi were positioned to prevent any move directed on Buq Buq. There were small forces at Half-way House, a precarious route down the escarpment about twenty miles west of Sofafi, and also at 'Hellfire' Pass, Capuzzo, and Sidi Omar.

Maktila, Point 90, the Tummars, and Nibeiwa were each separated from the next camp by about five miles. But between Nibeiwa and Rabia, the next camp to the west, where the ground was flat and featureless, with no vital or commanding ground, the gap was a distance of between twenty-five and thirty miles. Here, too, the escarpment was no obstacle to movement.

Nor were we wasting our time. Each and every move of the Italians was watched by patrols. Their new camps were carefully marked in on the maps and were attacked by the infantry in night forays, the aim of which was to discover the strength and identity of the Italian formations garrisoning each of them. By day the desert outside the string of Italian camps was entirely dominated by our columns of infantry and guns, occasionally reinforced by tanks. As a result we held the greater part of six Italian divisions not only in physical check but also in a measure of psychological subjection.

3

Advance!

DURING October and November each of the squadron's officers had a week's leave. In Cairo and Alexandria we met the men of units and formations newly arrived from England, India, Australia, and New Zealand. We began to feel that we were alone no longer and to sense that preparations were being made for operations about which we had as yet been given no hint.

By the end of November our training as individuals, as crews, and as units had reached a pitch when it was logical that we should exercise as a Division. There was no great surprise, therefore, and indeed considerable relief, when we were told that there were to be two large-scale exercises in the near future.

Kinnaird was away for a whole day with the Colonel at Brigade Headquarters being given the instructions for our part in the manoeuvres. On his return he called all his officers and N.C.O.s together and gave us an outline of the plan.

'As far as I can see, it's an exercise mainly to test the Brigade and Divisional staffs. All we've got to do is to drive for some distance, halt for the night and drive on again the next day to our objective. The Indian Division will be out too, and they're going to practise attacking some dummy camps. We'll be away for three days. Early next month we do the same exercise again over different ground. That's all there is to it. Any questions?'

There wasn't much that anyone could say, and I was surprised to hear Egerton from behind me asking, 'What's the object, sir? It seems an awful waste of time. When are we going to do something worth while?'

I was ready for a sharp retort from Kinnaird, but the answer when it came was in a voice which was calm and thoughtful:

'I don't know any more than I've told you. But I'm doing some pretty good guessing. It might be a number of things. But anyway I'm sure we can be certain that it's not just designed to waste our time. We'll know soon enough, I expect.'

But no one was really convinced that it portended anything special, and Ryan voiced most of our feelings when he muttered, 'Roll on me next drop of leave. I'm browned off with mucking about.'

The exercise went off, as far as we could see, without a hitch. Our part in it was as boring as it had promised to be, except that we did see some new country. From our leaguer area we moved south-east away from the sandier parts near the coast, and on the second day we reached the edge of the Qattara Depression. We looked down the 1,000-foot cliff to the salt marsh below, where the sun glistened on the white crystals and shone on the smooth, flat surface.

The second exercise started on 7 December. The same routine was to be followed, and we expected to return after three days and to settle down again to the interminable waiting. I noticed with no particular interest that the Support Group had moved out earlier across our front and were now some miles ahead. Behind us I could see the dust raised by more vehicles. But soon a mist settled over the desert which shrouded all but the nearest vehicles and hid the country over which we were moving, so that I could not even occupy my time by surveying the scenes around me. The mist was thick enough to prevent any accurate reading of a sun compass and so, to my annoyance, I could not follow the course of our move. In wireless silence, shrouded in mist and resigned to another period of boredom, I spent a lonely and dispiriting day, perched in the cupola of the turret, in discomfort and chilled by the cold winter wind.

It was a relief and pleasure to get into leaguer that night and to be able to move about and speak to friends again. The warm meal that I and my crew cooked revived my spirits, and afterwards I wended my way to Kinnaird's truck for a gossip and in case there were any orders. As I climbed into the smoke-laden interior I was greeted by Morgan's voice, raised in argument:

'. . . you can say what you like, but I bet you I'm right. I followed the route we came and I recognized one or two places I've seen before. And I tell you we're now just south of Nibeiwa.'

'You may be right, Taff,' said Kinnaird, 'but the C.O. doesn't know where we are to go, and he's had no orders yet. We'll have to see what happens to-morrow.'

At dawn we dispersed into open formation. Before breakfasts could be cooked or we had had a chance to check Morgan's information of the night before, we were told that we were to light no fires and were to move about as little as possible.

By this time speculation was rife among those of us who had not, as yet, been let into the secret. An exercise so close to the enemy positions seemed to be an unlikely possibility, and the final positions of our leaguer areas in the gap between Rabia and Nibeiwa, so well known to all of us, indicated that something fairly important was afoot.

In the early afternoon Kinnaird was summoned to the Colonel for orders. Before he left he issued his own orders for his squadron officers and sergeant-major to gather at his tank so that he could pass on the orders on his return. While he was away we passed the time by trying to guess what was to happen. I thought that Maletti's armoured group were out of their camp at Nibeiwa and we were going to destroy them or round them up. Bolton considered that somehow we had discovered an Italian plan for a further advance and the Division was being positioned ready to threaten the Italian flank. Egerton, bored with the recent idle-ness, hoped we were going 'to give one of the outlying camps a good kick in the pants'. Templeton appeared to be not interested and tried to show an unconcern which he, like the rest of us, must have been far from feeling.

Kinnaird was back within an hour and immediately started to give out his orders.

'I needn't tell you in detail about the Italian forces we have against us. You all know of the string of camps he has built around Sidi Barrani. I have got them all, or anyway the ones we know of, marked in on my map, which I will pass round for you to copy.

'Now the plan. Western Desert Force is to destroy or capture all the Italian forces in the camps at Nibeiwa, Tummar, and Point 90 and then move north to cut off the retreat of the Italians in Sidi Barrani and Maktila, who can then be captured or destroyed. At the same time communications and installations between Sidi Barrani and Buq Buq are to be disrupted.'

An awed silence, except for an incredulous, low-pitched whistle from Egerton, greeted this information. Kinnaird watched the effect with some amusement, as we must have exactly reflected his feelings when he heard of the scope of the planned operations.

He continued, 'The 4th Indian Division and a regiment of Matilda tanks are now concentrated to our east. They will carry out the attacks on the camps and afterwards deal with Sidi Barrani. At the same time a small force from Matruh will keep the garrison of Maktila occupied to prevent them moving to help any of the camps.

'7th Armoured Division is to protect the flank and rear of the Indian Division. To do so the Support Group is to watch the camps at Rabia and Sofafi while we in 4th Armoured Brigade move through the gap to cut the coast road and to engage a force of enemy tanks believed to be in that area. 7th Armoured Brigade is to remain in reserve here until called forward. The armoured cars are to patrol the whole frontage of the Division. Any questions so far?

'None? Right, I'll go on. We are to move as the right-hand regiment of the Brigade, and C Squadron will be in the lead. We will move with two troops up, you on the left, Ryan, and you on the right, Egerton. To my flank and to Egerton's right rear will be Stannard, with Templeton behind him.

'Reveille will be at 0400 hours and we shall move off at 0430 hours, so that we shall be clear of the area just west of Nibeiwa in good time before the attack starts at 0700 hours. The Matildas and the Indian Division are going in by the back door on the north-west face of the camp.

'You should all have filled up with petrol by now, and if not you must do so. There are to be no petrol fires for the rest of the day and you will move about as little as possible.

'Wireless silence will not be broken until contact is made with the enemy to-morrow. Synchronize your watches with mine. The time is fifteen-thirty-seven – now.

'If there are no questions, get back to your troops and pass on the orders to them. I want to see you all in leaguer to-night to give you final instructions.'

All through the night of Sunday, 8 December, the R.A.F. bombed Sidi Barrani and aerodromes to the west, the Navy bombarded Maktila and the guns of 7th Armoured Division shelled the camps at Nibeiwa and Rabia. Under cover of this noise the final moves to complete the concentration were made. Guided by special posted marker lights organized by the Support Group, the Matilda tanks and the 11th Indian Infantry Brigade moved until they were in position to the west and north-west of Nibeiwa, facing the less heavily defended portion of the perimeter and a gap through which, the previous evening, twenty-three Italian M11 light tanks had been seen to move – a reassuring sign that it had not been mined.

Punctually at 0700 hours the next morning the guns began to register their targets. At 0715 the bombardment by about 200 guns started, and the Matildas and the infantry moved in to attack Nibeiwa.

Meanwhile we in 4th Armoured Brigade had begun our advance to the coastal road some thirty-five miles away. As the sky lightened in the east and the guns started their bombardment, I could not help feeling awed and exhilarated. To my right, as we moved, the desert was bare and deserted, but it was from here that in due course the enemy might attack or the desert might become suddenly filled with enemy surprised by our move. However empty and tranquil it looked then, there was the lurking threat of sudden action, and action on a scale that I had not experienced before.

However preoccupied I was with the stark, ominous desert to my right, I could not resist occasionally glancing at the scene on my left. As far as the eye could see, stretching across the horizon to my left front and flank and rear, there were vehicles moving: the tanks of the leading and the other flanking regiment to my front and left, and behind me the other two squadrons of my own regiment. Each tank was followed by a plume of sand, lit and highlighted by the slanting rays of the early sun, as it pitched and rolled and tossed over the uneven, stony surface of the desert. Within the three-sided box formed by the tanks were the supply vehicles, the fitters' lorries, the doctors' trucks, the ambulances. In the centre of the whole array I could see the few vehicles of the Brigade Headquarters. In front of them, and behind the centre of the leading regiment, was the small group of tanks from which I knew the Brigadier was controlling the whole move and ready to give instant orders the moment the enemy was met. The contrast between the scene on my left and that on my right continued to enthral me as we advanced towards the coast.

As the light spread over the sky to the east, I felt, rather than heard the dull concussion of the guns as they fired on Nibeiwa. I could imagine the consternation of the unsuspecting Italians and the confusion which would follow. In my mind's eye I followed the Matildas in their attack.

I took my head-phones off so as to get a better impression of the sounds of the battle. It was uncanny that out of the silent, motionless wastes of desert there should be coming so much noise. Interspersed with the duller, heavier explosions of the field-guns I could hear the sharper, vicious cracks of the high-velocity guns and the frenzied chatter of machine-guns and rifles. Gradually over the edge of the horizon there rose a pall of black, billowing smoke, touched here and there with a long tongue of flame.

As we moved over farther from the battle, so the sounds died away. But before they had completely faded I sensed that the tempo of the shooting had decreased – the smoke-clouds grew no longer and no new clouds blacked the sky. I wondered what had happened. The silence could only mean one of two things. I was not left long in doubt. I heard the Colonel's voice in my head-phones saying:

' . . . Nibeiwa is captured. Our friends have reported complete success, with few casualties. They have got a large number of prisoners and have captured much equipment. To our west, too, reports say that there is no sign of any enemy reactions. I will give you the news as it comes in. Off.'

By ten o'clock we reached and secured the coast road some ten miles west of Sidi Barrani, and thus cut the enemy line of retreat. We were on the alert to capture or destroy any unsuspecting enemy who were unaware of the trap that had been set. By the end of the day our tally was 300 prisoners and twenty vehicles captured and a further sixty vehicles destroyed. At intervals incredulous Italian officers appeared in staff cars from the direction of either Buq Buq or Sidi Barrani to convince themselves that there really was an enemy force sitting on their main line of communications. Once during the afternoon Kinnaird ordered Egerton to do all he could to capture a particularly impressive and venturesome car, but Egerton could only report later:

' . . . Afraid he got away. Some of our bullets went fairly close though, and I think we frightened him. . . . '

All through the middle hours of the day and well into the afternoon we waited for news of the fate of the whole operation now being decided in the attacks on the Tummar camps. No word, however, came of the course of the battle, and not knowing the timings to which the attacks were planned, we were all beginning to lose hope that they had gone as intended.

Inside the turret my crew sat huddled in their positions. Probably they weren't as dejected as their attitudes implied. Nevertheless the long hours of waiting for more news were clearly an anxiety to at least Tilden, the operator, who appeared out of the loader's hatch and inquired:

'Ought to hear something soon, oughtn't we, sir? Wonder how them Tillies has got on? Gets you jumpy, 'anging about waiting for news, don't it, sir?'

'We'll hear soon enough, I expect,' I answered, more in hope than certainty. 'Hop out and make a brew and get out something for us to eat.' This would at least keep us all occupied and help to pass the time away.

At last, soon after four o'clock, the news for which we had been waiting came, as before, from the Colonel over the regimental control net:

' ... Tummar West has been captured and the attack on Tummar East has already started. Everything has gone according to plan so far. Other friends are now moving up on our right to help us seal off the camps that remain during to-night. Watch out for them, and for God's sake don't shoot at 'em. Be ready to give them any help they may need. Off.'

So it was that, just before five o'clock, from my position on the right flank, I saw and made contact with the leading troops of the 16th Infantry Brigade. By nightfall they were disposed to cover all the small tracks and routes to the west and were busily preparing for a strenuous night of patrolling the forward enemy positions in readiness for an attack to be launched early the next day.

As the light faded we moved into a regimental leaguer. I could sense an air of excitement and elation all round me.

When we were at last in position, Sykes climbed out of the driver's seat with a broad grin on his face, saying, as he pushed his goggles up on to his forehead:

'That's a great day, sir. Let's have some smack-up grub to celebrate. If we'ad knowed what was on we could 'ave stocked up ready. Alf, what've we got?'

'We ain't got damn all to celebrate wiv, 'less you think a bully stew is good enough,' answered Holton, rummaging in the bins.

'That do you, sir?' asked Sykes.

'I could eat a Wog, I'm so hungry,' I answered. 'I'll be back in a moment to give a hand. I must go to the O.C. first and see if he has any orders.'

'Tell you what,' said Tilden, released at last from the tyranny of the wireless, which had now closed down. 'Let's make a slap-up bivvy and eat our grub in style. That'll make it seem more like a celebration, though it'll still be bully stew.'

I left them preparing an elaborate bivouac which they were going to build by using the tarpaulin sheet tied to the tank track. Normally, during operations, we just threw the sheet over our bedding to keep the rain and dew off.

'Come on in, Tony,' Kinnaird greeted me as I climbed into his truck. 'Have a drink to celebrate.'

We all welcomed the occasion to rejoice in a day of triumph and success, all too few so far in the war. Here, at last, was the outward and visible vindication of the months of relentless pressure by which a moral ascendancy over the Italians had been created. Even so, we were all aware by what slender margin our successes of that day had been achieved.

At length I returned to my crew and ate the festive dish of bully stew and shared with them our sense of triumph and talked of all our future hopes.

Later, exhausted, dusty but replete, I lay down to sleep with an elation and confidence which I had not felt before.

The next morning dawned clear and sunlit, but, as so often happened in the desert, a sudden strong westerly wind sprang up by about six o'clock and whipped the light coastal sand and the loose dust, disturbed by the tracks and wheels of the previous day's advance, into a blinding sandstorm. Throughout the day we fought in an eddying mist of dust and sand, which not only caked our faces and clothes, but, on occasion, effectually hid our moves from the eyes of the Italian gunners. The storm also made these moves more difficult to execute when they depended on the close co-ordination and co-operation of a number of units who were only visible to each other at intervals through the swirling blanket of dust.

Already, to the east, we could hear the sounds of battle. I remembered that the Indian Division had planned to continue their advance to envelop Sidi Barrani before daylight revealed them to the Italian gunners. The sounds we now heard could only mean that their advance had been observed, and we were impatient to move as soon as possible.

The Colonel gave out his orders as we moved off:

' . . . We are to help in the capture of the remaining camps still holding out. Other people will continue to watch to the west. At present our friends are being attacked by Italian forces trying to break out to the west. We are to help break this attack first. Conform to my movements in your present formation and report when you have made contact with any friends. Off.'

By 0800 hours our squadron was in position some 1,000 yards south of a line of Italian guns which covered the ground to the west and south-west of Sidi Barrani. The remainder of the regiment were moving into line on our left. Farther still to the west, the regiment which had led the previous day's advance reported that they had swung east and were facing the seaward end of the Italian defences and here, where there were fewer guns, had managed, in concert with the infantry, to probe the outer defences of the town itself.

I found it difficult to control the exasperation I felt at being forced to sit so ineffectively watching the Italian guns firing at us. My inclination was to charge the whole line with my troop. But I knew that, though it would perhaps serve to relieve my feelings, it would be a useless gesture. I would not be able to achieve much before the whole troop were either knocked out or crippled. So I was forced to content myself with doing what damage I could with the machine-gun, while I avoided the attentions of the Italian artillery by careful movements of my tank to disrupt the calculations of any Italian gunner who was trying to range on me. I wished I could do more to help the infantry who were lying all round in the shallow holes and trenches they had quickly dug as some protection against the shell-fire. Apart from making my tank a target, which I was already doing, and trying to keep the Italians well occupied with the machine-gun, there was no other assistance I could give. I knew that the last thing any of the infantry would want to do would be to climb into my tank for shelter, for, though I invariably felt naked and terrified when under fire outside my tank, I knew from previous experience that they felt equally uncomfortable when cooped up inside the turret.

So for some time we lay in face of the enemy. Once or twice I felt like reporting that the infantry near me were in need of help but that there was nothing I could do. But each time I resisted the temptation. Kinnaird was close enough at hand to see the position, and in any case we were no worse placed than the other squadrons of the regiment. At length I heard Kinnaird reporting to the Colonel on the regimental net:

' ... We can't do anything here for ourselves or friends who are suffering a fair number of casualties. The enemy are too strongly defended for us to advance. I suggest we must either have very heavy gun support or be helped over the first part of an attack by others like us but heavier. I have looked to see whether we can move farther to our flank, but it's no better there, so there's not much point. Over.'

The Colonel replied, ' . . . Quite agree. I've already reported back that we can't do anything. They haven't got any means of helping us and are finding out what can be done. We shall just have to contain ourselves in patience for a bit. Do what you can to make life bloody for the Wops. Off.'

We were not left to our own devices for long, for within ten minutes the Colonel was again on the wireless saying:

' . . . Heavy relations are moving up to support us now. They will be with us soon and will advance to attack immediately so as not to give the Wops a chance to reorganize. I have already told them where we are and what they can expect. Stand by to follow them. Off.'

The arrival of the Matildas would be none too soon for our health and comfort and that of the infantry we were supporting. In the prevailing sandstorm we suddenly found ourselves for some minutes in an oasis of calm, clear daylight, sitting targets for the Italian guns, whose visibility was now unimpaired.

Their rate of fire increased until the whole squadron and the infantry were being deluged by a hail of shells. Our tanks were relatively in less danger, since, closed down, anything other than a direct hit could do us little harm. But the infantry were suffering a good many casualties, exposed as they were in the very shallow trenches which were all they had had time to dig. From the safety of the firmly closed down turret of my tank, I watched through the periscopes with awe and horror the scene of destruction and suffering which surrounded us. Some of the shells fell wide of their mark, leaving behind them only a cloud of dust and black smoke which drifted slowly across the battlefield, carried by the little breeze there was in the sudden calm. Others fell near the tanks, and we could hear the dull metallic clang as the bits of shell-splinter hit the armour plate. Others fell among the small groups of infantry, leaving behind the twisted, mangled, and distorted bodies of the dead and wounded.

As I watched I held my breath, as if expecting without doubt that the ghastly holocaust must have a climax, must leave a sight or scene which could only be violent and which would leave an imprint on my mind for ever. And it came as I sensed it would. Ten yards to the right of my tank was a small group of infantry – a platoon headquarters, consisting of an officer and three men. Even as I found my eyes fixed involuntarily on this group, there fell among them a large-calibre Italian shell. For a split second all that I could see was the dull red flash of the explosion. Then in the swirling dust and black smoke I saw with shocked dismay what was left of the three men. One was dead; there was no doubt of that, since all that remained of his face was a dull red mass of flesh and bone which seemed to have been pushed almost to the back of his head by an enormous weight. Another was staggering with hesitant, tottering steps away from the scene, clutching with both hands where his stomach had been and where now, through the gaps in his outspread fingers, a red mass of straggling entrails was hanging out. The third man was apparently untouched, and as the realization came to him he turned slowly and in an utterly dazed fashion to give what help he could to the officer, who lay looking at his legs. At first, as I watched, there was on the officer's face only a stupid, bewildered look, as if he entirely failed to understand what had happened; but this soon changed to an expression of incredulous dismay when he at last realized that where he had had two beautifully booted feet a moment before, he was now left with only one and, where the other had been, there was only a frayed end of bone and flesh, the dull, blood-red colour of the flesh thrown into sharper relief by the startling whiteness of the stump of the bone. I flung open the flaps of my cupola and jumped down.

'Anything I can do?' I said. 'Have you got a shell dressing? We must put on a tourniquet at once.'

Still dazed, the officer slowly turned an uncomprehending gaze on me and said, 'I don't feel anything. My foot's gone and it doesn't hurt. I can't understand it. All I can think of is that I shall be lame for the rest of my life. Oh, God, I can't bear the thought!'

But he soon pulled himself together and with surprising calm said, 'Call for a doctor, can you? I can't feel anything yet, but when the nerves wake up it'll be bloody hell. Besides, this poor chap here will need some pretty careful attention. For God's sake get one along soon.'

I clambered back into my tank and called on the wireless for our doctor, who moved, in his truck, near Kinnaird's headquarters. While we waited I did what I could to help the wounded with the first-aid kit we carried on the tank. I gave a shot of morphia to both of them. Sykes did what he could for the man with the stomach wound, but he died in agony. It was with infinite relief that I handed over my patient to the skilled hands of the doctor.

A few minutes later the leading Matildas, with a wave from their commanders in the turrets, swept past us and towards the line of Italian guns which were still firing furiously. It was the very heaviness of this fire that had drawn the Matildas towards this sector of the front, for in their move forward they had found it impossible, through the sand and smoke, to distinguish any part of the battlefield from another, and had at last determined to go where the noise was loudest and clearest to follow.

In the next moment I heard the Colonel's voice again calling Kinnaird and giving him further orders:

' ... As the relations have passed through your front you will lead behind them. As soon as you are through the enemy defended area, swing right. Take no notice of the relations, as they are to go left. We are to go east until we have joined up with other friends about whom you have heard. Off.'

This was a reference to the force from Matruh who were now faced with the Maktila garrison in strong positions. Without the help of tanks they could make no further progress.

Waiting until the Matildas were about 500 yards ahead, Kinnaird then gave the order to advance and to follow, as closely as possible, in the wake of the heavier tanks, so that we could take the best advantage of the gap they made in the line of guns. Once through, we swung east, being fired at whenever the sandstorm cleared, by a further line of guns on another ridge on our left.

It was here that I had my first experience of being hit squarely by a shell, though, luckily for us, it was not armour piercing and did no internal damage to the tank. Nevertheless it was an unpleasant occurrence and served to give me a clear indication of what would happen when the day came when I was unfortunate enough to have my tank penetrated. On the other hand, it left me with the reassuring feeling that all the rumours and opinions I had heard about conditions inside a tank which was hit were nonsense. I had often heard it said that a tank could be knocked out by even rifle and other small-arms fire, since the effect inside the tank was that the armour flaked off and small splinters of steel would cause serious injury to the crew. On this morning we were hit by two shells in fairly rapid succession. It was true that these hits jammed the turret so that we could not traverse it, and damaged the gunner's telescope so that, until he had replaced it with the spare one, he was unable to engage any targets. But for the rest, except that the dull metallic thud of the hit and the following crash of the explosion stirred up all the dust in the tank, making it difficult for a few moments for us to see each other, I and the other members of the crew only suffered from headaches for a short while afterwards.

Hindered by wide stretches of soft sand and blinded by the sandstorm which still raged, we at length joined the Matruh force, and with them did our best to harass and destroy the Italian rear-guards. It was a frustrating business. Often as we were just about to launch a quickly but carefully co-ordinated attack in concert with the infantry the sandstorm obliterated the objective. And when the view was clear again we found the Italians had slipped away and installed themselves further back on a new position. Here and there we were more successful, and the haul of prisoners and equipment captured or destroyed increased slowly but perceptibly.

But compared to the previous day the results were less startling. When darkness fell I found that the elation I had hoped to share in leaguer was tempered with disappointment, until news came that Sidi Barrani had fallen and the enemy before us were the last holding out of the string of forts which had stood only yesterday.

4

Chase Beyond the Frontier

I AWOKE next morning to find the air still heavy with dust and a high wind which made the chill of the December day more biting. The sunrise was thin and watery seen through a film of sand. With visibility cut down to so short a distance, we could achieve little more than on the previous day, though we managed to push the enemy back slowly but surely. At ten o'clock we were suddenly told that our plans were changed and that we were to move at once to rejoin the Brigade, who were in open leaguer between the Tummar camps and Nibeiwa. Here the Colonel gave out our new orders. Tilden and I stared at one another in surprise as we listened.

' . . . Orders. We move in figures one five minutes. Anyone who is not ready then will be left behind. The camps at Sofafi and Rabia are reported clear and enemy columns have been seen moving from there to the west. Buq Buq is clear and an attack will start very soon to clean up Italian positions about a mile to the west. It is expected that the enemy east of Sidi Barrani will have given in by this evening.'

He paused, and we could hear him drawing in his breath before giving the news which he must have known we would receive with excitement.

'We are to advance to the frontier to discover whether the enemy is holding any of his camps there. Owing to this change of plan we shall have to be short of food and water so that we can continue to be supplied with the ammunition and petrol we shall need. That is all. Move when I move, in your present formation. Off.'

South of Nibeiwa we were already above the escarpment, and here we turned west. Throughout that day and the next and the next we moved farther and farther west, until on the morning of 14 December we crossed the main Bardia-Tobruk road and finally sealed the western exits of Bardia. From the frontier onwards we were into country which few of us had ever seen before. Of the enemy we saw little. The camps and depots which they had set up in Egypt they abandoned, and fled into the defences of Bardia. Despite the discomfort and our increasing weariness, each mile that we covered acted as a spur to go yet farther, especially when we were in Italian territory.

At this stage – after our long period of relative inactivity and the softness and delights of leave – those of us in the tank crews found hardest to bear the continual lack of sleep and the physical effort required to meet the perpetual rolling and pitching of the tanks across the uneven desert. Our days started with the first flush of morning, and not until the sun was well below the western horizon did we normally withdraw to leaguer. Even then the work did not finish. Breakdowns to the tanks and casualties among the crews entailed hard work and reorganization within the squadrons. The tanks had to be filled with ammunition and fuel. The engines and tracks, suspensions and transmissions had to be inspected and repaired or adjusted as necessary. Orders, codes and wireless call-signs for the morrow were issued and memorized or filed away. Clean clothes were available sometimes from the squadron quartermasters; the doctor was at hand for minor wounds and ailments. In addition to these numerous duties and tasks, this, too, was normally the only time when we could get a hot meal and drink. During the day we existed on biscuits, margarine and cheese, occasionally varied by jam and tins of cold bully-beef. There was usually no time nor chance for even a quick brew of tea, so that the evening stew of tinned meat and vegetables and the brew of tea, sometimes with a tot of rum added if the Divisional Commander authorized it, assumed considerable importance in the minds and lives of each of the tank-crew members. It was seldom that the leaguer was quiet and asleep much before midnight, so that, with a turn of guard duty to perform and reveille a quarter of an hour before first light, each man got between four and five hours sleep each night at the most. If there were repairs to be done to the tank, then that crew, as well as the fitters who normally helped, got little or no sleep at all. And if the repair was of a major part of the tank, the crews of the tanks nearest on each side of the damaged one had their sleep disturbed by the inevitable noise and movement.

During the days of the battle and the subsequent chase, when the tanks were on the move for most of the hours of daylight, it was a test of endurance to exert the continual physical effort required to prevent actual injury caused by the rolling and pitching. The dust and heat of the engine, the fumes from the empty cases of the main armament and the more trying acrid smell of the Beza machine-gun cartridges were the least of the worries. Even so, looking ahead, I dreaded to think what hell of discomfort these would cause in any prolonged battles fought in the heat of full summer. These trials, in a very mobile campaign, were less exacting than those imposed by the movements of the tank. The rolling of the tank was the easiest of the unexpected movements to counter; a side slope of a hill or the more violent slopes of the small depressions in the ground were usually visible some way off, if one happened to be looking in the right direction at the right time. Forewarned, each member of the crew who could see could brace himself for the essentially limited sideways movement of the tank. The operator, working his set or loading the guns in any battle movement, and even at other times provided with very little vision, suffered most through being unprepared. It was the pitching and tossing movements which were the most violent, most unexpected and least possible to guard against. We usually moved fast, sometimes at a speed of between fifteen and twenty miles an hour, across all types and surfaces of desert, through the solid tufts of the sand-choked roots of scrub, over boulders often a foot in diameter and across ground of which every crevice and dip, undulation and hole was flattened to the eye by the almost perpendicular rays of the sun, which, except at the extreme ends of the day, cast no shadows at all. In these circumstances it was impossible for the driver to avoid most of the crashing bumps which we suffered and equally difficult for the crew members to brace ourselves in time. It was tremendously exhausting never being able to relax completely without being bruised or hurt. Even with the tank at rest, while we sat in watch on the enemy, the crampedness of our several positions gave us no chance to relax, so that, though only the commander needed to be always on the alert, the other members could doze only fitfully.

Another factor which contributed in no small measure to the exhaustion of tank commanders and operators was the wireless. From the moment we stood to at first light until we were finally settled into our positions in leaguer an hour or so after last light, the commanders and operators had to be fully on the alert. We only courted the vilest and most vehement abuse if, after failing to catch fully any message when it was first transmitted, we had to answer 'Say again'. The realization of the need for this instant and continual alertness and the degree to which it was achieved were the measures of efficiency and effectiveness of any armoured regiment. Laxness in this respect or undue volubility on the wireless detracted from the speed of manoeuvre of a regiment and could, and often did, make it a prey to any unforeseen quick move by the enemy. The alertness was not the only cause of exhaustion. When no messages were being transmitted and, in the early evening and first half of the night as a background to the messages that were being passed, there was a continual crackling, wheezing, whining, whistling noise in the head-phones, which had to be kept close to the head in case a distant faint transmission was missed. The concentration needed at all times and the persistent noise often gave to each commander and operator a violent headache which the glare of the sun on the sand did nothing to relieve.

Even when we reached Bardia we did not halt, for, handing over our duties on the perimeter, we moved south again along the route we had already come, and farther south still, until we reached the Italian frontier fort of Sidi Omar.

Here for a morning we halted to repair the ravages that the miles had wrought on our tanks and to get some rest for ourselves. Of the tanks nearly all required repair in some way or another. Of the crews, despite the long hours, the poor food and the lack of water, few needed to be restored either physically or mentally. Success was a heady tonic.

Our capture of Sidi Omar was a fitting climax to the chase, from which we passed now to the tedium of the watch on the perimeter of Bardia.

This was the final chapter in what had been a memorable week. The prisoners, the equipment captured, the positions taken and the country occupied were the signs of success to the outer world.

More important at the time to those of us taking part was the fabulous nature of the loot which fell into our hands. In the captured camps and stores we found pistols and automatics to delight the eyes of all; cameras, brilliant dress uniforms, gorgeously jewelled swords, silver and gilt belts and emblazoned leather equipment. Some found huge quantities of Italian money. Most important to anyone living on the barest rations, as we in the Western Desert Force were compelled to do, were the stocks of food which we captured; rich red and white wines, cases of matured brandy and liqueurs, bottled fruits, frozen hams and anchovies, tins of beef, sacks of macaroni, potatoes, onions and carrots, minestrone soup. I was not surprised when I heard Sykes, my driver, summarize our feelings by saying, 'What I says is, we want more wine, women and war with the Wops, and—the bloody songs.'

5

Templeton Falters

WHEN they had completed the capture of the camps and Sidi Barrani, 4th Indian Division were withdrawn and went south to Eritrea and other battles. We were sorry to see them go, and in later years welcomed the chances we had to serve alongside them again, to remind us of these first great occasions. Their place was taken by the 6th Australian Division, who, supported by the Matildas, captured Bardia on 4 January and Tobruk on 22nd.

Though we took no major part in the assault on either, the weeks since we had first crossed the frontier were not without action and discomfort. Day in, day out we were required to exercise a relentless vigilance in our watch on the western exits from each town. Before Bardia our alertness was especially important, since the Italian forces within the defences were so superior numerically that the chance of an attempt by them to break out had to be carefully guarded against. At Tobruk, with one Armoured Brigade watching the enemy front at Gazala and the other Brigade and the Support Group taking their share of the guard on the extensive distances of the perimeter defences, we were again fully occupied.

We were all desperately tired, until sometime during the siege of Tobruk, when I, for one, got my second wind. Starting with the sandstorm during the attack on Sidi Barrani, the weather had been persistently bad. High winds had either lashed the desert sand into storms of unusual intensity or had brought torrential downpours of rain, which had swamped the pits we dug for shelter or penetrated the hastily rigged bivouacs and seeped through every crack and crevice in tank or lorry. After the intense heat of the summer I found that I took time to get used to the cold and wet. Nor, to begin with, was I accustomed to the endless lack of sleep and the inadequate food. Eighteen hours of intense watchfulness and alert wakefulness, followed by six hours of so-called rest disturbed by a tour of guard duty and the ceaseless turmoil and noise of the leaguer, for forty days at a stretch – that had been our lot. When, at last, at the end of each day I crept into my blankets to get what sleep I could, I found that my earlier life of ease and luxury made it difficult for me to sleep soundly in these conditions. Either the blankets were wet from the day's heavy rain, or, muffled beneath a ground-sheet as protection against more night rain, the air was too close for comfort; or the ground was hard and pebbly; or it was just too cold for the blankets to afford enough warmth for sound repose. Whatever the reasons, I found that each night it was an effort to sleep.

Our food during most of this time consisted of a hot stew of tinned meat and vegetables cooked in leaguer at night, and during the day only biscuits and corned beef, and occasionally a cup of tea which we were able to brew if we withdrew out of range of the Italian guns or if the enemy were not on the alert. In time we all began to feel the need for fresh vegetables, more particularly so with some men who came out in boils and sores on all parts of their bodies.

Before Tobruk finally fell to the Australians we were already moving again in search of the enemy. West of Gazala, on the coast, the rocky, hilly country of the Gebel Akhdar, the Green Mountains, began. Our course had to be to the south of this area, which was in the main unsuitable for tanks. We moved on a line which was south of west towards Machili, the Italian fort at the southern foot of the Gebel.

Though we had little or no opposition, we had to curb our natural eagerness to press on, so as not to dislodge the Italians prematurely from their positions round Derna, which the Australians planned to encircle.

Carefully as we probed, however, the Italian tanks at Machili eventually took fright, and for three days we engaged in a fruitless chase into the foothills, vainly trying to bring them to battle.

The cold, the lack of sleep, the discomfort, the dangers, were beginning to take their toll on our nerves. We were all inclined to be irritable, not so much with our crews, whose hardships we directly shared, as with our fellow officers when we met in leaguer at night. Conversation in Kinnaird's truck was never very brisk now, and even Egerton seemed unable to summon the energy to make fun of events. We found we could only get on with one another if nothing was demanded of us, and for this reason we increasingly ignored Templeton. He appeared to make less and less effort to be friendly, but would sit huddled in a corner, shut in on himself, a bitter look in his eyes. None of us had the reserves of nervous energy required to cross the barrier he had built up, and on the few occasions we tried, our advances were so quickly rebuffed that we soon desisted. Indeed, he now became a subject for conversation, and gradually we became aware of his deterioration. We could see that he was almost desperate with anxiety and a fear which grew each day and fed on any incident or word which spoke of dangers passed or of the uncertain future. He had grown more and more morose and unapproachable. His experiences had been no worse than those of the rest of us up to this time, but he seemed incapable of making the effort to control the reactions we all felt when we were oppressed with fear. We all felt fear when we went into action – a fear aggravated by the frequent battles, the inevitable hits by shell-splinter and anti-tank shot thudding against the armour. Each time we engaged the enemy we could imagine what might happen. Despite the cold air which whipped and lashed my hands and face, I sweated as I stared down into the close confines of the turret and pictured the shambles that would replace the ordered scene if we were penetrated. Imagination and a quick mind were essentials to be able to take part in the swift-moving changes of an armoured battle, but in Templeton the imagination had taken command and led him on a gloomy labyrinthine course of mental horror and physical terror.

It was at Machili, just before we entered the foothills of the Gebel, that Templeton failed to spot a small Italian 20-mm. anti-tank gun which was dug in on his flank. The first indication he had of its presence was the sharp clang of a hit by its very high-velocity shot, a gush of flame and fumes which seemed to pass across the turret, just missing his knees, and a further clash of metal as the shot went out of the farther side of the turret. For a moment there was silence. Then from inside he heard the startled, horrified voice of his gunner shouting hysterically, 'For God's sake, sir, 'ave a look at Clements. 'E's been 'it good an' proper, an' 'e's spewing blood all over the — place.' When Templeton

70

bent to look he saw the operator sprawled on the floor of the turret with the blood pouring from a huge hole in his throat. As he watched, the last spasms of life crossed the face of the dying man, and with a croak he died. That had been bad enough, but clearing the mess from the turret later that day had been torture of the worst kind. And, since our tanks were then much depleted in numbers, he had to go in the damaged tank, with the holes on each side a constant reminder and warning for some days.

In leaguer that night we all went out of our way to commiserate with him on being penetrated, but he was completely unapproachable. Egerton's cheerful remark that he would now get a nice draught through the holes to keep his legs cool in summer was not well received.

After this incident he became even more aloof and unpleasant, so that we were not prepared to offer help even if we realized the need; yet he still had enough pride to prevent him from putting his troubles to either Kinnaird or the doctor. More and more each day he became a prey to his nerves and anxieties. We were none of us very sympathetic. We understood too little of fear and were too uncertain of our own control of our reactions to it to be charitable to others. We felt that we had either got courage or we had not, and if not there was little we could do for ourselves or anyone else. Later, with more self-confidence and a keener awareness of the nature of fear, we were to feel differently.

By 29 January our numbers were so depleted that we could neither press on nor try to encircle the Derna garrison, with the latent threat of the Italian tanks on our flank. We were told to withdraw, and settled down to rest while we waited for reinforcements which could not arrive until the second week of February.

6

We Surround the Enemy

OUR short rest was suddenly disturbed by the need for urgent action. During Monday, 3 February, it became clear from the sum of the air-reconnaissance reports that the enemy had realized the risks involved in holding their whole force in the mountain region and had decided to withdraw. As a further indication of a general retreat, the Australians reported during the morning that they had lost contact with the main body of the enemy west of Derna. So far it was impossible to say whether the enemy were withdrawing to defend Benghazi more closely or whether they had decided to evacuate the whole of Cyrenaica, in which case time was getting short if they were to be intercepted.

That day 7th Armoured Division was ordered to be prepared to move on the following day with all speed and all available strength.

At about midday Kinnaird was summoned to Regimental Headquarters to receive his orders. This sudden acceleration of the move was almost beyond the capacity of the supply resources, which had then only just started to be built up. Each tank was issued with two days' rations of food and water, some ammunition and fuel, just sufficient for the estimated needs, but the margin was very close. It was about 150 miles from Machili to the road south of Benghazi, and at least part of the route was known to be very bad and rough and might entail considerable detours. At the end of the march we would be faced, if we got there in time, by the whole of the remaining Italian forces. We could expect a very hard fight to stop the enemy, who would make every possible effort to succeed in their last hope of escaping total encirclement.

At dawn on 4 February we moved off. Preceded as usual by the armoured cars, 4th Armoured Brigade led the rest of the Division, spread out over a large frontage to make use of every available bit of good going. Mine was this time the centre troop of Kinnaird's squadron, the leading squadron of the regiment, which was itself the leading unit of the Brigade. All reports about the roughness of the country we found to be true after the first half-dozen miles of relatively good going. For mile after mile I was faced with a vista of huge, forbidding rocks and boulders through which I had to pick my way carefully to avoid the risk of shedding a track. All the time I was being nagged and harried by Kinnaird and the Colonel to speed up and press on. In the mind of every one of us was the vision of the Italians streaming out south of Benghazi, every moment more and more of them eluding the trap which was gradually closing in.

Revived by the short period of rest, I found that the fever of the chase kept me at a pitch of excitement throughout the day, despite the many frustrations of the incredible country through which we were passing and the uncertainties of the highly inaccurate maps on which we were forced to pin our faith. Movement for most of the day was at an average of not more than walking pace. Where the ground improved we accelerated in frantic anxiety to make the best possible time. Where the ground was again cut up by slabs of rock and outcrops of boulders, we learnt to contain ourselves in patience and to pick a slow, laborious route through the obstacles, trying desperately to keep the number of mechanical failures to a minimum. We succeeded at last, at about five o'clock in the evening, in reaching better ground. Ahead of us the armoured cars had already reached Fort Msus, which, after a short, sharp skirmish, they managed to capture, together with the few bewildered occupants whose quiet evening had been shattered by the sudden arrival of the enemy from what they must have regarded as the safety of the inner fastnesses of the desert.

When night fell shortly afterwards we continued the advance in the moonlight. To me this was a new experience, and not one that I particularly enjoyed. It was bitterly cold, so that my face soon became frozen and raw and was painful to touch. Yet the agony was made bearable as being an earnest of the indomitable purpose of the march. Occasionally I glanced down into the turret to reassure myself that I was not dreaming the whole situation. In the eerie light cast by the single red warning bulb of the wireless set I could see, beyond the glinting metal of the gun-breech, the huddled figure of Tilden. At my feet, crouched forward peering through the gun telescope – his only view of the outside world – sat Holton, on the alert, as he had to be, since we were one of the leading tanks of the Division. Beyond, and farther down and forward, I could see Sykes' head and shoulders silhouetted against the panel and instrument lights on the forward armoured bulkhead.

At one o'clock in the morning, when the moon had set and further movement would have been impossibly slow and even dangerous, we halted, still some way from Msus. The night remained bitterly cold, and a north-westerly wind which sprang up soon afterwards brought with it in due course torrents of rain. What little rest we might have had was curtailed by essential tasks. First there was the inevitable maintenance to be done. On my tank we had to replace a bogie wheel, one of the main ones which tensioned and moved along the lower run of the track, a task which involved a great deal of energy and time. Fortunately for us there were only a few other major tasks to be done in the squadron, so we had the help of Morgan and his fitters. With further luck the repairs went smoothly and were done quite quickly. Then there was the food – our only real meal of the day – to be prepared. No fires were allowed, so it was impossible to produce anything either hot or really appetizing. All in all it was a disturbing and restless night, with each of us still keyed up with anxiety lest in the end we should be too late to catch the retreating Italians.

At first light on 5 February the Division was divided into three detachments. To the first was allotted half the armoured-car regiment, a motor battalion of infantry and two batteries of artillery. These were ordered to make all possible speed to reach the main road south of Benghazi. Behind them, and on the same route, 4th Armoured Brigade were to endeavour to reach the coast at our best speed also. The third detachment was the now fairly depleted 7th Armoured Brigade, reinforced by the remainder of the Support Group, who were to make for Benghazi.

So the march continued. We were further urged on by the air reports, which spoke of large bodies of enemy forming up in and around Benghazi and starting to move south. The country beyond Msus was considerably better, nevertheless we could maintain no great speed without risk of further mechanical breakdowns.

So far, except for the minimum of orders, the move had been made in wireless silence, but at last, at about 1230 hours, the welcome news for which we had all been waiting with such anxiety was announced by the Colonel with the brief information, 'Hello, all stations BODO; BODO calling. The road is cut. I say again, the road is cut. Off.' The leading wheeled vehicle force had reached the coast where, in an area of low sand dunes, the main motor road to Tripoli and a lesser track along the coast came nearest to each other and the sea. They had won their race by

74

only a narrow margin, for not a hundred minutes later they sighted the leading vehicles of the first Italian detachment moving serenely on what they fondly imagined was their safe passage out of the clutches of the Australian forces who were pressing hard on their rearguards in their advance through the Gebel.

Towards evening a large enemy column, mainly consisting of artillery, met the block and, surprised at the spirited intensity of the opposition, which no doubt persuaded them that they had met a larger force, surrendered, yielding some 5,000 prisoners. Meanwhile we in 4th Armoured Brigade had reached Antelat, where we were told to halt for the night until the enemy intentions were clearer. We were well placed to deal with any possible advance by the enemy through the open desert east of the main motor road in an attempt to avoid the blocking force. 7th Armoured Brigade, after a short action at Sceleidima, were about ten miles short of Soluch.

Early on the following morning the enemy's main columns were reported moving south on the motor road. We were ordered to advance to the area of Beda Fomm, about eight miles from the road and approximately the same distance north-east of the block. Here, in the open, undulating country, we would be admirably placed to intervene against the eastern flanks of the enemy, who were still keeping religiously to the road or only just off it. Kinnaird's squadron was still in the lead, and we were all eager to be in at the kill. As we moved towards Beda Fomm the latest reports of the enemy's movements from the armoured cars ahead of us were continually passed on by the Colonel. At the same time we got reports from the blockading force.

'Hello DOMO; DOMO calling. Friends to our south-west report being attacked by about figures three zero tanks and two zero guns. They are very hard pressed, and we are to engage the enemy as soon as possible to relieve them.'

This was the first intimation that heavy fighting had started, and was followed shortly afterwards by, '... Patrols to our immediate front report being engaged by about figures five zero tanks and are being heavily shelled by a large number of guns massed in the dunes to the west of the road. They too want help as soon as we can give it to them. Off.'

More news followed, '... Friends to our north report they

have captured Soluch and a number of prisoners. They say that about figures three zero tanks were seen moving in a southerly direction towards us. Watch out for them. Off.'

As our move continued I marked each new piece of information on to my map and counted up the opposition. At least 100 tanks had already been located, and I wondered how many more there might be. The gunfire, as we drew nearer the coast, was distinctly audible and sounded as heavy as anything we had met so far.

Again the Colonel's voice, 'The road-block force say they are being attacked with great determination and that unless the pressure is relieved soon they do not think they can hold out. We will change direction left by figures two zero degrees and increase speed to the maximum possible. On reaching the road do not await further orders, but attack immediately. When we have made our presence known we will rally for a more concerted attack. Off.'

In a swirl of dust and at a speed which bucketed us about in the tank and put our hearts in our mouths lest a track or suspension should break and leave us stranded and out of the battle, we changed direction and moved in on the enemy. As my tank came to the top of a ridge about two miles east of the road I was staggered by the amazing scene before me. South, to my left, I could see the puffs of the shell-bursts on the brilliant white dunes which marked the positions of the blocking force. From there, and directly in front of me and to my right, stretching as far as the eye could see, the main road and the flat ground on each side of it were packed tight with every conceivable type of enemy vehicle and equipment. At this point, where the Italians were still unaware that they were being menaced, groups of men were wandering about between the equipment as if they were out for a Sunday stroll in the park. With black clouds low in the east, directly behind us as we moved in to attack, it was difficult for them to see anything clearly against the gloom of the background. About 2,000 yards from the road there was a further fairly prominent ridge, and here Kinnaird halted us temporarily so that he could more easily direct the moves and operations. I moved straight on to a small crescent-shaped sand dune about half-way between Kinnaird and the road, and took up a position on this piece of ground, with the other two tanks of my troop disposed on each side of me. I found on arrival that the dune was solid enough to take my tank when I moved up the eastern face, and that it was just high enough, when I was at the foot of the slope, to hide my tank completely from the enemy. It was in fact so ideal a position that I had no hesitation in reporting to Kinnaird:

'... Am in position one thousand yards to your immediate front on a perfectly shaped and positioned crescent dune. I suggest I stay here and do not move any further forward, but make this into as strong an outpost as I can. By digging and moving some boulders I think we can make the position almost impregnable. Over.' And Kinnaird replied:

'... Good. I agree. Stay where you are, and keep me fully informed about your ammunition supplies and any casualties you may suffer. I will try to keep your position up to strength all the time. Off.'

Using my troop position as a pivot for the manoeuvre of the rest of the squadron, Kinnaird then gave the order to advance. Maintaining a steady pace, so that no one tank should out-distance the rest and thus make itself prominent as a target, the squadron moved in to close quarters with the enemy packed on the road so that they could use their machine-guns to full effect. Twenty Italian tanks which had been moving down the east side of the road to join the vanguard attacking the blocking position wheeled left at once and engaged. The first sounds of machine-gun fire and the crack of the high-velocity tank guns turned the attention of the Italian gunners to this new menace. In a matter of moments they, too, had switched to engage the new targets. As they closed to within 800 yards of the road, the squadron were met by a withering fire from the enemy tanks and guns, but without pause they continued their advance to create as much disturbance and confusion as they could. In a momentary lull in the firing to my immediate front my attention was drawn to the area just to the north, where the crashing clamour of the guns announced the arrival of another of our squadrons to engage the enemy.

Along fifteen miles of closely packed road the Italians were hammered by our guns and tanks and, with unaccustomed fierce vigour, they replied. So near to their final salvation if they could only break through our thin lines, they fought with a courage and determination which they had not equalled so far in the campaign. Their attacks were, however, ill-conceived and unco-ordinated.

Our squadron held a vital position in the whole fabric of the attack, stationed as we were on the left flank of the mobile screen threatening the road and linking these forces to those of the blocking position to the south. Here, where there was a gap of a few thousand yards between the two forces and where, except for my small dune, there were no convenient features to defend, the Italians made their major efforts to break through. Backed by their numerous artillery and urged on by the knowledge that this was their last chance, their attacks were pressed home with the utmost vigour, added to which was the strength provided by a reinforcement of about sixty of their M13 medium tanks, which were either new or had only recently been overhauled.

After the first assault on the road, Kinnaird withdrew the squadron to the ridge behind me on which he had first halted. Almost before they had taken up their positions I reported, '... Figures two zero enemy tanks advancing against my position now. Over.' And Kinnaird replied, '... O.K. Devote your attention to those on your right, and we will deal with those moving round your left. Off.'

This was the first of many similar attacks which continued throughout the morning. Groups of Italian tanks formed up out of range, the Italian artillery bombarded my position and what was visible of the rest of the squadron, and then the tanks advanced. Mechanical breakdowns and one or two casualties were already seriously reducing our strength, and by midday our supplies of ammunition were running very low. Each tank had been engaged so continuously throughout the morning that as yet there had been no time to refill with ammunition or petrol, let alone get anything to eat. It was with surprise that I realized what the hour was and that the nagging hunger was due to my complete lack of food that day, since my attention had been so fully occupied that I had not even been chewing the interminable biscuits.

Again the Italians formed up to attack and again when they had advanced so far and were halted by the fire of my troop,

Kinnaird, from the ridge behind which he had hidden the squadron after each attack, suddenly swooped on one flank of their advance. They had no counter to this manoeuvre, which depended on my holding my ground on the vital dune and on Kinnaird being ever on the alert to come to the rescue with the rest of the squadron whenever the Italians advanced. After another of these actions we were forced to consider seriously the supply of ammunition. The battle had gone on so long by now that each tank was down to its last dozen rounds or so. We had been reduced in strength, too, by six tank casualties, mostly mechanical. We were therefore in a serious position. Taking advantage of the fact that the Italians had this time withdrawn farther than usual, Kinnaird gave me the order, '... You will stand fast on your present position while we refill. If you are attacked you must resist as long as you can by using your ammunition sparingly. As soon as we are ready we will move forward to cover your position and allow the lorries to come forward to refill you. We are so low in rounds now that we cannot help much until we refill. Off.'

For a time the enemy showed no signs of attacking. In the lull I became acutely aware of my own weariness and discomfort. Inside the turret I could see Tilden and Holton slumped in their positions. I would have given anything for a brew. My mind was abruptly taken off such thoughts when I saw the enemy tanks moving forward again.

I immediately reported this new threat to Kinnaird, who replied, '... Yes, I see what you mean. I had begun to wonder what those movements were. If they attack in the next ten minutes you will have to do the best you can for a bit and I will send all the help I can as soon as possible. Don't bother to report anything unless it is vital, as I am still in a position where I can see all that is going on. Off.'

The attack was started as usual by heavy artillery fire, which was immediately followed by an attack by twenty enemy tanks, which moved forward in two groups, one on each side of my position. The Italian tanks were engaged by our artillery, whose accurate and heavy fire caused casualties and confusion among them. But despite this they still came on. Mindful of Kinnaird's warning that for a period at least I would be on my own, I held my fire. The Italian tanks drew closer on both flanks, my left being more seriously menaced, as the other squadron on my right flank had fortunately just replenished with ammunition and were moving forward to help. At a range of 1,000 yards the enemy opened fire. With their first salvo of shots they scored a telling hit on Sergeant Wharton's tank on my left. The barrel of the gun was hit by a million-to-one chance, which left it bent and distorted, and the lugubrious voice of Wharton would have been funny if his news were not so disastrous when he reported:

'... We've 'ad it. Me bloody barrel's bent like a winkle-pin and it would shoot me own arse off if I fired it. What shall I do? Over.'

I replied, '... Stay where you are and look blood-thirsty. Do what you can with your machine-gun. Off to you.' And to Kinnaird I said, 'You will have heard that. I don't want to move my right-hand position because it will give the show away and leave him exposed while he moves, and in any case he is doing good work where he is. Can you help? Over.'

There was a long pause before Kinnard replied, and when he did it was Egerton to whom he gave the order, '... Stop your refill now and move immediately with what you've got to Number One's left flank and engage the enemy as soon as you can. Over.'

Egerton was half-way through his refill and had got a brew well on the way. 'Damn and blast!' he said aloud to his crew, but on the air he said, '... O.K. Off to you. Hello, One – have much pleasure in accepting your invitation and will be with you in figures five. Off.'

Meanwhile the Italian tanks closed the range still further. Some were already at no greater distance than 500 yards. Their movements were beginning to be slower and distinctly hesitant in face of the unusual and quietly sinister reception they were getting. When in due course they closed to less than 400 yards I decided that I could afford to wait no longer. Picking my target with care, I gave my gunner the order, 'Two-pounder traverse right – on – enemy M13 tank – range 400 yards – fire!' The whip-lash crack of the gun released me from my pent-up tension and fear, and from then on my mind was absorbed with the matter in hand to the exclusion of all other worries and apprehensions.

It was my left flank which was still most threatened. With

Sergeant Wharton unable to take any decisive part in the battle the Italians had in a short time worked two or three tanks so far round that flank that they were able to shoot from the rear into my otherwise well-protected position. But in doing so they had left themselves very vulnerable to any attack which Kinnaird could launch from his ridge behind. So embroiled in the heated exchange of shots had I been that I was only brought back to a realization of my precarious position by the loader's remark, 'Only two more rounds left, sir.' A moment or two later Sergeant Wharton reported, '... Have been hit again and penetrated. I have two casualties and can take no further part in the action. What are my orders? Over.' With reluctance I replied, '... Stay where you are for the present and do what you can for the wounded. I hope we can get you out soon. Off to you.' And to Kinnaird I reported this latest news and again inquired about the help I was desperately hoping to get.

Kinnaird replied with the same calm, deliberate assurance as ever, and his voice did much to make me realize that I was in good hands; the news he had to give was even better encouragement. '... Help will be coming in about one minute and should be very effective. At the same time your casualty will be replaced by another, so he should be prepared to move back now. As soon as we have driven the enemy back, they will be shelled heavily, and under cover of this supplies of ammunition will come forward to you, and when they reach you for God's sake be quick. Off.'

The whole action went according to plan. Egerton's troop appeared, not a moment too early, to menace the Italian flank, and when he was followed soon afterwards by Templeton, they both advanced to the attack. The Italians were taken by surprise, and suffered a number of casualties before they fell back to a position about 600 yards west of my troop. Here they stayed for a while until Ryan and his troop, making very clever use of the small amount of cover afforded by my dune, moved forward round the northern end of it and fell on to the other flank of the enemy force. Their hurried retreat was made even more confused by the heavy shelling of our guns. Under the cover of this fire Sergeant Wharton moved back, and was replaced by Morgan in one of the squadron headquarter tanks, and the supply lorries moved forward and refilled my own and my other tank.

All along the rest of the front the battle had been as intense. There was no question, as there had been earlier in the campaign, of the Italians sitting docilely awaiting whatever fate was in store for them. This was their last chance to escape, and they fought with the utmost determination. By the early afternoon 4th Armoured Brigade were so depleted by casualties of all kinds that 7th Armoured Brigade was ordered south at the best possible speed to bolster our weakening line, which was only just containing the Italians.

Two hours later they were almost in a position to help us. Before being able to advance into action they were forced to stop to replenish their nearly expended petrol and to take on more ammunition. This unavoidable delay was nearly fatal. The enemy pressure had been so great and so continuous throughout the afternoon that we had been unable to afford, with our then depleted numbers, to withdraw any tanks to refill and refuel, so that by this late hour nearly every tank was again down to its last few rounds of ammunition. It was with very real anxiety that we watched and listened for the approach of the reinforcements and with great relief that we at last hailed their arrival and thankfully pulled out troop by troop to replenish.

The Italians were unaware how close they had been to success. When another attack towards Beda Fomm would almost certainly have met with a large degree of success before 7th Armoured Brigade arrived, they suddenly turned their full attention and efforts to trying to smash a way through on the road. The position here became so serious that we, in our turn, were ordered to complete our replenishment as quickly as possible and then go to the aid of the road-block. Kinnaird's squadron was obviously the best placed to give the quickest help, so every available supply lorry was sent to us. Despite the extreme urgency with which we all laboured to complete the refill with the utmost speed, it was nevertheless half an hour before we were ready to move. By this time the situation at the road-block was almost desperate. Italian tanks had penetrated right into the position and were reported to be engaging the Headquarters itself.

In view of this, Kinnaird moved us due west from our refilling area so as to engage the enemy as soon as possible. He then turned us south to sweep down the flank of the enemy column, engaging any and every target as it presented itself, in the manner of our successful assault against the Italian mobile column on the frontier during the skirmishes of the previous autumn. The disruption caused by this sudden onslaught and our arrival in the positions on the road served to turn the scales. Further chaos was added to the confusion we had already started when, towards last light, we were ordered to return to our original position, doing what damage we could on the way. By this time there was little fight left in the Italians, and both to our marauding force and all along the front prisoners began to swarm in in ever-increasing numbers. Wherever we were able to launch even a minor attack or whenever one of their own attacks failed, the Italians immediately laid down their arms and waved any piece of white material they could put their hands on. But these troops belonged only to the fringes of the massive enemy column, and behind them there were still others who had no idea of surrendering as yet.

So the day ended. As the light faded, battered and depleted, we drew together into our various night leaguers to lick our wounds and repair what damage we could in preparation for the next day's fight. There were many among us who wondered how we could possibly resist for another day the same scale of determined Italian attacks, and it was with a confidence bolstered only by resolute determination that we settled down to the night's work, for of rest there was to be very little. All through the hours of darkness the many tanks which had fallen out with mechanical failures were brought into the leaguers and worked on. The battle casualties were also recovered, and by cannibalization of the worst, some at least of the less seriously damaged were repaired sufficiently to render them battleworthy. Crews had to be made up for these tanks from those who had not been wounded in the tanks which were destroyed. Guards were vitally necessary, as in most cases the enemy were no more than a mile or so away. A night attack seemed more than probable, as a means of trying to break out of the cordon. Food was prepared and eaten in the intervals between our other tasks. It was the first meal of any sort that most of us had had in twenty-four hours.

7

Victory at Beda Fomm

BEFORE first light the leaguers were astir, and as the dawn reddened the eastern sky behind us, it lit the long, straggling, inert mass of the Italian column where it lay still in its positions of the previous day. The Italians had been harassed throughout the night by our guns and a number of roving infantry fighting patrols which had kept them on the alert and deprived them of rest and any chance to reorganize. From my position on the dune I watched an attack which was launched soon after dawn by about thirty Italian tanks against the position on the road. This was beaten off quickly and with little difficulty.

For a time there was silence on both sides. For all the efforts of the previous day, the Italian column still looked huge and threatening. I watched with apprehension the movements of the mass of vehicles before me. On either side of me, hidden behind the crests of other dunes and ridges, I knew that there were other eyes just as anxious as mine, surveying the scene before them. In the mind of each one of us was the sure knowledge that we were well outnumbered. Each of us knew by what slim margin we still held dominance over the battlefield. Our threat was but a façade – behind us there were no more reserves of further troops. Even the supplies of the very sinews which could keep us going had almost run out. If we lost now we were faced with capture or a hopeless retreat into the empty distances of the inner desert. It was a sobering thought. I felt that the day, with all its black, wet dullness, was heavy with ominous foreboding. The scene before me was made gloomy enough to match my mood by the black clouds of acrid smoke which shrouded the battlefield like a brooding pall.

Gradually I became aware of a startling change. First one and then another white flag appeared in the host of vehicles. More and more became visible, until the whole column was a forest of waving white banners. Small groups of Italians started to move out hesitantly towards where they knew we lay watching them. Larger groups appeared, some on foot, some in vehicles.

Still not able to believe the evidence of his own eyes, the

Colonel warned, '... Don't make a move. This may be a trap. Wait and see what happens. Off.'

But it was no trap. Italians of all shapes and sizes, all ranks, all regiments and all services swarmed out to be taken prisoner. I felt that nothing would ever surprise me again after my loader suddenly shouted: 'Look, sir, there's a couple of bints there coming towards us. Can I go an' grab 'em, sir? I could do with a bit of home comforts.' We took the two girls captive, installed them in a vehicle of their own and kept them for a few days to do our cooking and washing. I refrained from asking what other duties were required of the women, but noted that they remained contented and cheerful.

Out of the first confusion, order was slowly restored. Each squadron was given a part of the battlefield where we were to collect the prisoners and equipment and to keep careful tally of the captures. It was a novel but exhausting task, and Kinnaird, anxious to be done with it as soon as possible, pushed and harried us to clear our portion of the area.

The battlefield was an amazing sight. It was strewn with broken and abandoned equipment, tattered uniforms, piles of empty shell and cartridge cases. It was littered with paper, rifles and bedding. Here and there small groups of men tended the wounded who had been gathered together. Others were collecting and burying the dead. Still others, less eager to surrender than the majority, stood or lay waiting to be captured. Some equipment was still burning furiously, more was smouldering. There were many oil and petrol fires emitting clouds of black smoke.

There were few incidents. Soon the generals and the high-ranking officers had been discovered and taken away. The remaining officers were piled unceremoniously into Italian lorries and driven off. The thousands of men were formed into long columns guarded at head and tail by only one or two of our impassive, imperturbable and perpetually cheerful soldiers, who shouldered the unaccustomed new duties with the same confident assurance with which they had met and mastered all the other trials of the campaign.

It was the work of some days to clear the battlefield of all that was worth salvaging and to muster and despatch on their long march to the prison camps in Egypt the thousands of prisoners.

At last the work was completed and the enemy's losses could be computed. At Benghazi, which had fallen into Australian hands on the same day as the surrender to us further south, and at Beda Fomm, the Italians had lost some 20,000 men killed and captured, as well as 1,500 lorries, 112 tanks and 216 guns.

In the brief period of two months, never numbering more than about a quarter of our enemy, we had captured or destroyed the cream of the Italian Colonial Army. The much-heralded might of Mussolini's Empire had been shown to have been a sham. Of the thousands who had marched with Graziani to the promised glory and riches of the capture of Egypt, few had escaped. Some 134,000 had been killed, wounded, or captured. We had taken thousands of lorries, hundreds of tanks and guns, as well as enormous supplies of food, ammunition and equipment. Against this gigantic total, our losses were 604 killed and 2,360 wounded.

We were well content. Except for the Matildas, our equipment had not been greatly superior and we had had at no time a superiority in numbers. Speed of manoeuvre and preparation, determination and the confidence born of a great and growing moral ascendancy were the weapons which had brought the final victory.

But, though these were enough to defeat the Italians, we knew that the scarcity of adequate equipment could be of no avail against an enemy with superior weapons and practised and dedicated to the rites of war. Behind the triumph and the glory of the campaign there lurked in the mind of each of us the threat of a more potent, more determined enemy – the Germans. For even as the battlefield was being cleared and, as ever before, the advanced patrols of the Division were moving farther south and west to Agedabia and Agheila, German aircraft began to strafe the road and attack the forward positions.

It was on this note of a great victory precariously won and of more difficult trials to come in the near future that the campaign came to an end. For some of us in the forefront of the advance there was to be no comfort nor good food after endless days of hardship; no port after the storm.

PART THREE

1941 : DEFYING THE GERMANS

___

1

We Meet the Germans

BUT with the end of the campaign there came at last a relaxation of alertness. The lengthening days which marked the spring brought with them a welcome warmth and the promise of a new year with all the hope that went with i . It was early yet for our memories of the heat to be revived, and it would have been churlish to think of the discomfort it would bring later. The even tenor of our days was in marked contrast to the hectic weeks of battle, culminating in the frenzied days of victory and the accompanying labours which the clearance of the battlefield entailed. There was now a holiday atmosphere, a natural and blameless sequel to hardships endured and triumphs achieved. But it was an atmosphere tempered by a degree of preparedness made essential by the attentions of the German Air Force, who attacked any sign of movement on the roads and in the desert south of Benghazi. The German fighters and dive-bombers were the first indication of their interest in the war in Africa, but their threatened participation elsewhere was to have an even greater influence on the campaign in Cyrenaica.

There was every indication that they were preparing to move in support of the Italians in their abortive attack on Greece. The British forces available in the Middle East were entirely insufficient to meet both threats, and taken all in all it was considered that resistance even of short duration and with only limited success would pay bigger dividends in Greece than in Africa. A large proportion of the available forces were therefore sent to Greece.

By the middle of March 1941 only a very depleted and ill-equipped 2nd Armoured Division, which had taken over from

7th Armoured Division, faced the ever-mounting power of the German Air Force and prepared to hold for as long as possible the now clearly inevitable German land advance. Behind was an Indian brigade, recently arrived, and the 9th Australian Division reorganizing before its move forward into the desert. In Cairo the majority of 7th Armoured Division were resting after the long months of hardship.

In the desert, near Agedabia, the 3rd Armoured Brigade, of which we were now a part, waited for the attack which was bound to come. In front of us the armoured cars patrolled the dunes and salt marshes near Agheila and beat off the daily heavier attacks of the German Air Force. A regiment of light tanks was deployed immediately behind the armoured-car screen. Behind them were a newly arrived armoured regiment, equipped entirely with light cruisers, and our regiment, which had been re-equipped with Italian M13 tanks, as no British tanks were available.

By this time we had at least accustomed ourselves to the new equipment, though we were not yet, and would never be, content or enthusiastic about the Italian tanks. We knew too well with what ease our guns had been able to penetrate and destroy their armour in the battles only recently over, and were grimly aware that the guns of the German tanks we were soon likely to meet would be at least as good.

We were spread out in open leaguer and remained in these positions at night, since we were so far from the enemy. Nevertheless we stood to at dawn each day in case there were sudden alarms to be met, and to guard against a surprise attack by para-chutists, the threat of whose action was clear in all our minds since the attack on Holland the previous year. During the last half-hour of the night there would be a faint lifting of the darkness in the east. Through binoculars the horizon would lose its shadowy shape and take on a harder outline, and the tanks which lay in the line of sight would shed their vague silhouettes and grow into solid forms again. By the time we were roused and dressed, with bedding packed and stowed ready for action, it was possible for us to distinguish in detail the lines of the turret and gun and the faces of each other as we stood grouped round the front of the tank. And then – within moments, so it seemed – it was dawn and the start of another day. I would stand and survey the flat landscape dotted here and there with the shapes of other tanks and vehicles and lit by the thin, watery rays of the young sun. Tilden would climb into the turret to switch on the wireless set and to go through the rigmarole of the morning's 'net' with the control station. Holton would wipe the moisture from the front end of his telescope and then, with a great noise and clatter, open the various bins on the side of the tank to get the implements for the day's first brew and breakfast. Sykes would climb into his seat to start and warm the engine. Very few words were ever spoken until hot, steaming mugs of tea were in our hands and we stood huddled round the petrol fire for what warmth we could get in the first chill of the day until the sun was high enough to provide all the heat we could want. The grey, silent, bristly faces grouped round me always brought warmth to my heart, as in the months since I first joined the Regiment I had grown to know well and to like each member of my crew.

On 25 March the German Army advanced against us, while the fighters and dive-bombers of their Air Force attacked anything and everything on the roads, and at Agedabia and Benghazi. To begin with, the ground attacks were made by light mobile forces, probing to discover our strength – or weakness, as it was – and our dispositions. They were searching for gaps in the defences, for the flank in the open desert to the east, for crossing places of the obstacle that was the sandy-bottomed Wadi Faregh. The German eight-wheeled armoured cars were more than a match for our own, which were more thinly armoured and lightly armed.

After five days of this incessant patrolling, each day the Luftwaffe ranging farther and farther afield to pick off stray vehicles and to bomb and harass our dispersed leaguers, the Germans were aware of the nature and size of our force. Unimpeded air reconnaissance made it possible too for them to watch and counter any move that we made, so that the swift manoeuvres and lightning strokes of our previous campaign were of little avail. They were always seen too soon, and the forces to counter them moved with a speed and precision of which the Italians had never been capable.

Throughout 30 and 31 March we met the vanguard of the Italian and German divisions in the desert south of Agedabia. In the confused and fast-moving battles in which small groups of tanks and armoured cars were engaged over a large area of the desert, both sides suffered losses but, scattered and depleted as we were, we were relentlessly driven back by superior weight and by the outflanking moves of yet more enemy forces, which, though not directly engaged, nevertheless forged their influence on the battle by the threat of being able to cut off our escape unless we kept pace with them in our withdrawal.

On the evening of 1 April, when what was left of the regiment had drawn together into night leaguer, Kinnaird was sent for by the Colonel to receive the orders for the following day. We had all begun to see the inevitability of a long withdrawal and knew that if it were not ordered soon we had little chance of survival. As it was, our chances were small enough. Faced by a far superior force, better equipped and better supplied, and fighting always blindly and desperately against an enemy who was enabled by his superior air-power to see and plan each move more accurately, we had behind us only the weak and half-trained brigade at Machili and the Australian Division still moving forward. Otherwise there was only the empty, neutral desert, brooding alike on friend or foe and offering no help nor haven if, in the course of the battle, we were wounded or left behind. Unless we escaped there was only death by thirst or starvation, or capture by the enemy.

We were all gathered in the back of Kinnaird's truck, crowded uncomfortably into the very limited space and choking in the haze of cigarette smoke, when he returned from the Colonel. His orders were short and to the point.

'Orders for to-morrow, and the days following, for that matter. The Brigade has been ordered to withdraw on Benghazi. I don't think the withdrawal will stop there. You know as well as I do what we are up against and you know that our job is to delay them as long as we can. Make every shot count and don't be too rash in pitting yourself against larger numbers. We shall do better to withdraw each time before we are cut off than to try and fight it out. If any tanks are knocked out the crew will have to fend for themselves. We can't afford to lose any other tanks doing

90

rescue operations. If you have to bale out, walk due north to the Gebel – 150 miles will get you into the foothills, where the Arabs will probably look after you, and you can get news of what has happened and where to make for. That's all I can say, except to wish you all the best of luck. It's not going to be an easy battle, but it's vital that we should all do our best. Any questions?'

Inevitably it was Templeton who asked in a voice which was clearly on the edge of hysteria, 'Is there no help? Aren't there any other forces anywhere? Have we got to fight the whole bloody war ourselves?'

Kinnaird's reply was sharp.

'That's enough of that, Templeton,' he said. 'We're all in this together. I have no doubt other forces are being organized, but that's none of our business at present. We have been ordered to fight a withdrawal, and that's all there is to it. Pull yourself together, and don't let me hear any more of that sort of talk from you. If there are no more questions, that's all I have to say.' As we climbed out of the truck he called, 'Good night'.

2

Templeton Dies

THE first three days of fighting had jerked us abruptly from the relaxation of the lull, had started to tune us again to the instant reactions and to the endurance that would be demanded of us. Already we were almost back to the old routine, and the next day or so, if there were any left, would see us fighting fit again. As usual after the boredom of the intervening weeks, there were some who were even glad to be back on the job again. I was not one of these, but I could guess how they felt. They were free from the doubts and anxieties caused by the uncertainty of an impending fight, they were released from their jealous, envious longing to be with the rest of the old Division in Cairo. To some extent it was a relief to all of us. This was our real task, for which we were well trained and qualified, and we turned to it with a single-mindedness which was an effective blanket to our other thoughts and desires.

Throughout the daylight hours of 2 April the battles moved

91

with a wayward direction and unpredictable speed over the desert to the north and north-east of Agedabia. Always we were driven back; sometimes slowly and imperceptibly as we contested each ridge and hillock against the pressure of the superior weight of enemy armour; at other times in a wild flurry of speed and disorder as we found that we were again being outflanked by yet more of the enemy. By nightfall the Germans and Italians were within striking distance of both Msus and Benghazi, within easy reach of our two vital main supply dumps of all types of fuel, food, and ammunition.

Early on 3 April these main dumps were destroyed before we had time to refill and replenish. It was one of those things which happen so often in war despite the best-laid plans, and in this instance the plans were not too clear and the confusion was growing worse each day. So our depleted numbers were even further reduced. As with the other squadrons, we had to reorganize our tanks and men to take account of the small amount of petrol which remained. There were, as a result, only eight tanks left in our squadron which were both battleworthy and filled with petrol and ammunition, some perfectly good ones having to be destroyed at Msus, as they could neither be moved nor fought without the vital supplies burning so tantalizingly before us. Kinnaird arranged the squadron into two troops, each of three tanks, with the remaining two forming his headquarters. With himself and Bolton in the H.Q. tanks, he put me in command of one troop, with Sergeant Wharton and a corporal under me. Ryan having been transferred temporarily to another squadron whose officer casualties had been heavier, Kinnaird had no option but to give the other troop to Templeton, who had preserved his tank intact with every conceivable supply. It would have been impossible to take it from him, however much both he and Templeton would have wished it, without inciting the most strong and pointed comment from the other crews.

Egerton, Morgan, and the remaining officers and men who were now out of the fight, climbed into the now empty petrol and ammunition lorries preparatory to starting the long drive back to Tobruk in the first instance, and then wherever else they were sent, in search of other tanks to take over, in which they could join the fight again.

92

I said good-bye to Egerton before he left. We were both at a loss to express our feelings and took refuge in bright, banal remarks.

'I wish you'd been given a troop instead of Templeton,' I said as we shook hands.

'I don't,' he laughed. 'It's a nice day for a bus ride to Tobruk, and a free one too. Join the Fathers' Union and see the world! You be careful, Tony, or you'll find yourself walking there, and it's a hell of a long way.'

But behind the banter I knew he would rather share the dangers of the retreat with his companions of so much hardship than set off to possible safety and have to face the adjustment required in a new unit.

'It looks as if you're about to go,' I said, seeing the driver climb into his cab. 'Well, good-bye, Alan. Look after yourself. I expect we'll meet up again.'

'Surely,' he said. 'Be good, and don't forget to wear your woollies at night.'

With a grin he clambered over the tailboard of the lorry, and as it drew away he gave a half wave, half salute. I returned it, and as I walked back to my tank I knew we were each wondering if we would see the other again.

Throughout the rest of the day the withdrawal continued as before, except that, when at about midday we reached the rocky, atrocious going half-way to Machili, the German advance slowed down, as they were clearly doubtful whether their tanks could cross such an obstacle. We, who had already passed that way once before, were therefore able to put a greater distance between ourselves and the enemy than at any time since the Germans first advanced. In the mid-afternoon, when we had taken up positions on a good, commanding ridge, we even had time to cook our first hot meal for three days, and to be able to enjoy it undisturbed by shell-fire or the threat of attack.

Towards evening the German armoured columns caught up with us once more and the endless procedure of withdrawal, halt, fight, withdrawal, started again. By this time we were all weary beyond belief, dirty, unshaven and caked with layers of the dry dust and sand which enveloped our tanks whenever we moved at speed and whenever the wind blew from behind us. Again it was in this initial period – the first week or so – that we found it most difficult to combat the exhaustion, both mental and physical. It was relatively easy to fall back into the highly-tuned reactions, to acquire again the instant efficiency and resourcefulness; but the toll taken on the human frame could only gradually be accepted as a matter of habit, and during the days while this was being done extra determination and will-power were demanded of us all. As my tank bumped over the broken rocks, I wondered whether it would not be better to finish the whole thing off there and then. I could either stop and fight it out with the German tanks, following so closely behind, or I could just halt and surrender. There would then be an end to perpetual fear and anxiety, the uncertainty would be over one way or another.

Instinctively, while my mind was still toying half-heartedly with these thoughts, I turned my tank and took up a position on the next suitable piece of ground. On either side of me my other tanks did likewise. Away to my left I could see Kinnaird positioning himself, while beyond, Templeton and his troop were already in position. Even as I looked, my thoughts were abruptly interrupted and I was jerked back to full awareness of the battle by the sight of some ten German tanks emerging from the broken ground beyond Templeton and moving at speed, in a solid phalanx, as if determined to drive a wedge behind the squadron and so to cut us off from the rest of the regiment. The enemy were already behind the flank of Templeton's troop, all of whom were so preoccupied with keeping a watch on their front that they were as yet, so far as I could see, unaware of the much greater danger behind them. Frantically I groped for my microphone, and forgetting all the usual procedure, blurted desperately, 'Look to your left. For God's sake look to your left, Templeton.'

But I was too late, for before I had finished even this brief message, I saw by the spurts of flame and smoke coming from the gun-barrels of the German tanks that they had opened fire. The first concentrated salvo, though mainly inaccurate, as it was fired by the enemy tanks while they were still on the move, nevertheless achieved sufficient strikes on the outer flank tank cf Templeton's troop to reduce it immediately to a smoking, crippled hulk, which a moment or two later burst into flames.

Meanwhile Templeton and his other tank were desperately

trying to escape, a task made simpler for the inner flank tank, as it was as yet beyond the effective range of the German tank guns, and had time to turn and move off before the enemy had closed the vital distance. Templeton turned his tank away from the advancing enemy. It was just gathering speed when it was brought to an abrupt and jerking halt by a strike through the rear armour into the engine compartment. There was always this risk to be run in any attempt to make good an escape from the enemy, for in turning away the weakest armour of the tank, at the back of the hull and turret, was exposed to the fire of the armour-piercing shot, which, except in a few fortunate cases, it was unable to resist. This was Templeton's fate, and though two or three of the enemy tanks detached themselves from the main body to press on against Kinnaird's headquarter's tanks and my troop, the remainder concentrated on the destruction of the cripple. A great weight of shot was poured towards Templeton's tank, which was helpless and incapable of any return fire. I dreaded to imagine the shambles and horror there must have been within the cramped confines of the hull and turret. No crew could possibly undergo such punishing fire without death or serious physical injury, and I felt that the sooner this tank blew up and put the crew out of their misery the better.

But for some inexplicable reason tanks did not always blow up quickly, however often they were hit, nor did they always catch fire. Unfortunately, Templeton's was one of these, and the agony was prolonged both for the crew and for the rest of us, who still watched with fascinated horror. Kinnaird voiced the thoughts of each one of us when he gave his orders, '. . . There's nothing we can do to help, I'm afraid. There are too many of them against us and if we don't move now we shall . . .'

The rest of his sentence was drowned by the high-pitched, wailing note which meant that there was another set transmitting at the same time and jamming the signal. The noise continued for about another half-minute and then as suddenly ceased, when Kinnaird had completed his orders. Now all that we could hear was the thrumming carrier wave of a set transmitting and inter- mittent, indistinct sounds which gradually increased and became distinguishable as mumblings and groans. Suddenly, with start- ling clarity, we heard a voice which we immediately recognized as Templeton's. 'Driver, why the bloody hell have you halted? I told you to go on, blast you! Go on, I said; can't you hear me? ... Oh my God, my leg.... I can't stop the blood. ... Where's the rest of the squadron? They ought to be helping soon, but I can't hear them shooting. Where are they, blast 'em? Oh God, if they've deserted us, we haven't a hope in hell. ... The bastards, they've gone. ... Hanshaw, we're alone. D'you hear? We're alone. ... Blast it, can't you answer me when I speak to you? ... Hanshaw ... Hanshaw, damn you! ... I must kick him. ... If only I could move about better. ... That's better; now I can reach him. ...' There was a long pause, at last ended by a maniacal scream – then Templeton's voice again, croaking and breathless with hysteria, 'My God, I can't stand it. ... My foot's fallen off. ... Where is it? Hanshaw, where's my foot? ... Why doesn't he answer? ...' Another long pause punctuated only by the quick, harsh gasps of Templeton's breathing, then, 'He's dead. He must be dead. He won't answer. ... The driver must be dead too. ... Where's Collins? ... Collins. ... Damn you, answer me. ... Collins, blast you, where are you? ... They're all dead. ... God, they've gone, and the rest of the bastards have deserted me. ... They all hated me, and now they've left me ...' Then clearly over the air came perhaps the most unnerving sound of all, the wailing, uncontrolled moans and sobs which denoted Templeton's complete breakdown. But these too, with a sudden intake of breath, ceased, and for a time we heard nothing but the ceaseless hum of the set. Suddenly there was the sharp crack of a shot – clear and deafeningly loud – followed only by the now eerie thrumming of the set. Then this, too, abruptly stopped, the microphone presumably having been dislodged from wherever it had been stuck by the pull of the body falling to the floor of the turret.

In the meanwhile the battle had continued unabated elsewhere. With our communications dislocated by the one set transmitting on our frequency and jamming all other signals, we had been unable to fight any co-ordinated action and had had further casualties as a result. Soon after the jamming ceased I lost one of my tanks, which was first immobilized by a severed track and then made completely unbattleworthy by a further hit, which jammed the turret and the elevating mechanism of the gun. The crew were miraculously unharmed and had time to bale out before worse befell them, the tank commander – a very good corporal – first reporting in his inimitable Cockney manner, '... We've 'ad it. We're all baling out. See you in Berlin at the end of the bloody war. So long. ...'

Bolton, his tank and crew all disappeared. One moment they were with us in our hasty, hectic retreat – for it could no longer warrant being called a withdrawal – at the next moment, when we had time to take stock of our position and what remained of our meagre force, Bolton's tank was no longer with us. He and his crew were gone. And though in the months to come we kept a careful watch on the lists of the men who had been taken prisoner, it was all in vain, and in the end we had to make up our minds that another crew were either entombed for ever in their tank or that their bodies had perhaps been buried by the enemy in lonely graves which were never likely to be found.

At last darkness came, a welcome curtain to hide the stage for a few hours and to give us some relief from exhaustion and a chance to reorganize for the battle to be joined again on the morrow. By now it was a hand-to-mouth existence. Hot meals were a rarity; indeed, rations were extremely short and we were already existing mainly on biscuits. Water was severely rationed and proved only just sufficient for the few brews which were possible. There was certainly none to spare for washing, and by this time we had all grown at least enough of a beard to have passed the stage when it was a mere uncomfortable stubbly growth. In the course of the battle most of us had lost both our bedding and our spare clothes. The loss of the bedding was the most hard to endure, for as a result the only way of getting any warmth was for each crew to huddle uncomfortably into the turret and there to work up what fug they could. Sleep in these cramped positions was disturbed and unsatisfying. Of the spare clothes, the majority of us felt most the need for clean socks. After a few days we found that those we had on became soft, gluey masses in our boots, uncomfortably hot and sticky during the day and damp and soggy at night, but necessary to endure even so, as to be without socks would have been worse. After a time we were able to see these hardships in the right perspective, and we indulged each day in a morbid game of trying to decide at what range our odour was most offensive to each other. At first the distances were measured in feet, but later yards were a more accurate indication!

3

A Desperate Race

BEHIND our disordered but determined resistance in the forward areas, we knew that those other forces that were available were being mustered and positioned for battle. The 9th Australian Division, we were told, were busily occupying the perimeter defences of Tobruk. At Machili the 3rd Indian Motor Brigade were preparing to stand and fight. The best news for us who knew them was that 7th Armoured Division were being sent forward again to take part in the battle.

On 4 April we were ordered to withdraw to a line from Derna to Machili. In the open desert we were still being hard pressed, and were daily becoming more depleted in numbers and less effective as fighting units as we ran out of fuel and ammunition and found no more dumps from which to replenish.

Our squadron had been reduced to a mere four tanks: Kinnaird's, two of my troop, and the remaining tank from Templeton's troop. The other squadrons of the regiment were no better off. All that could be mustered from the regiment was a weak squadron in which I was given command of three tanks. I found that my companion troop leaders were Ryan, whom I had not seen for weeks, and a subaltern named Charlton from one of the other two squadrons, whom I had met only briefly once before soon after the battle of Beda Fomm.

The day started with no greater promise than any others since the beginning of the German offensive. Shortly after first light, when the desert was still lit only by the reflected rays of the early sun, which had not yet risen above the horizon, we had our first brush with the enemy, who must have been leagured very close to us throughout the night. They would have had greater success but for our alertness. In the first exchange of shots Charlton's tank was knocked out. The whole crew hurriedly baled out. As we moved back to other positions we watched with frustrated helplessness all four men being ferreted out and rounded up. We last saw them, lit by the first direct rays of the sun, walking away towards the enemy with their hands above their heads.

Charlton's was but the first of a number of tanks that went that day. Before noon I lost Sergeant Wharton and his tank in another short, sharp engagement with a superior force of enemy. Before I had time to brood on this loss my own tank was hit in the suspension, and though thereafter each yard of progress was accompanied by a frightening, doleful noise made by the rough edges of the distorted metal rubbing together, the tank managed to run for the rest of the daylight hours.

In the early afternoon Ryan's tank was hit at long range by a chance shot which penetrated the front armour. Ryan himself was hit by part of the flying fragments of metal and suffered a compound fracture of the thigh. This was a wound which was often fatal. With the limited medical resources immediately at hand and the long distances back to the base hospitals, where alone adequate treatment was available, few managed to survive the severe shock to the system. Ryan's wound was as bad as any. But still he would have had no chance to recover at all if it had not been for the doctor's cool gallantry in going forward in his open unarmoured truck to his rescue. In full view of the Germans, who surprisingly held their fire, he picked up Ryan and his companions and carried them back to safety.

Ryan's still unquenchable spirit was a tonic to all who saw him. Seriously wounded as he was and suffering no small degree of pain from the merciless chafing of the ends of the broken bone in the uneven motion of the truck, he apparently was more concerned that his own vital organs were not damaged in any way. 'Are you sure they're all right, Doctor? No damage at all? I would feel really miserable if I couldn't still give the girls a treat.'

Towards last light we were ordered to withdraw into the thinly defended perimeter of Machili. We had fought an ever hopeless, losing battle for ten days on end and over a distance of more than 150 miles. We had seen the capture or destruction of many of our closest friends. There were many others too who, in the hectic, scrambling haste of the withdrawal, had had no more time than to become a face and a name to be recognized when we met for a brief moment in leaguer at night. They had come, some from other regiments, others as reinforcements from the base, had been with us for a day or two only in some cases, and had then been killed or captured. The endless daily repetition of this slaughter had developed in all of us an unconscious capacity to take it all for granted. We became hardened to pain and destruction. We were no longer overwhelmed with pity when watching the dying or burying the dead. Occasionally when one whom we had known or liked particularly had been killed, his loss was felt as an aching pang for a few days, and then we grew accustomed to his absence. Death was not very different from leave. Whoever it was we mourned had gone away and we would not see him, and the deep feeling of tragedy was only revived by the thought that he would never be seen by human eyes again. But it was unprofitable to devote much time or thought to these events. We had to develop a detached, unfeeling attitude, or we would have been swept away in the horror and in the expectation of our own fates. It was better to concentrate on the task in hand and to fight back with all the cunning and efficiency that we could muster, and so leave little time for other considerations.

My crippled tank managed to reach the leaguer area for the night, but a close inspection of the damage revealed that it was unlikely to last much longer, so I took over a tank of another regiment who were leaguered with us. It was an A9, old and battered, but nevertheless, to my prejudiced eye, better than an M13.

This meant that after so many months of danger shared, the close companionship which had grown within the crew had to come to an end. I had to say good-bye to Sykes, Tilden, and Holton, for I could not take them with me to my new tank, which already had a crew. We had only a moment or two to say our farewells, but these were enough, despite the lack of words, for us to sense our deep regret at this parting.

Feeling a little lost, I joined my new tank. The driver, small, dark and lively, greeted me as I crawled into the bivouac. 'I'm Tomkins, sir. You're just in time for a brew. We thought you might like one – and we've made a good bully stew. There you are, sir – is that how you likes it? You're the boss, sir.'

I thanked him and took the food gratefully. The operator, Chandler, and the gunner, Oxton, less voluble than Tomkins, busied themselves with tidying up and laying out what bedding there was.

Later I made my way across to Kinnaird's truck. He greeted me wearily.

'Come on in, Tony, and have a cigarette. I'm afraid it's a fare-well offering. From now on you'll be under the orders of the Machili garrison commander – you'll be given the frequency on which to net later to-night. You are to move out at first light to the east of Machili – about five miles will do – and take up a position where you can watch that flank. There'll be another troop about a mile away.'

'What about you, sir?' I asked.

'I've got to go back to the frontier with the rest to pick up new tanks. If we get them in time we'll probably come forward to re-join you. If not' – he shrugged – 'I don't know where we'll meet again. Anyway, the best of luck.'

As I walked back in the darkness I felt an almost overwhelm-ing loneliness. A mere four days ago the squadron had been at full strength. Now Templeton and Sergeant Wharton were dead, and Bolton probably so. Ryan was dangerously wounded, Egerton somewhere on the way to Tobruk. Other N.C.O.s had been killed or taken prisoner. And now Kinnaird was leaving me, as it seemed at that moment, to fight the battle alone.

That night I hardly slept at all.

At dawn, in company with an A13 light cruiser which, with my own A9, now formed my troop, I moved out east of Machili to protect that flank. Here, for two days, undisturbed by friend or foe, we stayed on watch, in contact with the Machili garrison and our companion troop only by wireless. During the afternoon of the 6th we heard gunfire and the wireless told us of attacks by the Germans which continued with increasing strength during the following morning.

Towards midday we received the last message from the be-leaguered garrison, '... We cannot resist any longer. Some are going to try to break out and make their way back as best they can. It will be every man for himself. Make for Tobruk. Good luck.'

Both crews heard this news with heavy hearts. Each one of us was filled with doubt that we had any more chance. It was 100 miles to Tobruk, and there were no supplies of any kind on the way. It would indeed be each man for himself, and the Germans would take the hindmost.

I gave orders to move off immediately at the best speed we could make on a bearing which was just north of east. This would bring us by the shortest route to the main coastal road, where I hoped to meet other parts of the British force which was withdrawing through the Gebel. On this bearing, too, we were more likely to keep out of the way of any German tanks which might be moving on the direct route from Machili to Tobruk.

In the early afternoon the intense concentration I was devoting to the move and to an estimation of our chances was interrupted by Chandler, the operator, saying, 'Look, sir, we're being followed. See that cloud of dust behind us, sir? Well if you watch you'll see it's made by tanks. ... There, sir, see them at the top of that ridge? Do you think they're Jerries, sir?'

Reluctant to delay our move for even a moment, I tried to look through my binoculars while the tank was still in motion. But I was unable to identify what they were and replied, 'Can't make 'em out, Chandler. They may be that other troop who were to our west this morning. We'll see if we can contact them on the wireless. If we can't, then they must be the enemy. See if you can get any reply.'

We tried in vain to get an answer from the other troop. Not only did we fail to make contact with them, but discovered we were no longer in touch with anyone else either. The tanks behind us could have been friends, but our doubt about their identity invested them with an ominous quality, and both Chandler and I watched them with intense and anxious interest from then on. We decided to take no chances and to keep as far ahead of them as we could.

The sinister race continued throughout the afternoon. Gradually, imperceptibly the tanks behind us closed the distance, so that by early evening we could plainly see the squat turrets, the high-standing commander's cupolas and the six small road wheels on each side which identified them as German Mark III tanks. Before this, though, the sergeant in the A13, unaware of the situation, asked by wireless whether we could not halt and have a meal. I was amused to see his reaction to my reply, which was, '... Don't look now, but I think we're being followed.'

With a bound as if it had been prodded by a gigantic pin, the A13 leapt forward, and thereafter maintained a position some distance ahead of my tank.

When the sun set and the light in the west began to fade, when in fact we were within half an hour of salvation and probable escape during the hours of darkness, the German tanks overhauled us sufficiently to bring us within range of their guns. In the main their shooting was not very accurate, but the sharp crack of the shots passing and the occasional angry buzz of a ricochet were enough to bring my heart to my mouth. A foot or so either way in the height or direction of the shots would make all the difference between a miss and a strike into the thin armour at the rear of the engine or turret.

As the light faded, the Germans increased the rate of their fire and the speed of their move, so that in the last ten minutes of fighting light their shots were flying thick and fast, and ever closer. With the further reduction in range, I decided that, despite the very poor visibility through the cloud of dust behind my tank, it would be leaving our fate unnecessarily to chance not to reply, in the hope that one of our shots might be lucky.

But as always, so it seemed, the fortunes of war went to the strong, luck to those who were least in need of it. A loud spluttering and coughing of the engine of the A13 as it first drew level and then fell behind told me that it had been hit, and the sergeant's report when it came was an unnecessary comment. 'We're hit in the engine and have a fire in the turret. I'm going to stop and give up. It's no good trying to fight it out, 'cause I reckon we shall blow up soon and we'll all go with it if we don't bale out. Best of luck – Cheerio.'

I watched as the A13 came to an abrupt halt, counted the four figures as they erupted frantically from the now heavily smoking tank, saw them dash away from the vicinity of the impending explosion and watched with apprehension until it came at last with a shock which I felt even at the distance separating us. The force of the explosion blew the tank to bits, strewing the desert with burning debris and fragments of metal.

With this success to encourage them the Germans redoubled

their efforts against my tank. Night was almost upon us, and each minute we we were being engulfed more and more into the enveloping darkness, except that the small pinpoint of light of our red-hot exhaust pipe continued to give away our position. We had survived too long for our luck to last for ever, and by now I felt a gloomy foreboding that something was bound to happen. I would almost have welcomed any incident as a release from the gripping exhausting tension of the past six hours. Our future seemed so hopeless. Even if we were not hit, our petrol would not last for much longer, and then we would have to abandon the tank and walk for goodness knows what distance until we met friends again. While we walked the enemy would be overtaking us on all sides, so that we were more likely to be killed or captured at the end of it all than to escape and live.

I laughed grimly to myself as I recalled Egerton's parting remark: 'If you're not careful you'll find yourself walking to Tobruk, and it's a hell of a long way.' It now looked almost certain that we would have to walk.

As if fate was reluctant to disappoint me, I heard in the next instant the clanging thud of a hit and felt the jar of the strike. It was followed by a grinding crash of torn and tearing metal as a track was severed and its two flying ends, whipped upwards and outwards by the motion of the still-moving tank, ripped the thin metal of the track-guards and side-bins to shreds. The damage was aggravated by the speed of the tank as it slid down the steep incline of the side of a wadi, which, in the darkness had been invisible to both Tomkins and me, but which was to be the main cause of our salvation. For lying as we now were at the foot of a small, steep cliff some fifteen feet in height, we suddenly disappeared from the pursuing Germans and were as effectively hidden from them as we could ever have been.

The abrupt halt had stalled the engine, and for some moments in the silence that followed no one moved. In the distance above us I could hear very faintly the engines of the German tanks. They soon faded away as, baulked of their prey, they moved back to rejoin the remainder of their force. So our race was ended, and from now on we would be on our own. I was too exhausted and anxious for sleep and rest to be willing to consider immediately the new problems and trials that lay ahead of us all. Release from danger and tension had been so sudden and unexpected that my first reactions were of triumph and joy. I almost wanted to sing aloud. I was brought relentlessly back to our immediate predicament by Chandler's voice from within the turret shouting urgently 'Sir, can you come and have a look? Tomkins says he's wounded and can't move one foot, sir. He says he thinks that last hit knocked a bit through the side of the tank and hit his leg. He can't feel nothing, but he can't move neither, sir.'

'All right, Chandler,' I answered. 'You come with me to the front of the tank, and tell Oxton to help Tomkins from inside. We'll get him out somehow, and then we can see what's wrong with him.'

In the gathering gloom, which was already beginning to blur even the closest outlines, I climbed carefully down to the front of the tank, followed closely by Chandler. There, through the hatches of the driver's compartment, which he had managed to open, Tomkins, his face faintly lit by the dim lights of the dials before him, greeted us almost cheerfully:

'Lucky it 'appened when it did, sir. We were down to about the last drop of petrol, too, sir, and I was wondering 'ow much longer we could move. But we've beat them Jerries now, 'aven't we, sir? 'ow far is it to Tobruk, sir? I can't come with you now, sir, but you must get started soon. Leave me with a Very pistol and I'll soon attract someone's attention. Seems stupid for us all to be captured when only one need be. You'll do that, won't you, sir?'

Overcome by the generosity of Tomkins' suggestion and awed by the courage that lay behind it, I found it difficult to give an immediate reply. Instead I bent to the task of getting Tomkins out of his driver's seat through the narrow hatch and placed on the ground to the front of the tank, where his leg could be examined and tended. In the process I answered briefly, 'We'll talk about that later, Tomkins. We must get you out first and see what's wrong with your leg. Oxton will help you from behind and Chandler and I from here. Come on now, and tell us straight away if we are hurting you.'

So soon after the actual hit, Tomkins' muscles and nerves were still numbed by the shock of the wound. Later, when his nerves came to life again, I knew he would feel the full agony of his injuries. It was therefore important to work fast. We quickly had him out of his compartment, and made him as comfortable as possible on all the available bedding. By the light of a hand-torch I examined the damage to his leg. This was a task I always loathed and however often I was forced to do it, and whatever degree of adeptness I achieved after innumerable experiences, I could never be entirely confident that the next time I would not fail; that the sight of blood and the terrible damage to flesh and bone would not unnerve me; that the obvious agony of some wounded, the hopeless pain or the inevitable creeping hand of death already shadowing some others, would not unman me. I tried not to betray any of these feelings, and with a briskness and honesty which I hoped would instil confidence remarked:

'You've a compound fracture of the bone just above your ankle, Tomkins. We'll put a splint on it to keep the bone in position and lash it with bandages, and you ought to feel fine.'

This I did, and when the job was finished I sat back on my heels with profound relief and satisfaction that I had managed to do enough for Tomkins to make him comfortable and even, judging by his next remark, confident that he could accompany the rest of us.

'That's a fine job you've made of it, sir,' he said. 'I feel I could almost come along of you all, my leg seems that better.' And then after a pause he added, 'But you must all be off now, sir. Give me the Very pistol and the whole stock of cartridges and I'll soon attract someone's attention, even if it be them Jerries. You get a move on an' get away.'

The logic of his reasoning was unarguable, but nevertheless neither I nor the other two were keen to grasp this ray of hope, entailing as it did leaving behind Tomkins, who, even in the few days that we had lived and fought as a crew, had grown immeasurably in our esteem and affection. I was to notice this again many times in the months and years to come. I would take over a new tank and crew in leaguer one night, and if we were together still there would have grown by the next night a sense of companionship, of mutual reliance and almost affection.

After spending some time in discussion of other ways and means and after coming back always to Tomkins' obvious but courageous suggestion, I and the other two set about collecting the few things which we could take to survive the long walk to

Tobruk. We divided the water carefully, each of us taking a full water-bottle and leaving the rest with Tomkins. With the food we did the same. After I had buried the various codes and orders which were in the tank, we were ready to start.

Chandler and Oxton said a brief and inarticulate farewell to Tomkins and moved off into the night, leaving me alone with the wounded man. In the dim light of the stars, all that I could see was the shadow of the blanket-clad shape propped against one of the road wheels at the side of the tank.

'I wish I could think of some other plan, Tomkins,' I said quietly. 'I hate leaving you like this, but I'm sure we ought to try and escape.'

'That's all right, sir,' answered Tomkins. His voice was hoarse, and as he cleared his throat I realized that the pain of his leg was probably getting worse. 'You 'aven't picked the easy way out, sir. It'll be a bloody miracle if you get to Tobruk without being captured, sir. A 'undred miles to walk and not much food nor water. It'll need some guts, sir. I'll be all right. I expect it'll be like a Bank Holiday, with Jerries milling round 'ere, sir.'

I could think of no answer to that one. I knew as well as Tomkins that the chance of his being found even in a well-frequented part of the desert was by no means certain. Where there were no tracks each vehicle picked its own way through the scrub and boulders, and it might be a week or a month before anyone came near enough to see that there was a man lying beside the derelict tank.

'The Very lights will soon call all the bloody Jerries round me, sir,' Tomkins repeated, as if reading my thoughts. This was the only factor which still convinced me that our plan was right, so I said:

'Well, good-bye, Tomkins. Give us five minutes to get clear and then start shooting off those lights. Good luck. I shall always remember this, and after the war you must tell me how you got on.'

'After the war,' said Tomkins evenly, 'there'll be better things to talk about. Good-bye, sir, and good luck.'

On Foot to Tobruk

WE walked all that night, stopping at half-hourly intervals so that I could take a bearing and pick another star on which to march. It was cold, with a fresh breeze blowing in from the sea. Even if we had not been eager to cover all the distance we could, we would have found it too cold to stay still, in view of the limited clothing that we could wear or carry. The night was clear but without a moon, and we soon found the ground treacherous and became exhausted by the need for constant alertness, to prevent a fall over the rocks or the occasional tufts of scrub. Otherwise nothing disturbed our progress after the first alarm, which caught us all unawares and left us in a nervous condition for some time afterwards.

We had been walking in single file for perhaps ten minutes when suddenly behind us there was the sharp crack of a pistol shot and, as if that were not enough, in the next instant the desert behind and in front of us was lit by a brilliant light. Instinctively each of us dived for cover, expecting to hear the sharp chatter of a machine-gun and to see the desert around us kicked up by bullets. After a moment of complete silence while we watched the light gradually fade and drift to earth, Chandler said with a laugh:

'We're like a lot of bloody girls frightened by a mouse. That's only Tomkins letting off the — lights.'

We walked at a steady pace throughout the night, and by daylight we had, by my rough reckoning, reached the escarpment which marked the start of the wadi running down to the sea at Tmimi. Unused as we all were to this sort of exercise, by morning we were footsore and leg-weary. Months of living and moving in a tank had only conditioned us to the peculiar character of the endurance required in those circumstances and had left us untrained for any long march. At first light we halted and had a brief meal of cold bully beef and water. Afterwards we wrapped ourselves in all the clothes we had, found a cleft in the cliff which would not mask the rays of the sun, lay down and fell into an exhausted sleep.

I was the first to wake up early in the afternoon. From our resting-place I could see a wide stretch of the desert to the south. Across this, spreading east astride the many tracks, I could see, through my binoculars, the columns of enemy moving forward to invest Tobruk. I sat for some time watching, and wondering whether I had done right in leaving Tomkins behind the night before. The scale of enemy movement was a reassurance that he had probably been picked up, but I still had a lingering sense of guilt about the whole affair. I could not help marvelling again at the courage with which he had accepted the position and the calm assurance with which he planned to get himself rescued.

Towards evening the other two woke up also. We divided our food and water again and ate a meal which was just sufficient to stave off the worst pangs of hunger. We all found the tepid water tasteless and lacking in any power to quench our thirst. For the most part we were silent, both while we were walking and in the periods of wakeful relaxation before and after sleeping. There was not much that we had in common except a feeling of close comradeship and mutual reliance. Beyond that there was little we could discuss on even terms. Besides, we were all still far too busy with our thoughts, adjusting them to our new conditions and making continual laborious estimates of our chances of survival. But the stale and tasteless water at last provoked Oxton into venting his feelings.

" Bloody hell, what couldn't I do with a bloody good brew? This — water tastes like cat's pee. When I get home after this — war, I'm never going to drink water again. If my old woman ever tries to give me any, she'll get a bloody good kick. For — 's sake, I'm — fed up. Let's get going again. I can't stand all this bloody sitting around.'

This was how we all felt. The safe cover of the squadron commander and the C.O. had been removed, and I for one felt lost, bewildered, and abandoned. We had all been too buried in our own thoughts to recognize the comfort we could obtain by sharing our anxieties. Oxton's outburst at least served to relieve the tension, and it was almost with surprise that I awoke to full awareness of my two companions. Even so, the incident might well have poisoned our relations had not Chandler answered quietly, 'Come off it, mate – it's the same for all of us.'

The thunder cleared from Oxton's face and he grinned guiltily, ashamed of his outburst.

The light was now beginning to fade, so we decided to start again. I led the way, with Oxton and Chandler flanking me on each side and a pace or two behind. We walked for a time in silence. When Oxton spoke, his voice seemed unusually loud in the surrounding stillness of the night. Its unexpectedness and the close echo of my own thoughts startled me.

'What's our chances, sir?' he said.

After a moment I let my own thoughts speak for themselves.

'Pretty good, I think, if we can get across the main road without being seen. We'll get to Tmimi to-night, I hope. Then we'll lie up again for the day. Next night we'll get down to the sea. There'll be more chance there. The desert's swarming with Jerries and Ities. We'll make for the coastal end of the defences at Tobruk. I hope the enemy won't be watching there as closely as in other places. We'll manage, I expect.'

'Well, you sound — cheerful, sir,' Oxton answered. 'I hope all this bloody walking won't land us up in a prison camp. Sort of waste of effort, wouldn't it be?'

Chandler sniggered, and I could think of no adequate reply. We walked for the rest of the night in silence, except for the frequent curses from one or the other of us as we stumbled or fell in the darkness. Our strength and determination to cover as much ground as possible were weakening. This and the soreness of our feet made periodical halts a welcome relief. I found that I had to exert the utmost determination to prevent these halts from occurring too often or from being too prolonged. Our progress was noticeably slower than on the previous night.

When daylight came we could see Tmimi. Again we lay up during the day, sleeping and eating, and trying to keep warm. It was a cold, damp day with a northerly wind blowing a light mist in from the sea. In the early afternoon two Arabs saw and approached us. After indicating with much talk and gesture where we were on the map, they gave us an Italian water-bottle filled with warm but weak tea. It was a gesture of friendliness which was so unexpected and yet so spontaneous and genuine that I was deeply touched. I felt churlish in suspecting that they might give away our position, and rigidly suppressed any such

110

ungrateful thoughts. Nevertheless I thought it safer to start off again as soon as it was dark.

In a gap in the fairly incessant stream of traffic we crossed the main road at a point where it was close to the sea, and then turned east, following the shore. But all our luck was against us, as we continually came to large waterways which ran up to half a mile inland. We were soon wet and cold after our efforts to cross them, and decided to give it up as a bad job and wait until first light to see where we were. Our disappointment was the more acute after the relatively better progress we had made on the previous nights. We shared two tins of bully beef between us and spent the rest of the night walking about to keep warm.

Daylight showed us that we were about a mile and a half east of Tmimi. As there seemed to be no sign of life near us, we headed for the shore, and walked on throughout the day till in the late afternoon we sighted Gazala Point. Here we were held up by a party of Italians who were bathing from a camp which was about 100 yards from the shore. There seemed to be no way round, so we lay up in the scrub and watched with intent interest the preparation of the evening meal at the cookhouse, which was no more than 100 yards from us. At seven o'clock the Italians had their meal. Leaving no sentries, they then all went to their tents. I gave them an hour in which to become completely settled. Then we crept up to the cookhouse. From the water-cans which stood ready to hand we filled our water-bottles. In a big iron container we found the remains of the hot food, no doubt mixed with the refuse of the day, as it smelled so peculiar. But it was hot and tasty after the endless cold bully beef, and we ate until we could eat no more. The unaccustomed quantity and the richness of the food were to cause us trouble later. Our raid had been so successful that we became careless in our movements. Chandler stumbled in the dark and knocked from a hook a large tin bucket, which fell with a resounding clatter, making enough noise to wake the surrounding countryside for miles. We all crouched with bated breath, tensed to make whatever frantic move might be necessary. But, except for one shouted sentence in Italian from a tent nearby, there was no alarm, and with relief we continued our journey.

We walked for another three hours, passing further camps on

111

the way. At last we were faced by an escarpment which blocked our route and which we were forced to climb, as we could find no way round. It was nearly dawn by the time we reached the top, and by then we were much too exhausted to go any farther. By now, too, the food and drink which we had taken in such unwise quantities the night before were beginning to have an effect, making us weak and sick at intervals.

At daylight we took stock of our position and got the shock of our lives. A few yards away from the bushes in which we were lying was the main road to Tobruk, along which a constant stream of traffic was moving. There was only one thing to do. We buried ourselves deeper into the bushes, pulling our coats closely around us and lay and hoped for the best. The sun beating down on us during the day caused us acute discomfort, as we were unable to move much. Our thirst, induced by the quantity of rich food of the previous night and aggravated by the sun, distressed us considerably, and by nightfall we had drunk half the water which was to have lasted us for two days. The performance of our normal daily functions disgusted us in the close confines of the bushes. These were all the more frequent as a result of the disorders of our stomachs. The stench and the flies it attracted were two more burdens to be borne.

At dusk we set off again and made some progress unobserved. But we were too weak to go far, and after a few miles lay down close together in an effort to get the warmth we now so desperately needed before we could sleep.

Before dawn we started off again. Our progress was slow, as the coastline here was dotted with a string of camps. Nor had we recovered from our stomach complaints, which still made us feel weak and dispirited. By late afternoon we decided that it was useless to continue and that we all needed a good night's rest. We found a safe hiding-place, and after a frugal meal of biscuits, which was all we could face, we carefully divided the small amount of water remaining and lay down to sleep.

We made an early start the next morning, passing several German camps in the semi-darkness and making good progress until about midday our way was completely blocked by another camp. There was nothing we could do but to lie up again and wait till darkness came. The continual halts had been a considerable drain on our meagre supply of water and in the afternoon we shared out the last drop. When night fell we decided to push on as far as we could get and hope that we would come across another Italian camp which would be less well watched and guarded than the German camps we had seen recently.

Our luck was in, for after a short distance we walked into a small Arab encampment. Here we were given all the water we wanted and pressed to accept hot food which smelled appetizing, however revolting it looked. With the memory of our previous large meal still clearly in our minds and still to some extent suffering its ill effects, we reluctantly refused. The Arabs could not understand this rejection of their hospitality, and watched us depart with a quiet disdain which marked their hurt pride. I knew too little of the language to explain the reason for our refusal, and our send-off gave me much anxiety, lest our presence should be reported to the enemy on the following day. As a result we determined to make as much progress as possible during the night.

This was to be the cause of our undoing. For, intent as we were on speed, we neglected the elementary precautions, and before we knew what had happened we had stumbled in the darkness into the perimeter of another German camp. The first indication was a shouted challenge from the darkness just to our right. This was followed almost instantaneously by a shot which missed us and, ricocheting off the rocks, went wheeing off into the night. After that there was pandemonium. Lights appeared in all directions and shouts seemed to surround us. In the confusion I yelled to my companions, 'Run for the sea. Separate. We haven't a bloody chance if we stick together.'

So saying, I headed off into the dark away from the other two, found the beach by a miracle and stumbled along it, making all possible speed. Gradually the noise died away behind me as I increased the distance from the camp and as the Germans gave up their search. When I was out of earshot I dropped exhausted to the sand, where I lay for some time trying to recover my strength and hoping I would hear Oxton and Chandler. At last I decided to wait no longer and, staggering to my feet, I stumbled off along the coast. At dawn I found myself a hiding-place, where I collapsed into an exhausted sleep.

I did not wake until late the following day, and was then too weak and exhausted to move. Throughout that day and the following night I slept by fits and starts, gradually regaining my physical strength, but losing for a time my mental equilibrium. I found myself mumbling incoherently at frequent intervals, and once or twice woke with a start from my fitful sleep at the sound of a voice, only to find that it was my own. I dreamt of my home in Somerset. I fought again the battles of the recent past. I had long conversations with Tomkins, explaining at elaborate length to him my exact reasons for leaving him. In a fevered way I planned my next moves. These thoughts were abruptly halted by my sudden idea that Tobruk, too, was taken and that I would have to walk to Sollum. At last my mind cleared. I ate all the biscuits that were left and half a tin of bully beef, then lay down to sleep until nightfall.

I woke with a start to find that it was pitch dark, and with a feeling of alarm that something had disturbed me. I sat still and listened. I was not more than thirty yards from the shore and could now clearly hear the crunch of footsteps on the sand. I waited with my heart in my mouth, listening intently to try to determine how many men there were. As they drew level with my hiding-place I felt sure that there were not more than two, in which case it was unlikely that it was a German patrol. Suddenly the most English of all sounds broke the silence and assured me that I had nothing to worry about. One of the figures stumbled against a rock, and the next moment the silence of the night was shattered by a hardly suppressed voice cursing all and sundry, ' — hell. That's another of them bloody rocks. I'm about — cheesed off, Alf. For —'s sake let's stop till morning, when we can see what we're doing.'

I stood up. The noise of my movement brought the other two to a halt, and when I called out there was no answer from the two motionless figures I could now see silhouetted against the phosphorescence of the surf. In the silence that followed suspicion began to grow on both sides, until at last I determined to risk all and called, 'Is that you, Oxton and Chandler?'

After that there was no further hesitation. The warmth of our mutual welcome was a stimulant to all of us, and the knowledge that I was now no longer alone did for me what no amount of additional rest and food could have done. It was good to have these two with me again. Their conversation might be limited, their adjectives monotonously repetitive, their thoughts crude and direct, but there was a wealth of fellow-feeling and genuine comradeship in their concern for my condition and their anxious attempts to revive and encourage me.

The formalities and chatter of our reunion took so long that we only made a short distance during the night and at first light dived hurriedly for a sheltering hiding-place when we saw the wire and sandbags of a M.G. post outlined against the lightening eastern sky. By day we established that it was the German front line. Behind us we saw further signs of the enemy. We took advantage of the daylight hours to work out our route to what we were sure was the British front line on the crest farther to the east. To this moment we had been in doubt as to who held Tobruk. There was, till then, the nightmare thought that we might have to continue our march for another 100 miles to the frontier. The knowledge that we were so near the British lines was another boost to our spirits. Yet we were still so far that on further reflection about the hazards yet to be overcome our exuberance was dampened, and it was with sober determination that we planned our moves for the night.

As soon as it was dark we started. The seashore again seemed to offer the best chance. From the high ground of the British positions it was entirely overlooked, and try as we did during the day we could see no sign of any enemy positions close by the sea. After dark this part was no doubt closely patrolled, and it was in order to forestall these that we had made so early a move. Indeed, it was so vital that we should reach the shore before any patrol that we cast all caution aside and walking at a fast pace made all possible speed over the broken rocks and tangled scrub. The enemy could not have failed to hear us, but we relied on the chance that those who did might think that it was their own patrol moving forward to take up position. And so it seemed to work out. In any case, there was no sudden burst of fire, no Very light was put up to light the scene, and we made our first objective without incident.

On the shore we halted and rested. Unfit as we were, the exertion, albeit brief, had exhausted us, and we lay for a time breathing heavily and slowly recovering our wind and strength. At last

I said, 'Come on, let's go. Stick close together and do as I do. We haven't far to go if we don't get lost. We're off.'

All night we crawled, so as to avoid appearing on the skyline to either side. Our hands and knees became badly cut and raw and it was agony to put any weight on to them. Our high optimism of the afternoon evaporated, and as each hour passed with yet no sign of rescue we became gloomier and gloomier. For some time we climbed gradually in the bed of a rock-strewn wadi, until I suddenly realized that this probably marked the centre point between the two front lines. The British line was at the top of the ridge to our left. With a muffled curse of disgust at my own stupidity, I turned left and started to climb the steeper side of the wadi. The other two followed, but only just, as my sudden change of direction had taken them unawares and they nearly passed me going in the original direction.

We continued slowly and laboriously on the new course, pausing frequently for breath and rest. Our movements, careful as they were, were to our own ears enough to wake the dead. Each move dislodged a rock or stone, each patch of scrub we passed through seemed to make more noise than the last, and we felt sure that our deep, stertorous breathing must have been audible for some distance. Despite the noise we were making, we all heard the sharp click of metal against metal somewhere in front of us. As one man we stopped, not daring to breathe. For minutes which seemed to turn into hours we remained rigid, until our rigidity caused acute and agonizing cramp. At last I decided to risk all on one throw and called in a harsh, whispered croak, 'Don't shoot. We're English.'

In the darkness before me I could sense the presence of more than one person, and as I heard them move there was a muffled reply, 'How many?'

'Three,' I answered.

Again there was a pause and a muffled consultation, then, 'O.K., come one at a time.'

I called quietly to Oxton that I would go, and started to scramble forward. Suddenly I was seized by strong arms, lifted to my feet and hustled off into the night. Behind me I heard a voice say, 'Next', and, reassured, followed obediently the directions of the hand on my arm.

After a walk of perhaps ten minutes we came to the entrance of a shallow dug-out. We entered, and my companion, after carefully fixing the flaps over the entrance, said 'Let's have a look at you,' and shone a torch in my face. 'O.K., you'll do,' was the cryptic comment. 'We'll wait for the others.'

It was too good to be true. The other two followed soon afterwards, when we were all three taken to the Company headquarters of the Australian battalion into whose hands we had fallen. A hot drink, a meal and as many blankets as we wanted, and we were soon asleep, and sleeping as we had not slept for weeks.

5

In Tobruk

So ended for me and my crew what was later to be known as the 'Benghazi handicap'.

Tobruk was invested by the Germans on 11 April. The garrison consisted of the 9th Australian Division reinforced by various British units, among whom was a composite regiment of tanks from 7th Armoured Division armed with light, cruiser and Matilda tanks.

My arrival in Tobruk coincided with the end of the first German attempt to seize the fortress, which had started during the early hours of 14 April. They were to make only one more major attempt at the close of the month, and thereafter, both attacks having been beaten back so conclusively, they did not try again.

After a day of rest with the Australians, the three of us were sent back to the Transit Camp near the harbour. On the following day we joined the tank regiment which had only arrived by sea the previous week, just in time to take its part in the repulse of the first German attacks.

I was given command of a troop and took over a tank with an already established crew. Oxton and Chandler were allotted to separate tanks to fill gaps in the crews. We saw little of each other in the days that followed and gradually grew farther and farther apart. Our close comradeship of the hectic escape faded with time and was replaced in me by a feeling of loss, until this in turn was slowly effaced by the new comradeship with my new crew.

It took some few days to recover from the physical and mental strain of our ordeal, and during this time the incessant bombing attacks left me weak and afraid. Soon, however, I found, as so often in war, that I had mentally valued this new danger, had assessed the risks, and gradually the air attacks were no longer novel and unusual, and so held less terror for me. It was always the unknown that caused the greatest fear. A danger, however great, well comprehended was as nothing. Only so could some men achieve with the utmost calm and cool calculation the supreme deeds of clear-headed action.

After the second German attack we settled down to our watch and to the improvement of the defences. All our energies and ingenuity were required to guard effectively the twenty-five miles of the perimeter, at any point of which the Germans might have attacked. The defence lines were in the form of a semicircle, whose radius was about ten miles, with Tobruk as the centre. Within this area we, in the tanks, had to be prepared to move at a moment's notice to any part of the perimeter which was threatened.

The hardest task of all was merely to exist in the relatively confined area of the fortress, all of which was within range of the enemy guns and subject to continual air attack.

The ever-present sand which blew up into periodic sand-storms; the flies, mosquitoes and insects; the lack of fresh veget-ables and food or any variety of diet; the warm, distasteful, brackish water which only served to aggravate the thirst instead of quenching it; the difficulty of keeping clean or of cleaning our clothes; the lack of any of the small comforts of civilization; the weeks and months without even a sight of a woman – these were the main trials and tribulations.

The daily patrols and later the incessant air attacks were in a way a relief to the sorely tried spirit, and the many small successes were at least subjects for conversation and gave no little excite-ment in the performance. There was humour in every situation, if only there was a will to see it. The effort to keep clean, to shave each day, was one means of beating back the incipient lethargy and melancholy.

In the middle of May I was at last told that I was to return to Alexandria for a few days' leave before rejoining my old regiment.

Before leaving I went in search of Oxton and Chandler. They greeted me with polite and respectful courtesy, and our relations remained distant and formal while I promised to try to get them back, too, and we discussed what fate might have befallen Tomkins, since we had had no more news of him. I couldn't help thinking of the reception that I would have been given a few weeks ago when, after our miraculous escape, we had all grown so close. It was surprising how even a week or two separated from soldiers whom one thought one knew well and regarded as friends, could build up again the wall of constraint which had been broken down in so short a time. But it was always so, and I, now less sensitive to the feelings and attitudes of others, was content to leave it so.

That night I went down to the harbour. While I sat waiting to embark, I was aware of the many noises around me – cranes clanking and creaking; shouts and oaths; the bump and thump of loads being landed; the clatter of the loads being manhandled along the quay. In all that was being done there was a note of urgency. The ships had to be unloaded while it was still dark so that they could be safely away by daybreak.

The organization was, after so many trials, a perfect instrument, and all was accomplished with surprising smoothness and speed, considering the blackness of the night and the total absence of lights. There was, too, the occasional crash of a shell landing in the harbour area. On this night for once there was no air attack.

At last we went aboard and were packed into our allotted places. I was kept awake by the usual sounds of departure; the pounding of feet on deck; the clatter and clank of the winches; the shouts. At length I felt the vibration of the engines as we moved, and soon after fell asleep.

At dawn the hatches were opened and, a few at a time, we were allowed on deck. Away to the south, like a dark smudge on the horizon, I saw the coastline of Africa. Somewhere there, behind the cliffs and coastal greenery, I could imagine the camps and leaguers of the troops who were watching the Germans on the frontier. They would have broken their close night leaguers by now and have fanned out, some to their positions of observation, others merely to wait and wait, as we had waited for months

119

before and as we would wait for many months more in the years to come.

That evening we came to Alexandria. I was taken to Mustafa Barracks, past the bright lights of the city centre and opulent flats along the Corniche. I was back to civilization again, but I felt a complete stranger and a little lost.

6

We Move to Relieve Tobruk

AFTER a week's leave I rejoined the regiment, who were in the throes of the urgent preparations for another offensive.

I went back to Kinnaird's squadron, and was delighted to find Egerton and Morgan had also returned to it. Morgan was now second-in-command in place of the vanished Bolton, and I was given his old job of supervising the fitters in addition to, since we were short of officers, commanding a troop.

The reunion was celebrated in such style that I felt like the Prodigal Son, and we talked away the hours of night recounting our adventures and laughing over our misfortunes.

Egerton was the same as ever. The other two troop commanders I had not met before. They were not new hands to the desert and had already established themselves in the squadron. However fast the slaughter and the resultant replacements of officers and men, it was only a matter of days before the new face blotted out the tragedy and loss of an old and trusted friend. I did remember, however, to inquire after Ryan, and was told that he had lost a leg.

Perhaps endeavour was the keynote of all we did at that time, endeavour and an unquenchable optimism and confidence. The past, with all its errors and tragedies, was only to be remembered so that we could learn from our mistakes.

We were determined that we would do all in our power to relieve Tobruk, but we were soberly aware of the difficulties we faced. The Germans were now in complete control of the frontier areas, they had been reinforced and we had had a first taste during May of their prowess in the close collaboration of their tanks and anti-tank guns. We already knew the worth of their tanks.

When we moved forward on 14 June there was none of the elation we had felt before the advance against the Italians, however much we were reminded of it by the presence of the 4th Indian Division, now returned from their triumphs in East Africa. Even Egerton was subdued and remarked, 'If I'm killed, will someone write to my Mum and tell her I was brave and good? She'd like to hear it even if it isn't true.'

At 0230 hours on the morning of 15 June we started to move forward to our battle positions. All through the remaining hours of darkness the long columns of tanks, guns and lorries moved slowly north. I peered through the choking clouds of dust and petrol fumes to pick up the pin-point of red light from the vehicle in front. The creak and clatter from the tank-tracks, the clink and rattle of the gun limbers and the thump and bump of the lorry-loads, were the only sounds to be heard. Later I was sent on ahead to the start point to give warning to the regiment when they were due to move. I watched with wonder the silent host as it passed. No one spoke to me, indeed it was only once or twice that I realized that there were men in the mass that was moving before me. Occasionally a tank commander bent to look into his turret, and the interior lights lit a taut or laughing face for an instant. Once, as a gun-towing vehicle passed me, the faces of the occupants were visible for a moment through one of the apertures lit by the quick flare of a match. A few lorry-drivers at the rear, less disciplined and less aware of the hazards they risked by betraying their position, drove for a short distance with their side-lights on until a violent shout from a military policeman caused the lights to be doused immediately.

Each column was led by the navigator. The regular halts to correct the bearing were understood by those just behind him, but each check had a worse effect the farther down the column it was felt. Those in front knew the reason and halted smartly, waited patiently and moved off again when they should. Farther back each halt was construed as being unplanned, caused by some mischance or alteration to the plans. Here, as in any column on roads or tracks, in daylight or darkness, where the dust was worst and the confusion of many vehicles on the move was most marked, tempers were soon frayed.

Moving only a short distance behind the navigator, I was

121

unaffected by these worries. True the dust was bad and I had to be on the alert the whole time to warn my driver if he approached too close to the vehicle in front. But there was still time for my mind to wander to other subjects. I had acquired the habit of living outside my immediate surroundings. In the boredom or stress of battle I was beginning to find that my main diversion was to detach my mind and to concentrate on thoughts of leave, or my home in Somerset, or anything else that was pleasant.

When dawn came at about 0430 hours we were still moving almost due north. The clear air of morning was a relief. Though it was hours since I had had any sleep, I stretched as if I had just woken up. The night, even at almost midsummer, had been cold, with a heavy dew. The gradually increasing warmth of the sun was welcome at this early hour, though later in the day we would curse the heat. As the light increased the vehicles and columns moved farther apart. This was perhaps the greatest relief. At last the begrimed drivers could take off their goggles and wipe the caked dust from their faces and clear their mouths and noses. Though less affected, I did the same.

Inside the turret Basset, my gunner, and King, the operator, stirred, and I felt a tug at my trouser leg. Basset asked:

'Any chance of a 'alt, sir? I could do with a leak.'

'Afraid you'll have to hold it, Basset. Could do with one myself – and a good hot brew too,' I replied.

'O.K., sir,' answered Basset cheerfully; ''ope it won't be too long, though, or there might be a nasty 'orrid haccident.'

'You'd better bloody well not,' was King's ultimatum, who had moved over behind the gun so as to catch what was being said.

'O.K., O.K.,' said Basset. 'Don't get so narsty about it. I said I 'oped as 'ow it would be O.K. But if it isn't, you watch out . . . you just watch out!'

This dire threat was accompanied by a roar of laughter, and the two figures disappeared from my sight as they fell to the turret floor good-naturedly wrestling with each other. I could not help marvelling at their good temper and humour, even as we moved towards battle. I supposed it was due either to a complete lack of imagination or, more probably, to a power which was almost a national trait, which enabled each one, whether a tank crewman in battle or a London housewife in the blitz, to see all events in their right perspective in history and not to be over-awed by any incident. Sometimes perhaps we overdid this habit, but it was a fault on the right side. I grinned as I imagined the possibility of the German crews advancing to battle, sitting to attention and singing national hymns with great solemnity.

7

Brewed-up

BY 0600 hours we were near the German position at Point 207. We had shaken out into our battle formation of the day. Our squadron was in the lead of the regiment which formed the right flank of the Brigade. Here we were virtually up with the leading regiment in the centre, and our task was to extend the frontal reconnaissance screen as far as possible to the right. My troop was on the extreme right of the squadron, and I had been given the added role by Kinnaird of roving out as far as I thought prudent to extend the screen even farther.

We moved past Point 207 in a wide sweep never closer than about 1,000 yards and changing direction meanwhile to the left on to a course which was just north of west. This was to bring us to a position slightly to the south of the German defences at Point 206, some two and a half miles to the west. There was a short halt while the various navigators set their new course, and then we moved forward again. Except for some half-dozen shells fired at long range, there was no sign of life from the German positions at Point 207.

An hour later we were in battle formation in positions overlooking the defences at Point 206 and also disposed to keep a watchful eye on the open desert to the west. Kinnaird was ordered to screen the eastern edge of the German position and so to watch the gap between Point 206 and Point 207 behind us.

He sent me to a position about half-way between the two, where I found a good commanding feature which gave me a wide view of the country to the north. From here at 0730 hours I heard, about four miles away to my north-east, the first sounds of the battle being fought for 'Hellfire' Pass by the right-hand columns of our advance. One column was advancing at the foot of the escarpment along the coast, while the other, just visible to me, was moving in a wide encircling sweep along the top of the escarpment.

It was a fine sight. Silhouetted against the bright sky to the east I could see, in the van of the attack, a squadron of Matilda tanks moving majestically forward, followed by the infantry and guns. They looked irresistible – squat, heavily armoured, powerful and invested with all the prestige of their victorious attacks against Nibeiwa, the Tummars, Bardia and Tobruk. Behind each tank was a plume of dust, which made the squadron look for all the world like a fleet at sea, closing at speed to engage some luckless foe.

But this rosy picture was quickly and rudely shattered. Up to this point the Germans at 'Hellfire' had been engaging the forces on both its flanks with only long-range artillery fire. Suddenly above the confused rumble of battle I heard the unmistakable whip-lash crack of high-velocity shot. Even so I was expecting it, for in the instant before the sound reached me I saw three of the leading Matildas stop abruptly and burst into flames. In another minute there were five Matildas disabled or in flames, and the attack which had looked so triumphant a moment before had lost a third of its tank strength and was still some 2,000 yards from its objective. I watched, fascinated and almost unable to believe the evidence before my eyes. I realized with dismay that the Germans now had an anti-tank gun to which even the Matildas were not immune. It was a sombre and depressing thought. I understood clearly in this moment that none of our future battles would be as easy as those of the previous year, now that even the Matilda was matched, and indeed, overmatched.

I was so engrossed in what was going on in front of me that I failed to report anything to Kinnaird. Before I could do so there was a further development. From the German positions at 'Hellfire' there now emerged some tanks which, advancing towards the now disorganized British force, compelled it to retire. It was a well-co-ordinated withdrawal, and the Germans were not allowed the opportunity for a quick follow-up, but nevertheless I itched to be able to help and reported:

' ... Our force advancing to my right front has been stopped by fire from very heavy anti-tank guns and has now been forced to withdraw by enemy tanks. Shall I move to support? Over.'

Kinnaird's instant reply was, ' ... No, repeat no. Certainly not. Stay where you are. You've been given a job to do, so do it and don't start dashing off anywhere else. If you've got any gumption you'd get something to eat now. There won't be much chance later. Over.'

I answered briefly, ' ... O.K. Off,' and bent down immediately to Basset and said, 'Brew-up, and be quick about it,' and signalled my other two tanks to do the same.

Whatever else we may have neglected to practise during the period available for training, at least we had established a quick and efficient drill for the preparation of our food and tea. While King and I manned the set and kept watch, Newman, the driver, and Basset had soon got a fire going and the brew-can on it. There was not much choice for breakfast so, as speed was essential, they had cut two bully-beef tins in half, and the ends of these they had stuck into the fire.

In fifteen minutes the meal was ready, but as Basset climbed on to the front of the tank with two steaming cups of tea, Kinnaird ordered:

' ... Move now and join me. The advance is to continue in figures one five minutes. You will now take up position at the rear. Off.'

This happened too often to be funny. Just as the meal was ready and each of us was mentally enjoying the few quiet moments during which we could suck at our tea and meditate, we were ordered to move, or a truck would come and fetch me to take me to Kinnaird's tank for orders, or a lorry would arrive to refill us with petrol or ammunition. There was a wild scurry as Newman kicked over the fire-can to extinguish the last flames and Basset emptied the brew-can of the last dregs and stowed all the equipment. We had to do the best we could to eat and drink as we moved back to join the squadron.

'A bloody waste of a good brew,' was King's sour comment as, with his head and shoulders stuck out of the operator's hatch next to mine, he tried vainly to measure the jerks and bumps so as not to lose too much of his tea.

We rejoined the squadron and almost immediately the advance continued. We now turned south to avoid the tail of the two columns which had earlier been moving to our south and which had now swung north for their attack on Point 206 and on Fort Capuzzo, farther to the north-west.

By the middle of the morning we had skirted the two northern columns, had crossed the wire and were in position to protect the open left flank of the whole series of attacks. To the south I could see occasionally the trucks and gun-limbers of the Motor Brigade, who were extending our line farther south past Sidi Omar to Bir Sheferzen. While we waited, the first reports began to come in of the attacks on Sollum. They were not pleasant hearing. Each one spoke of the strength of the German guns, and particularly of the 88-mm. anti-aircraft guns which were used against their tanks. It was with a dismal apprehension that I heard the Colonel's warning:

' ... Our shooting must be very accurate. Shoot to kill with the first shot, or our chances will be slim. The Mark IIIs and the 88s can both be expected. Off.'

Just before midday the attack on Point 206 and Fort Capuzzo started. To my right rear I heard the short, sharp tumult of the bombardment and the subsequent fire of the tank two-pounders and their machine-guns. The action was brief and successful. But though quiet settled over the desert again, the lull was ominous. A feeling grew and grew within me, however much I tried to dispose of it by logical arguments and optimism, that I was going to be unlucky. I had never felt it before. It sapped my confidence and resolution. I tried to find a reason for these thoughts, and could only assume that I had been out of action too long and that as a result all my forebodings, natural enough before any battle, were magnified. I found myself praying for some activity – anything to occupy my mind. I was at least sure enough of myself to know that when the demand came I would be able to try to meet it. I had not long to wait.

Some three miles west of Fort Capuzzo was a prominent piece of high ground known as the Hafid Ridge. Behind this the Germans were now reported to be concentrating, no doubt in readiness for a counter-attack on our advance. We were ordered to engage this force, which was reported to be not large. The orders were passed on by Brigade to us, the right flank regiment, the one best placed to carry out the attack. The Colonel in his turn passed them on to Kinnaird.

'Hello, DONA; FANO calling. Enemy force of guns and tanks reported to be forming up west of Hafid Ridge. Move now to engage. They must be prevented from attacking Fort Capuzzo. Report the extent of their positions and numbers as soon as you can. If necessary I will reinforce you. Over.'

'Hello, FANO; DONA answering. O.K., off to you. Hello, all stations DONA. You have heard our orders. Advance now on a bearing of figures nine degrees. Two and Three leading, with One and Four on my right and left. Over.

While I waited to answer as Three troop, I thought, 'Well, here we go, and the Lord save us.' I acknowledged in my turn, dropped my wireless microphone and picked up the Tannoy mike to speak to my crew:

'Driver, advance – right – a bit farther right – too far – left a bit – that's it – on – speed eight miles per hour until I tell you to go faster. Gunner – two-pounder and machine-gun action – be ready to shoot well and fast. Loader – load both guns and stack some more ammunition handy.'

That seen to, I turned my attention to my other two tanks to make sure they were in the battle positions I wanted. I checked my position with Two Troop on my left and looked behind to see that I was correctly located in relation to the Squadron Headquarters – that I was not going too fast or too far off the bearing. Although we had all been given the line on which to advance, it was for the troop leaders only to make sure that we were heading roughly in the right direction, as the accurate navigation would be done by the Squadron Navigator – in our case, the sergeant-major. Incongruous as this had at first seemed to me, I soon realized that the sergeant-major had an absolute flair for these unusual duties, and the fact that he had gave him a degree of prestige among the soldiers which he would never have acquired if he had been only the conventional disciplinarian.

I had slipped naturally back into the routine of battle, the battle drill. All my earlier worries were now forgotten and my whole mind was concentrated on the performance of duties which were now almost, but not quite, second nature. I watched my other tanks, checked my position with the other leading troop, commanded by Egerton, made sure by occasional backward glances to the navigator that I was going in the right direction.

As I came to each crest on the line of march I ordered the driver to slow down, and so crept cautiously to the summit for a careful examination of the ground ahead before moving on again. In this sort of life a tank commander's best friend was his binoculars. Only with them and adequate forethought and caution could we be sure of seeing the enemy in time to avoid disaster or to spring a surprise. So used had I become to relying on them that I felt lost without them. They were with me at all times, carefully kept clean and out of harm's way – tucked into my shirt while I was eating, held firmly when I climbed on to or off the tank, wrapped tightly in my clothes at night.

Twice on the move to Hafid Ridge my view was obscured by high ground to my right front. Although off the direct line of march, it was essential that the ground beyond should be looked at. The main body of the enemy might have moved, or a further small force might have been lurking there. I reported:

' ... Moving figures nine zero zero to my right front to observe. Over,' to be answered briefly by Kinnaird's, ' ... O.K. Off.'

We had been moving for just over half an hour when Kinnaird said, ' ... Navigator reports that he is now about figures two five zero zero yards short of the position given for the enemy. You should therefore be seeing them at any moment. Be bloody careful, as we do not want to be caught by surprise. Halt and report as soon as you see any signs. Off.'

I gave the necessary orders to my crew.

'Newman, slow down to figures five – close down – prepare for action. Basset, when I give the order, give the bastards all you've got.'

At reduced speed, I guided the driver over each yard of the way, so as to make full use of every fold and crest of the ground. I glanced quickly into the turret, and was satisfied to see Basset with his eye glued to his telescope, King standing by the gun with the next round clasped to his chest, and Newman peering intently through the thick glass block in his closed visor.

Another small crest loomed before us, and I felt certain that beyond this I would see the enemy. I signalled my other two tanks to halt and told Newman to slow down. At a snail's pace we crept up to the crest. As soon as I could see the ground beyond I called,

'Driver – halt,' so that only my head and shoulders and perhaps a very small portion of the turret would be visible to those on the other side. I moved slowly, in order not to attract attention, and surveyed the expanse of sand and rock before me. The heat of the midday, midsummer sun covered the desert with a shimmering haze which made observation beyond about 1,000 yards almost impossible. To my astonishment, I had been unaware until this moment of the intense heat. The movement of the tank, though slow, had been sufficient to fan a slight breeze over me, and my mind had been too intent on other things. The haze which masked my vision beyond a certain range reminded me now of the heat, and I was instantly aware of the sun beating down on the back of my head and toasting the steel of the turret to almost unbearable temperatures, so that my bare elbows, when I tried to rest them on the edge of the cupola, seemed to have been seared with a red-hot poker.

All this I forgot in the next moment. Their shapes magnified and distorted in the haze, some fifteen to twenty German tanks were visible in my binoculars. I counted them and tried hard to identify them, but to no avail, so my report lacked some of the detail I would have liked and had been taught to include:

' ... At about figures one two zero zero yards to my front, figures fifteen to twenty enemy tanks, stationary, facing this way. Impossible to identify them accurately, but I believe they are Mark IIIs. Behind them there is a mass of vehicles, among which there may be more tanks. Am halted in a position to observe, and do not think that I have yet been seen. Over.'

Kinnaird answered, ' ... O.K. Off to you,' and to Egerton said, ' ... Can you confirm the last information from Three? Over.'

I glanced to my left to see where Egerton had got to and, as I heard his voice answering Kinnaird, saw him in a similar position to my own, with his two troop tanks halted some way behind.

' ... Yes, I can,' was Egerton's reply. 'I think there are at least figures twenty tanks, and their position is extended on each flank by what appear to be dug-in anti-tank guns. The vehicles behind include some big guns. I don't think I've been seen yet either. Over.'

Kinnaird acknowledged the message and then told both Egerton and me to stay where we were and to remain out of view.

He then reported the news to the Colonel, who immediately ordered another squadron forward in support of us and himself came to take charge of the impending battle. The third squadron of the regiment was left behind in its original position to continue to watch to the west.

Some twenty minutes later the second squadron arrived and halted behind Kinnaird's headquarters, while the Colonel and the two squadron leaders came forward to look at the enemy. Their arrival, on the crest previously occupied by only Egerton and me, though slow and careful, was yet sufficient to attract the enemy's attention. Desultory fire by medium-sized field guns and the unpleasant air-burst of the 88s made the reconnaissance hazardous and unpleasant. In fifteen minutes the plan was made, and the exchange of wireless messages between the C.O. and the squadron leaders, though brief, guarded and laconic, was sufficient to tell the rest of us what our role was to be.

Almost immediately Kinnaird recalled Egerton and me with our troops to his own position farther back, and here we all re-formed and faced on to a new bearing. We were to move east behind the crest which now hid us from the enemy and, turning north and then west, were to advance on a close wheel on the eastern edge of the enemy's defences. Thus we would face only the flank of the anti-tank gun screen, and might pierce these outer defences and do damage to the vehicles behind before the German tanks could move in support. The second squadron was to extend the flank of the attack to our right and if possible, shielded by our actions, move into the rear of the enemy force. We were already detected, so success would depend on speed of manoeuvre and accurate shooting when the opportunity came.

Taking advantage of the haze, Kinnaird moved at speed behind the crest, swung north at its eastern extremity, and after 1,000 yards turned on to a bearing just north of west. Egerton and I were leading, with the two other troops of the squadron echeloned back behind my right flank, positioned so that they could see our moves and be ready to take advantage of any tactical gains. As we moved in over the last 1,500 yards, I glanced quickly round to be sure that my tanks were in position and to take final note of Kinnaird's moves. Inside the turret I knew that the crew were at their action stations, and could imagine King stolidly chewing his baccy – his standby in all moments of stress. Over the even, pebbly desert the tank moved smoothly at speed, and the breeze was a welcome relief from the heat, which was becoming oppressive. I edged my ear-phones more closely on to my ears, though by so doing some of the pleasant cool air was excluded and I could feel the sweat gathering almost instantly behind my ears.

Twelve hundred yards I estimated the range to be to the nearest object, which resembled an anti-tank gun – eleven hundred – ten – nine. 'Driver – halt,' I called down the intercom. The tank came to an abrupt halt, rocked forward on to its front suspensions and settled still. I braced myself with my forearms on the front of the cupola until the tank was steady, then swept the ground before me through my binoculars.

What I had thought to be a dug-in gun turned out on closer inspection to be only a large tuft of scrub. I glanced hurriedly to my left to check Egerton's movements, and was just in time to see him also come to an abrupt stop.

Immediately Kinnaird inquired the cause, 'Hello, Three. What's happened? Why have you halted? Over.' And I answered:

'Three answering – I thought I was in range of a target. It's only scrub – moving on now. Off.'

We moved on, with every nerve alert so as not to miss any cleverly dug-in anti-tank gun. On the move they were very difficult to spot. I could only hope and keep my eyes fixed to the ground in front. If I had missed one, we were close enough now for the first indication to be the impact and probable penetration of a hit. However, all went well, and after another 200 yards I was satisfied that I was in range of the nearest tank.

'Driver, halt,' I ordered. 'Gunner, two-pounder – traverse left – on – tank – German Mark III – eight five zero yards. Fire.' I watched Basset carefully turn the range-drum to the right range, saw him turn to his telescope and aim, noticed out of the corner of my eye that King was ready with the next round, and then the tank jolted slightly with the shock of the gun firing. Through the smoke and dust and the spurt of flame I watched intently through my binoculars the trace of the shot in flight. It curved upwards slightly and almost slowly, and then seemed to plunge swiftly towards the target. There was the unmistakable dull glow of a strike of steel on steel. 'Hit, Basset! Good shot! Fire again,' I

131

called. Another shot and another hit, and I called 'Good shot; but the bastard won't brew.'

As I spoke I saw the flame and smoke from the German's gun, which showed that he was at last answering. In the next instant all was chaos. There was a clang of steel on the turret front and a blast of flame and smoke from the same place, which seemed to spread into the turret, where it was followed by another dull explosion. The shock-wave which followed swept past me, still standing in the cupola, singed my hands and face and left me breathless and dazed. I looked down into the turret. It was a shambles. The shot had penetrated the front of the turret just in front of King, the loader. It had twisted the machine-gun out of its mounting. It, or a jagged piece of the torn turret, had then hit the round that King had been holding ready – had set it on fire. The explosion had wrecked the wireless, torn King's head and shoulders from the rest of his body and started a fire among the machine-gun boxes stowed on the floor. Smoke and the acrid fumes of cordite filled the turret. On the floor, licking menacingly near the main ammunition stowage bin, there were innumerable small tongues of flame. If these caught on, the charge in the rounds would explode, taking with it the turret and all it contained.

I felt too dazed to move. My limbs seemed to be anchored, and I wondered vaguely how long I had been standing there and what I ought to do next. It was a miracle that the explosion had left me unharmed, though shaken. I wondered what had happened to Basset and bent into the cupola to find out. Shielded behind the gun and the recoil guard-shield, Basset, too, had escaped the main force of the explosion. The face that turned to look at me was blackened and scorched and the eyes, peering at me from the black background, seemed to be unnaturally large and startlingly terrified. For once Basset's good humour had deserted him, and the voice which I heard was shaking with emotion.

'Let's get out of 'ere, sir. Not much we can do for King, poor bastard! – e's 'ad it and some. An' if we 'ang around we'll catch a packet too. For Gawd's sake let's — off quick.'

At last I awoke from my daze. 'O.K., Basset. Tell Newman to bale out, and be bloody quick about it.'

As Basset bent to shout at the driver, the tank was struck again, but this time on the front of the hull. When the smoke and dust cleared, Basset bent again to shout at Newman. A moment later he turned a face now sickened with horror and disgust and blurted out:

"E's 'ad it too, sir. It's took 'alf 'is chest away. For —'s sake let's get out of 'ere.' In a frenzy of panic he tried to climb out of the narrow cupola past me, causing me to slip and delaying us both. Through my mind there flashed the thought that the German would still continue to fire until he knew that the tank was knocked out, and as yet no flames would be visible from outside. Inside the turret there was now an inferno of fire.

Without knowing how I covered the intervening distance, I found myself lying in a small hollow in the ground some twenty yards from my stricken tank, watching the first thin tongues of flame and black smoke emerging from the turret top. Beside me Basset lay panting and gasping, the sweat pouring down his face washing thin rivulets of white over the blackness of his features.

Beyond the front of the tracks of my tank I could see the German tank still firing. No shots were now coming our way, and I assumed that we must have been seen emerging from the turret.

'Come on, Basset,' I said; 'we'll get back. Follow me and do as I do.'

I drew myself half upright and ran doubled forward for some thirty yards before dropping again into the next suitable hollow. I was trying to orientate myself and to locate Kinnaird's headquarters. From ground level, outside the protecting armour of the tank, the desert seemed so vast and different. My search was interrupted by a sharp exclamation from Basset.

'Christ! – look at that. The poor bastards!'

I turned and looked past and to the left of our burning tank, where I could now see what Basset was pointing at. Beyond the left-hand tank of my troop, which was still exchanging shot for shot with the enemy, I could see all three tanks of Egerton's troop halted and in flames. A large column of black smoke and a long tongue of flame shooting out of the cupola of Egerton's tank had caused Basset's exclamation of horror. A feeling of desolation settled on me. Hoping against hope, yet fearing the worst, I desperately searched the open desert for any signs of others situated like myself. As I watched, I saw a solitary figure detach itself from the distant shape of Egerton's left tank and stumble towards he enemy.

'Not that way, you fool!' I shouted and realized in the same instant the stupidity of my action. There was nothing we could do but lie and watch the distant figure until it disappeared, swallowed up in a fold in the ground and the haze of heat and smoke and dust which overhung the whole battlefield.

At last I came to my senses. The stupor of shock left me suddenly, and I looked round with a clear eye on the scene about me. I stood up and saw about 100 yards away the small group of Kinnaird's headquarters. Behind me the two other tanks of my troop were still in action. To my left, as I stood with my back to the enemy, I could see that one tank of the next troop had also been knocked out. Beyond that my view was obstructed by the ground, so I could not tell how the fourth troop had fared.

I knew that I should not go back, but that I should take over one of the other tanks of my troop. The nearest was that of my troop sergeant, but I could, even then, imagine the reception I would get if I tried to take that over.

'You go on back, Basset. You can see where to go, can't you? O.K., report to Major Kinnaird – I'm going to take over Corporal Whiteman's tank.'

'O.K., sir,' said Basset. 'Good luck, sir.' There was no hesitation in the reply. I half hoped that Basset might have suggested that I should go back, too, until a better moment to take over another tank. I knew that I would not be wrong to postpone it, and the desert behind me looked invitingly quiet and safe. But having made up my mind and given my order, it was no use delaying.

8

Our Advance Fails

As I alternately ran and walked towards Corporal Whiteman's tank, I was conscious of nothing more than the heat around me. The crack and whine of the shot being fired and passing overhead, the duller boom of the enemy field-guns and the explosion of the shells I sensed only as the accompaniment to the main action of the scene, the heat and haze. As I moved I could feel the cooling evaporation of the sweat from my face and bare arms and legs. Whenever I stopped and lay down for protection and rest I could feel the sun beating down on the back of my head and shoulders. The desert round me was a brilliant, brittle blaze of sunshine and the reflected glare of sunlight. The heat and the recent shock sapped my strength and determination, but there was still an inner spirit which urged me on to do what I knew I must.

At length I reached Whiteman's tank and clambered up over the back and the engine to stand behind the turret. The steel of the whole tank had been baked to a heat which scorched my fingers as I grasped the turret edge and leant over the cupola.

'Come on, Corporal Whiteman,' I shouted. 'I'll take over now.'

I was surprised to see the look of startled amazement on the Corporal's face, forgetting that however much the recent events loomed in the forefront of my own mind, others on the battlefield had probably only given it a moment's thought, engrossed as they were in their own actions.

'O.K., sir,' the Corporal at last shouted back; 'but I'll pull out a bit, sir, or we'll both cop it.'

I nodded in assent and held on while the tank reversed back over 200 yards or so. When it halted, the changeover was completed in a matter of moments, Corporal Whiteman shouted his good wishes and jumped off the back on his way to Kinnaird's headquarters, and I turned my attention again to the enemy and moved back to the original position.

After the first holocaust of disaster, the battle now settled to a duel at long range between the two tank forces. For an hour or so neither side made any major move. One by one Kinnaird withdrew us to the supply lorries to refill with ammunition. In the middle of the afternoon Morgan, who had come up with the reserve tank of Squadron headquarters to fill the gap caused by the destruction of Egerton's troop, suddenly reported:

' . . . I can see a number of enemy tanks gathering behind the vehicles. They look as if they are forming up to attack. Over.'

Kinnaird's reassuring voice answered at once:

' . . . Yes, I noticed something was going on, but couldn't make out exactly what. If they attack we will withdraw slowly, keeping just out of range. If any of their tanks are too daring we'll do what we can to finish him off. But no standing to fight it out. Off.'

Soon afterwards the enemy attacked with about thirty tanks. Their advance was slow and cautious, but nevertheless determined, and throughout the rest of the afternoon and evening our two squadrons were gradually pushed farther and farther back to the east. It was a slow, remorseless gun duel, neither side causing any great damage to the other. But not for a moment could we relax our vigilance. I found that the conditions were deceptive. Often when I thought that the enemy tanks opposite us had halted, and I had done likewise, I discovered that they had in fact been moving so slowly forward that their approach had been difficult to detect until they were almost on us again and we were well within the lethal range of their guns. As the day passed and the sun sank farther down into the west, it became more and more difficult to distinguish the enemy tanks in the glare, let alone determine their moves.

At last, when the light was almost gone, the final welcome signal came from Kinnaird:

' ... Withdraw now and form line ahead behind me in the order Four, One, Three, New Two. Off.'

In the gathering gloom this was no easy task to accomplish, and when we were all in position our troubles were by no means over. There were five mile to go before we reached the area where we were to leaguer with the other two squadrons. Five miles before we could get out of our tanks at last to relax and stretch our limbs, to talk to one another again and lick our wounds and count the cost of one day in our share of the war. During this move I became suddenly aware of an overwhelming sense of personal loss at the memory of Egerton's death. His gay laugh, his sordid wit, his abundant confidence and cheerfulness were no more. Another of the few who had been with me in the triumphs of not six months ago had gone: first Templeton's suicide, then Bolton's disappearance, then Ryan's crippling. I felt that we were like the ten little nigger boys – soon there might be none.

During battle the night leaguer was always like home – there was food and hot drinks and companionship. Though each crew was a closely knit community during the day, each man was so occupied with his own duties and each tank so engrossed with the enemy that the opportunities for talk and the easy exchange of

136

friendship were few. I was still shaken and somewhat shocked by my experience, and only gradually did the friendly, though inarticulate, companionship of my new crew thaw me out of my dazed condition. I dragged myself to Kinnaird's truck to get my orders for the guard duties that night and for my depleted troop on the following day. Except for a strong drink of whisky which Kinnaird made me take, my visit, as a reviver, was a failure.

Indeed, I returned to my own tank more depressed than I had been before, for in Kinnaird's truck there was an officer of the other regiment of the Brigade which had been engaged during the day, and I arrived in the middle of his account of the day's activities.

'Soon after you were ordered off to the Hafid Ridge a small group of Jerry tanks and M.T. came on the scene from the north-west. They must have passed just about under your bloody noses. Anyway, they looked a neat little morsel to gobble up, and as soon as we were sure they were not being backed by others we went after 'em. Everything looked rosy. The Jerries turned and ran, and we were after them in full cry. It looked too bloody easy. And then it happened. Before we knew where we were, we were being knocked out right, left, and centre. We'd bloody well run into an ambush of dug-in anti-tank guns. God knows how many there were, but they were artfully dug-in and hidden, and we hadn't a chance. They certainly know how to handle their guns and tanks as a team – and of course we had no answer. The gun O.P.s were miles behind and hadn't a chance of getting up to us. We've got to get that better organized – have 'em riding in tanks or something. The present set-up's bloody well useless. What do you think, Peter?'

'A tank gun which can fire H.E.' was Kinnaird's prompt and decisive reply. 'Having the O.P.s up with us will be better than nothing, but the field-guns aren't accurate enough. We don't want a lot of guns to plaster an area. What we want is an accurate gun which can knock out the anti-tank gun as soon as it fires. How many tanks did you lose?'

'Not sure yet until we've had a good check up, but I reckon it was sixteen or seventeen. And most of them were quick brews too, so few of the crews got away. God, it was frightful! How many did you lose?'

'Six from my squadron and four in the other,' replied Kinnaird. 'This chap here was brewed up.'

The other turned briefly to look at me, but, engrossed in his own disaster, gave me no more than a cursory glance and then said:

'Well, good night, Peter. Hope to God we do better to-morrow. At this rate there won't be many left to-morrow night, though. Best of luck.' He ducked out of the back of the truck and was gone, leaving both Kinnaird and me silent and thoughtful about our own losses and ruminating on his last remark.

I finished my drink and rose to go.

'Good night, sir,' I said. 'Thanks for the drink. It's done me good. I'll miss Egerton. He was a fine chap.'

'Good night, Tony,' answered Kinnaird. 'Get some sleep. I've told the sergeant-major to keep you off guard to-night. You'll need some rest. Have you seen the doctor?'

'No, sir. I'm all right. I could've done guard, but I won't say I'm not glad to be off.'

'O.K. Get along, then. There's not much of the night left. I've missed Egerton all this evening. I bet he'd have had some quip to make even about to-day's doings.'

I found the sergeant-major waiting for me at my own tank.

'I've got some blankets here for you, sir. Expect yours went up with the tank. Are you O.K., sir? I thought you'd like a mug of char too, sir. There's one on the front sand-shield. You're off guard, sir. Did the Major tell you?'

The kindness and friendly thoughtfulness brought a lump of emotion to my throat and I felt my eyes smarting. This was an example of the humanity which lurked behind the bleak exterior of the disciplinarian – evidence of the deep and perfect understanding of the needs of his fellow beings which this bluff and stern soldier had picked up in his long years of service in rough barracks and vile conditions – this was the lewd and licentious soldiery.

'How's Basset?' I asked to hide my own feelings and because I knew that the sergeant-major would have seen that he was looked after.

'He's grand, sir. Sleeping like a top in the back of an ammo.

138

wagon. But you have your tea, sir, and get some sleep. Good night, sir.'

For the four remaining hours of darkness I tossed and turned in my blankets on the rough ground. I heard the sentries being changed at hourly intervals, I felt and heard the distant rumble of the gun-fire of the Indian Division's attacks on Musaid and Sollum. My mind was too alert to allow my tired body any rest. At last, about half an hour before first light, I fell into a deep slumber, only to be awakened, so it seemed, almost as soon as I was asleep. My exhaustion was thus worse than it might have been if I had not slept at all, and my first series of actions on waking were performed in a daze. I climbed into my tank and listened vaguely to the palaver of 'netting'. I failed to acknowledge my orders to disperse to open leaguer and was soundly damned by Kinnaird, who, though no doubt aware of the probable reason, was nevertheless not one to allow any lapse to pass unremarked.

Once in open leaguer I watched dreamily while the desert before me to the west was gradually lit by the rising sun. The long shadow of my tank, with the outline of my own head and shoulders topping it, shrank with remarkable speed; the folds and crests of the ground so clearly defined by the low early sun gradually faded out of sight and the view was once more the flat, glaring expanse of sun-baked sand which would be all I would see until the sun at last began to set again in the west.

I was startled by Kinnaird's voice in my ear-phones when he gave permission to ' brew-up'. When the steaming mug of tea was in my hands and I had wolfed the greasy mass of half-cooked bacon which, even on a dirty tin plate, looked like a feast, I felt awake at last and more human. I rubbed the remaining sticky vestiges of sleep from my eyes and scratched the short, itching stubble on my face. The first few days of battle were always the most uncomfortable if there was no time to shave. Until there was about four days' growth of beard the hairs were still stiff and stubbly, catching on jerseys or scarves or coats. Thereafter the hair became softer and more pliable and the skin accustomed to the long period of dryness.

Already the sun was uncomfortably hot. As I stood on the engine-covers behind the turret to take off the overcoat which I had until then found very necessary, I heard the Colonel's voice blare with the rasping note peculiar to all ear-phones when they were not close o the head:

'... Enemy force consisting of about figures five zero medium and figures two zero light tanks and a number of other vehicles reported moving on a bearing between south and south-west from roughly the area of Hafid Ridge. We are to prepare to engage. Finish whatever you are doing now and get all crews mounted ready for action. Off.'

My crew was thrown into some confusion, as the driver had 'taken a spade for a walk' and had hidden himself so cleverly in what appeared to be flat ground that none of us knew in which direction to shout and all shouts seemed to be of no avail. However, there was one way which always worked. I started the engine and revved it hard. Almost straight to my front a head appeared momentarily and ducked away – a minute more and a figure came trotting towards us, clutching the spade in one hand and holding his trousers with the other.

'No bloody peace for the wicked nor for them what's minding their own business,' was the only disgruntled remark that he made as he climbed into his seat, hurriedly adjusting his belt and buttons.

Soon the German column was clearly visible at a range of 2,500 yards to the south-west. It made no attempt to turn and face us where we lay in battle positions ready to resist. Instead it continued to move past our front, its eastern flank being guarded, like sheep-dogs watching the flock, by an outer screen of Mark II light tanks and an inner screen of Mark IIIs. For a time we watched and waited. Our battle positions were good, and we were averse to leaving them unless it was absolutely necessary. But each minute made it more clear that the Germans were intent on out-flanking our position to the south and then, presumably, moving on to cut our communications and to disrupt the other units less capable of defending themselves.

Finally the inevitable order came from the Colonel:

'... Advance now in line. Watch what you do, as there will be friends to our left supporting us, probably. Off.'

No orders were needed from the squadron commanders. As one, the tanks of the Regiment moved forward to the attack. My troop was on the left of B Squadron, which was still depleted by the casualties of the previous day. To our left, C Squadron, which had not been engaged in any of the earlier fighting, was the strongest, with a depleted A Squadron on the other flank.

By now we were more than well aware of the capabilities of the German tanks and knew there was no sense in pushing our advance so far that useless casualties would result. The screen of German light tanks was no problem. Armed only with machine-guns, they were no match for us, and three were burning after being struck by lucky shots at long range.

At a range of 1,000 yards from the Germans, Kinnaird halted the squadron on a suitable crest-line and ordered us not only to engage any enemy tanks that offered suitable side-on targets, but to fire with our machine-guns at the massed transport in the further distance. He was groping for a way to fight the Germans so as to offset the great advantage they had in their superior gun-power. Within the limited tactical liberty which could be afforded any squadron commander in a battle which depended for success on the manoeuvre of as large a tank force as possible, Kinnaird was trying to induce the enemy to move in such a way that we could engage the thinner side armour of their tanks.

Not so wise as Kinnaird, or perhaps lacking his experience and the faculty for critical analysis of failure, however recent, the commander of C Squadron pressed on with his attack. In so doing he moved his squadron within range of the German tanks. Their flank screen immediately turned to face him and halted to engage. Two of the C Squadron tanks were knocked out, one a brew-up, from which only the commander was seen to escape. But this foolhardy action produced unexpected results.

Away to their left, still moving almost due south, the head of the German column had not halted. Inevitably therefore a gap was bound to occur somewhere in the line of defending tanks. The gap came opposite the centre of C Squadron, but it was not so large nor so vulnerable that the squadron commander, pre-occupied with his two quick casualties, noticed it soon enough to take advantage of it. Before he did so, the German tanks on his right, opposite us, saw the danger and moved immediately to fill the gap.

Try as he had, Kinnaird had been unable to create a situation

141

to our advantage, but here, suddenly, before his eyes, the German tanks were faced with two unpleasant alternatives. Either they turned to engage, and so allowed the gap to grow bigger. Or they moved to fill the gap at the risk of being engaged in the flank. Kinnaird was quick to see his chance, and his orders followed immediately:

' ... Advance now and engage. We've got 'em side on at last, where their armour is thinner. Close to ensure accurate shooting – we've got the advantage. Tally ho! Off.'

Quick as he had been, even so it was going to be touch and go whether the move would meet with success. The Germans were moving very fast to close the gap and were well aware of their vulnerability. I could imagine the quandary they were in. If any-one was going to get a shot, it was likely to be my two tanks, since, being on the left, there would be more time for us to move into range before the last of the German tanks moved away to he left and out of our field of fire.

As I moved forward I became aware that there was another tank on my left, and looking more closely I saw that it was Kinnaird, determined to be in at the kill, waving cheerily to me.

Another 200 yards and we both halted, and the crack of our guns was almost simultaneous, followed only an instant later by that of my other tank. We all three reloaded and fired again. The last but one German tank halted abruptly and burst into flames.

Hardly able to control my excitement, I quickly gave the next order, 'Gunner, traverse right. Farther – quicker, you fool! On now – enemy tank. Fire or he'll be out of range.'

Kinnaird had also switched to the new target, as I could tell when I caught a glimpse of both mine and another trace floating towards the target. Both appeared to hit, and this tank, too, burst into flames. Kinnaird waved triumphantly to me and then ordered, ' ... Conform to my movements. We will turn left and move south to catch up with the enemy. Off.'

From then on the battle resembled an action at sea, each side manoeuvring to outflank the other and to take advantage of any lapse of manoeuvre or slow-wittedness. The German advance continued by fits and starts, swinging first to the south and then almost south-east. In a wide arc they moved round our outer

142

flank, relentlessly and with little effective opposition, as their tank guns outranged those of our tanks by so wide a margin.

The Colonel was quick to grasp the significance of Kinnaird's brief but highly successful action, and throughout the further battles endeavoured at every opportunity to manoeuvre the German rear-guard into a position where one or other of his squadrons could engage them from a flank. The German force had clearly been ordered to move on, whatever happened, so that occasions inevitably occurred when they lost a few more tanks in the same fashion.

Just before midday we passed back through the Italian frontier wire. Shortly afterwards, with the visibility reduced to less than 800 yards by the haze of the intense heat of the sun, the Germans halted their advance and we took up positions to their front and flank to continue our wary watch, to lick our wounds and to relax after four hours of intense action.

One by one we were withdrawn to refill – only to find that ammunition was running short. I took a chance and ordered my operator and driver to dismount and to start a 'brew' at the back of the tank, where they would be unobserved and would have some protection from any shell-fire if it occurred. My gunner and I sat on in the turret to keep watch and be ready to shoot if necessary.

Throughout the burning heat of the afternoon and early evening the long vigil continued. In the middle of the afternoon the regiment was re-deployed, so that we lay in hull-down positions blocking the direct path of any further German advance. There could be no rest. We were now so depleted by casualties and breakdowns that each tank was a doubly vital link in the chain of defence. I longed to be able to get out of the cramped and boiling turret, to lie down in some shade somewhere and to sleep, if only for a few minutes. But I knew that to relax would be fatal – the first weakening would soon grow until my energy and determination to stay awake and to concentrate would vanish.

As hour after hour passed I came to loathe and detest the sun. At home on the beaches of Somerset and on the open moors I had always regarded it as a friend – bringing joy and gladness and banishing the mists and fogs. Here it was my enemy. Behind the glassy orb I could imagine a fiend chuckling with triumph and gloating that he could have fooled so many for so long. All around me, every object, animate and inanimate, was affected by the heat. From the burnished sands the glare was reflected and magnified – the air was burnt to a hot, opaque haze which shimmered and drifted nowhere more bewilderingly than between us and the enemy. Even the thick armour-plate of the turret had been cooked to a heat which made it painful to touch. Inside, where the res of the crew sat in huddled dejection, the air was thick and stifling, made worse by being flavoured with gun-fumes and the smell of hot oil and burnt petrol. There was not a breath of air – no breeze – no light stirring of wind. All was still and hot and burnt and stifling.

The 'brew' that we had had at midday had been a failure. It had not quenched our aching thirst nor had it revived our flagging spirits. I did not suggest another, and even after some five hours of watching and waiting, it was the not over-enthusiastic voice of the gunner who asked, 'Do you want a "brew", sir?' I answered wearily, 'Not for me, thanks – but have one if the rest of you want one.'

There were no more sounds after a short exchange of murmurs within the tank. Indeed, everything was so silent for so long that I wondered if I was the only one awake. Except for the incessant crackling and splutters in my headphones, there had not for some time been any sound on the wireless. It was now about 1830 hours and the first breath of evening breeze stirred the haze, so that I suddenly realized that the distant shapes I had been staring at for so long had in a moment taken form again as German tanks. In another moment I realized with a start that they were growing larger each instant, and the small plume of dust surrounding each one showed that they were advancing to attack.

Quickly I reported, ' . . . German tanks now advancing towards us. The leading Mark III is about figures one five zero zero yards from me, and coming straight towards me. Over.'

Kinnaird's voice, even and alert as ever, answered briefly, ' . . . O.K. Off to you. Hello, FANO; KANO calling. Germans advancing now. Off.'

Even as I prepared to engage, I wondered whether Kinnaird was really as bright and alert as he had sounded. Had he, during the afternoon, cursed inwardly at the heat and discomfort? Had

144

he mentally given anything for a short sleep and a cool drink? Or had he, with iron control, fought off these distractions and weak complaints to devote his whole mind to the battle?

But there was no time to wonder. 'Close down. Action stations. Gunner, traverse left – more left – O.K. on. Mark III – twelve hundred yards. Keep him in your sights and do not fire until I give the order. Driver, start up – we may have to move. Operator, get some rounds out of the racks and stack 'em handy. Tell me in good time if we are running short.'

The roar of the engine behind me was a reassuring sound, and served to jerk me to full wakefulness. The engine-fans drawing the air through the turret caused a small but welcome draught. I settled myself more firmly on my seat and gave a last wipe to the eyepieces of my binoculars. It would be almost dark in about three hours, but much could happen before then.

Until nightfall the battle continued. Over the comparatively flat surface of the desert in this area we and the Germans moved in parallel columns of tanks in line ahead. After the initial battle, in which I lost my remaining troop tank, though the crew managed to escape, it was a running fight. Losses on both sides were about even, though to us, with an already depleted tank force, each casualty was much more serious. By last light we reached an area just west of Sidi Suleiman, and the Germans had fallen far enough behind for me to have a moment to remember that it was here, almost a year ago, that I had first joined Kinnaird's squadron. How much had happened since!

9

We Withdraw

WHEN it was clear that the Germans were not following us up any farther, we moved into leaguer. After a day of heat and almost constant vigilance, the process of moving to the chosen area and the action of forming the leaguer were a last exasperating trial. When all was done, and food and sleep were only waiting for the replenishment of ammunition and fuel to be completed, there was an interminable delay before the lorries arrived. In the fast, running battle of the afternoon they had moved well to the east, so as to be out of the danger area. Inevitably they had gone farther than was really necessary, and the return journey, in darkness, had taken all too long.

At last the work was finished and my crew flung their bedding down by the side of the tank and were soon well on the way to sleep. I prepared my own bedding beside the others, sipped the last drops of tea from my mug and made my way carefully through the leaguer, stepping over the sleeping forms, to get my orders from Kinnaird.

At Kinnaird's tank I found the sergeant-major sitting, propped against the back of the tank on an empty petrol tin, almost asleep. He moved to get up when he became aware of me. I stopped him, saying, 'Don't move, sergeant-major. Where's the O.C.?'

'He's gone to get orders from the C.O., sir. Shouldn't be long now. There's some talk of a move at first light.'

I grunted and sank down on to the sand by the S.S.M. Already it was cool. The heat of the sun was gone, leaving only a memory to mar the thoughts of the morrow. Morgan arrived next, followed almost immediately by the only other surviving troop leader. During the day the squadron had lost, besides the tank from my troop, two others, one commanded by an officer and the other by a sergeant. In both cases the crews had escaped with only minor wounds, but the squadron was now reduced to a total of eight tanks. The other two squadrons were similarly reduced, and the strength of the Brigade was not more than about fifty tanks all told.

Kinnaird returned, and gave us his orders quickly:

'Tony, you'll make up your troop with Sergeant Weston and Corporal Shalford. Alex, you'll have Sergeant Trenton from S.H.Q. We'll be two troops of three with two tanks on S.H.Q. for to-morrow. Right. Now our orders. We move at first light on a bearing of 160 degrees to the area just north of Ruweibit el Warani. On arrival we turn and face north-west, ready to resist any attempt by the Jerries to move round to the south. If they try to move any farther east they must move between us and the escarpment. The other Armoured Brigade have had heavy fighting during the day and are reduced to about thirty tanks. They and the Indians have been heavily dive-bombed and shelled all day, and with their flank exposed by our move, it's not likely that

146

they can hold out at Capuzzo and Point 206 for much longer unless the Jerries relax a bit. That's all. Sergeant-Major, all guards and crews fixed? Good. Well, sleep well.'

I was soon back at my tank and, removing only my boots, wrapped myself into my blankets and fell asleep.

At first light we moved as planned, and on arrival formed into battle positions facing north-west. Throughout the morning the armoured cars reported that there was no sign of movement from the Germans force disposed in open formation where they had halted the night before, about four miles west of Sidi Suleiman.

When it was clear that we were to have some hours of inaction, Kinnaird ordered us to have a good breakfast and to attend to the major items of maintenance on our tanks. Thereafter each crew slept, two at a time. I found, as before, that with a relaxation of tension, my mind and body clamoured for rest and sleep. If there had been a battle I would have been alert and wide-awake, whereas now I found it needed a supreme effort to take my share of the duties and to drag my weary limbs about.

Shortly after noon the summons came. The armoured cars reported increased signs of activity among the enemy, followed soon after by the news that they were moving just north of east, a direction which would bring them to the escarpment just east of Battuma. This would have been no cause for alarm if 4th Armoured Brigade and the Indian Division had been in a position to hold their recently won gains. But their precarious predicament of the previous day had been made worse by fresh German attacks during the morning. They had to withdraw, and with the Germans still in possession of 'Hellfire' Pass it was vital that we kept an avenue open for them along the top of the escarpment. It was this that the new German advance threatened.

Just in time we joined with the depleted 4th Armoured Brigade and were disposed in battle positions about three miles west of Battuma in an inverted V formation, the open side being towards the enemy. The battle started almost immediately. We knew that there was to be no withdrawal, that any retreat would endanger the move of the Indian Division, whose safety it was our task to protect.

I crouched into my cupola and settled myself firmly for what was clearly going to be a long ordeal. On either side of me I could see my two troop tanks. I just restrained the impulse to wave them a few yards forward – it would make little difference and would fray the tempers of the tank commanders, besides making plain my own nervous impatience. Beyond my troop, on the right, were the remaining tanks of the other regiments of the Brigade, and farther off, marked only by the bursts of the first enemy shell-fire, was 4th Armoured Brigade.

To my left Kinnaird's and Morgan's tanks were ranged up in line with the rest of the squadron, and beyond them was the other troop. There was an ominous lull: for me, and I supposed the others, the worst part of any battle. It reminded me of the moment before the bell was rung to start a boxing bout in which I was to take part. All the worst that could happen was in the forefront of my mind.

From out of the glare of the sun, fairly low down on the western horizon, I could soon distinguish the squat, sinister shapes of German tanks moving at some speed towards our positions.

After that the events followed too swiftly in a bewildering kaleidoscope of impressions for me to be able to form a coherent picture of the course of the battle. The initial gun duel, lasting some ten to fifteen minutes, was fought at a range which caused no damage to either side. Then the Germans moved forward again. I was deliberately conserving my ammunition until the targets were more worthwhile. Since I was busy estimating the opportune moment to open fire, the time passed quickly for me. But to my crew, peering through their periscopes and telescopes, it must have seemed an age before at last I gave the order, 'Gunner, German Mark III – straight in front – seven five zero yards – fire.' The immediate crack of the gun showed that the gunner had already picked this as the probable target and had set his range in readiness.

To my left and right the distant sounds of firing came to my ears in the pauses between my own gun being fired. Dimly I was aware that a tank on my right was in flames. Then my own tank was struck on the turret, luckily without being penetrated. The dust and sand which had collected in every nook and crevice was dislodged and shaken into a choking cloud by the impact. On my left, I saw out of the corner of my eye Morgan's tank slowly reversing out of the battle with the gun barrel elevated to a ludicrous angle. I looked quickly to see how Kinnaird was faring, and saw the flash from his gun, which showed that he was still in the battle. It was a peculiarly reassuring thought.

To my front a German tank burst into flames. Almost immediately my view was clouded by black billowing smoke which drifted past me from my left, where I saw that the tank beyond Kinnaird's was a mass of flame. Perhaps five minutes elapsed before the flames and smoke died down so that I could see the enemy clearly again. In that time I had been able to take a quick glance farther to my right to see how the other regiment was faring. They appeared to be in no better state, the desert being strewed with either burning tanks or tanks which seemed derelict, deserted and silent.

I turned to devote my attention again to the enemy. However successful they had been, they seemed in no mind to advance any farther. I wondered whether they were only waiting to knock out every one of us and then to make an unopposed advance. If so, their calculations were disrupted by a new development which encouraged me as much as it must have surprised the enemy. Above the sharp crack of the small high-velocity tank guns I suddenly heard, close at hand on my right, the deeper bang of field-guns. Startled, I turned to see what had happened, and was amazed to find a battery of field-guns ranged in the gap between myself and the next regiment, engaging the enemy tanks over open sights.

Whether this was the turning point or not, soon afterwards the battle stopped as abruptly as it had begun. The Germans stopped firing, and gradually, as we became aware of this, we stopped, too, one by one. In the fading light of the last hour of the day we lay in silent watch on each other. Now and again the somewhat eerie silence was broken by the explosion of shells from a burning tank or the sudden splutter of an engine being started before a tank slowly reversed or changed its position.

I relaxed and eased the tired muscles of my arms and hands, which had been holding my binoculars steady for so long. I felt a wave of relief and elation that the battle was over and that none of my grim forebodings had come true. I felt human again and anxious for conversation and laughter, some close communion with my fellow beings.

So we continued to lie and watch until the light had at last faded altogether. Then we moved back into leaguer.

Our high hopes of relieving the defenders of Tobruk had been shattered. I could imagine in the following days the deep disappointment which must have been felt in the garrison. A battle which had started with so great promise had turned almost to disaster and had then petered out in anti-climax. After the last, desperate evening battle, the Germans did not follow up their clear advantage, and we withdrew slowly, chastened and thoughtful about the defeat we had suffered. The lurking doubt about our own equipment was growing each day into a clearer conviction that we would have to have better tanks if we were to defeat the Germans. We were confident that, given the new weapons, we had the skill and endurance to do all that might be asked of us.

It was in this sober mood that we heard the news that Germany had attacked Russia on 22 June. We had had five days to brood over our own defeat and to try to imagine how and when we could match, let alone defeat, the power that Germany had amassed on the Continent of Europe. As if in answer to a prayer, came the news of Hitler's latest gamble. There was no sympathy with Russia, after her dealings in the summer of 1939 and the rape of Poland. Indeed, I felt that the situation could not have been better put than by my driver, who remarked tersely, 'Thieves always falls out.'

Later in the evening on the same day Kinnaird walked over to my tank. He called to me when he was still about twenty-five yards away:

'Tony, here a minute,' and when I joined him he added, 'Don't answer straight away the question I'm going to ask you. I'm sure you'll want time to think it over. It's this. I have been given command of a regiment at present refitting in the Delta. They're short of officers, and I have been told to take someone to be my adjutant. Would you like the job?'

I turned and looked incredulously at Kinnaird. In the months that had passed, my respect and affection for him had steadily grown. I had always felt that a time must come when we would no longer serve together and that it would come to me as a great personal loss. Now that was not to happen.

'If you think I can do the job, sir, I'd like to try,' was my hesitant but hopeful answer.

'Good,' replied Kinnaird. 'I'm sure you can do it. We start to-morrow morning after breakfast. I'll send my truck over for your kit at about seven, and we'll start soon afterwards. We'll have to say good-bye to various people – and I want to be in Cairo for the night. Good-night, Tony. I'm glad you'll be with me.'

PART FOUR

1941: DEFEATING THE GERMANS

1

Cairo

FOR a week I was almost convinced that the war was a bad dream. I was living with the Kinnairds in their flat in Cairo. The change from the life in the desert, where I had been for so long, was so abrupt that at times I expected to wake up and find my crew asleep beside me. To my dismay at first, Celia Kinnaird fussed over and cared for me as I had not been looked after for a long time. I was scolded for the state of my clothes, bullied to eat and rest, cajoled to give a hand in her various household duties. I revelled in it all, and my devotion to her grew with each day. I was made to feel so at home and so much a part of the family that the brief holiday renewed and rested me as no other holiday would have done.

I was left to my own devices by the Kinnairds, who had many months of separation to make up for. I read from the well-stocked library I found in the flat and spent hours playing the gramophone. In the afternoons I usually went to Gezireh and either bathed or played tennis or watched the cricket or polo. It was all most pleasant. But at last it had to come to an end. The time had arrived for both Kinnaird and me to return, if not to war, at least to the tedious preparation for it.

There was the life in battle, exhausting, terrifying, cut off from the civilized world. There was the life in the concentration areas, endlessly boring, when we were not in battle but were not entirely out of it. There was the life on leave, peaceful, calm and comforting. And there was the half-way life in the camps of the Delta, refitting to return to the desert, not on leave, but not entirely separated from the pleasure of Cairo or Alexandria. Of them all, the life in camp gave us the clearest understanding of the size and complexity of the war effort and the diversity of the forces engaged.

Beni Yusef was one of the many camps dotted round Cairo to which the desert formations returned to be refitted, remanned and re-trained. It lay in the desert to the south of the western end of the Mena causeway, in sight of the Great Pyramids of Gizeh and the brooding Sphinx. Here the units returned for rest and renewal. Here, and at other camps round Cairo and at yet more near the Suez Canal, 100 miles to the east, the sinews of the Desert Army were given new strength.

Most of the heavy equipment we handed over to other units or returned to the workshops for repair. The only evidence of our struggle in the desert were the lorries, the trucks, the cars. Out of range at last of the enemy's bombers and fighters, these were now parked wheel to wheel, huddled into the batches belonging to each squadron – sun-baked, shabby, worn – yet with an air of achievement about them. These would be renewed in due course and to them would be added the new tanks. Even then they would not shine nor glisten like new equipment. Any surface which might catch the eye would be sprayed with camouflage paint and covered with sand. We would emerge at last from the camps to return to the desert that was our home, strengthened and with our endurance rekindled – the Armour of the desert which had withstood the trials of one testing year and would meet the new trials as they came.

The men were of the same stamp. In this summer of 1941 we and the Russian armies were the only major land forces at grips with the Nazi war machine. For us the war was almost a private battle, those taking part members of a select club – the numbers confined to those who had been in battle or on the fringes of it. We knew what war entailed – we had been under shell-fire, out on patrol, short of food and water. We had known fear and been almost overcome with exhaustion. We had seen our friends maimed and had buried our companions. We had killed and waited to be killed with our nerves taut, but still somehow managing to muster enough courage to carry on and not to show it. We knew our own jobs and roughly those of the other men fighting beside us. We could judge the temperature and condition of the battle; we could measure the value of each of our own formations and distinguish the quality of our enemies. Ours was a close, demanding comradeship, forged in the stress of battle and nurtured by the trials that each had seen the other undergo and survive. There was confidence and expertness in nearly all we did, but we were sobered by the knowledge that the odds were now against us. Better equipped, better supplied, more numerous, we knew the enemy of our next battles would test us to the limits of our courage and endurance.

This was especially true for those of us who fought in the tanks. In the broad expanses of the wastes of the desert it was on us that the brunt of the battles fell. As we sat now in the base camps after the swift attacks and savage assaults, after the slaughter and loss, after the exhaustion and miserable terror, we were very conscious of our responsibility. Wherever the enemy tanks attacked or threatened to attack, we would be called to go. It was only we, with our inadequate tank-guns, who could hold or delay the enemy armour. It was we who would carry out the relentless pursuit in victory. It was we who would be the tattered, broken rearguard in withdrawal or retreat. The papers and the public could talk of 'the armour breaking in' or 'the armour breaking through' or even of 'great tank battles'. But none of them could know of the scale of horror and exhaustion to be endured. Only in the secret minds of each of us who had fought was there a full comprehension of the nature of our own private and combined victories. And each of us was proud, with a quiet pride which rejected praise or sympathy, secure in the knowledge of our achievement.

My new job was very different from those of my previous experience. I found that to exercise the authority expected of me required a deal of effort and thought. The firmness necessary to decide between two courses, both of which appeared equally right, was not acquired in a day. The physical labour involved in preparing and maintaining a tank was no longer mine; gone, too, was the day-to-day contact and supervision of the men of a troop. But there were a hundred and one other things which went with my new position. New responsibilities had always to be borne in mind, and I was never free from the many and varied interruptions of my work or my supposed hours of leisure. Always there was the nagging worry that I had not done something vital or had forgotten to do something which ought to have been done. Gradually I evolved a system for myself, so that as far as possible my duties fell into a regular pattern. Day by day my confidence and authority grew, until I no longer felt hesitant and doubtful of any action or self-critical of a decision taken with firmness and despatch. More and more I began to acquire the knowledge of what had to be done and to see where the wishes and convenience of the few had to be subordinated for the good of the whole.

In essence my duty was to relieve the Colonel of all the daily routine business of dealing with other units and headquarters, and to see that his orders were transmitted to all those in the regiment who would have to act on them. I had never worked harder in my life. Nor had I fully realized before the great volume of work entailed in the efficient running of a regiment. There was no time to spare or waste in our preparations. We had been given twelve weeks in which to train and re-equip ourselves before we were required again in the desert. Though at first this seemed an endless period and ample for all that was to be done, as each week passed I began to realize that we would only just beat the time limit. The key officers and the senior N.C.O.s were already there, and could make a start with the first stages of their task. Other officers came each day and were fitted into their various places. The more junior N.C.O.s came and were sent away on the many courses at the Depot which had been started to meet the regiment's needs.

For this re-equipment was like none that I had known before. We were to be entirely armed with tanks from America. There were new guns to learn; new wireless sets to master; the mysteries of new engines, transmissions and tracks to unravel before we could acquire the techniques needed to handle them. Day after day the new equipment standing on the parks grew in number and with them the men to man them. The old battered lorries eventually disappeared, replaced by a new generation of vehicles, more efficient and more battleworthy than their tried predecessors.

All the time there were the daily growing responsibilities which tended more and more to keep me pinned to my desk. I was never free of worries. Either I had to adjudicate between harassed or angry squadron leaders about the relative value of the N.C.O.s or men each had been allotted, or I was embroiled in a reshuffle of the clerks or fitters or young officers, some of whom had proved either better or worse than expected. While the major items of equipment arrived, so the Quartermaster was gathering the many vital other pieces without which the tanks or lorries would have been valueless. In huts and dumps, in store-tents and binned lorries, the wireless sets, the spare parts, the ammunition, the sights were slowly gathered and checked, sorted and put away. And all the time the camps had to be run, the meals cooked, orders issued, kit inspected, guards detailed and mounted, men trained. Gradually order grew out of chaos, the raw material of men fashioned into the shape and form of trained and reliable soldiers, the equipment tested and adjusted and finally passed ready for battle.

Cairo felt the impact of the men of the camps on her outskirts. From armoured regiments, from infantry battalions, from the artillery, the engineers and the whole array of units which backed and supported them, hundreds of men swarmed into the city each day and night, intent on enjoying themselves. They crowded the streets, the bars, the cinemas. They got drunk and fought. They broke up the dance-halls and night-clubs. They violated the virgins, appropriated the professionals and encouraged the enthusiastic amateurs. Cairo was a seething, swarming mass of soldiers, swindled, cajoled and cursed by the crowds of impoverished and grasping Egyptians. The richer Egyptians lived a life apart, ignoring the war, the soldiers and their own less fortunate countrymen. The poorer Egyptians seized the fleeting opportunity to raise themselves above their usual filthy and depressing lives; they stole, and sweated at a hundred and one menial tasks with their eyes on the main chance and with little or no concern for the wider issues of the war.

When opportunity offered, I got away from camp in the evenings and at the week-ends. Kinnaird gave me two further pleasant week-ends at his flat. The small, comfortable rooms seemed more and more like home each time I saw them. The peaceful friendliness and comforting quiet were all that I needed to restore my energies. But more than these, Celia's watchful care and attention gave me the inner contentment which left my heart and mind at peace.

On other occasions I joined any party who were going into Cairo for the day or the evening. I went when I could to Gezireh on Sundays for the marvellous buffet lunches, followed by a lazy afternoon watching cricket. I played tennis and had tea by the swimming-pool, bathing occasionally, and spending the rest of the afternoons 'body-watching', as the pastime came to be known.

Our experiences and the knowledge that we would soon again be in battle coloured, as they were bound to colour, our feelings for those who had not stirred from the base. In the clubs and bars, in the Staffs and depots, we met a large variety of men who not only had not seen battle, but many of whom had no intention of doing so. There were certainly a great number who were hard-working, genuine and willing to give all the help they could, and who were eagerly scheming to get themselves away from their base jobs and into the desert. But there were others who had acquired so established an air of importance that they had already convinced themselves that their presence in 'G.H.Q.' was vital to the war effort.

Among the many soldiers we met often in Cairo were the men of the other armies of the Empire and of the allied nations. There were the fine, stalwart figures of the Indians, the squat, cheerful Ghurkas, the Australians, the New Zealanders, the South Africans, the Rhodesians. Each wore a distinctive uniform and was marked by his own badge of behaviour. They tended to keep to themselves in their own national groups, but occasionally at Gezireh or in a night-club in town we found that the natural bars of restraint and of different backgrounds were broken down and we began to feel that we were part of a huge family. There were the mutual suspicions to be swept away. We found it difficult to convince ourselves that the tough, noisy Australians and the equally tough, more silent New Zealanders were not in some respect sneering at our smoother ways and perhaps softer pre-war lives. They, too, were inclined to believe that we of the Home Country looked down on their ways and customs. So it was with the other Empire armies. But in fact there was already a degree of mutual respect and understanding which grew in each new test of action.

Of the other nationals, the ones we saw most often were the

men of the Free French Forces. There was about them a sadness and aloofness which were difficult to penetrate. Each man seemed to be hiding the guilty knowledge that his country had failed in the hour of need and had then gone from bad to worse by collaborating with the Germans. The stain had left its mark. In the inner deserts the patrols of the Long-range Desert Group had at this time seen more of the French than most. They were impressed and awed by their selfless dedication to the prosecution of the war, as if in their earnestness to test and try themselves, they were striving desperately to expunge the shame of a nation. They were tough and uncomfortable people to live with in action, and in more peaceful surroundings their Latin display of emotion and lack of restraint in sorrow or romance set them apart.

There were as yet no American forces in action anywhere in the world, but Lease-Lend had brought them into close contact with the conflict. It was at this time that the first American ships began to arrive at Suez and we began to see both Americans and the supplies of arms they brought. In the clubs and hotels we met the men of the merchant ships, the 'observers' from the American forces and the journalists.

Of more lasting interest and concern to us was the arrival of the American tanks, with which we were to be equipped. The M3 Light Tanks, which had been named 'Stuarts' after the great American Civil War cavalryman, soon came to be known more affectionately as 'Honeys'. They were no bigger than our cruiser tanks and carried much the same armour. Their 37-mm. guns were almost similar in performance to the two-pounders we already knew. It was their speed and reliability which were their most valued features.

Compared to the generous stretching of their legal neutrality by the Americans, the attitude of Egypt and the Egyptians was different and difficult for the ordinary soldier to understand and condone. While we and our friends were daily – year in, year out – risking our limbs and lives to defend the rights of the free world, the Egyptians lifted not a finger to help. Indeed, from the King downwards, throughout a large section of the powerful Pashas, their sympathies and hidden allegiance were clearly with the Italians. We saw the Egyptians as a craven and crooked nation, hiding behind the shield of our protection. To us all it seemed natural that a race who would not move in self-defence even when the enemy had actually crossed their borders should be reviled in word and deed whenever need or the opportunity arose. We could have no respect for them, no sympathy with their sufferings, no hesitation in thinking of them as 'Wogs' or 'Gyppos' or 'Gyppies'. The only words of their language which we bothered to learn were the more offensive and shorter epithets to summon or dismiss them.

2

A Squadron to Command

As the weeks passed we began to know each other better in the Officers' Mess. To start with, except Kinnaird, I saw them as just a blur of faces and I wondered if I would ever get to know them all by name. But gradually they sorted themselves out. Hutchins, the second-in-command, I came to know best before any of the others, as he had an office between mine and the Colonel's and was always willing to give useful advice and help.

The Quartermaster I saw much of during the hectic weeks while we collected our new equipment. Recently promoted from R.S.M., he was not yet fully sure of himself in the Officers' Mess and was inclined to retire to his office as soon as he decently could. He knew his job and was thorough and energetic, and as he slowly began to feel his feet, I found him an amusing and staunch ally, with many a ready word of advice or honest criticism or bawdy humour which relieved the tension.

There were four squadron commanders: Williams of H.Q. Squadron, Chesham of 'A', Stendall of 'B' and Fox of 'C'. These I saw frequently, and in time began to spend many of my spare hours with Chesham and Stendall at Chesham's flat, where Angela, his wife, soon captured our affection by her beauty and the excellence of her cooking. Williams was a quiet, aloof man who had no particular friends, while Fox was the social lion of the regiment, always in Cairo, at parties, dances or in a rowdy crowd of other men and girls playing tennis or swimming at Gezireh.

The atmosphere in the Mess was already an encouraging sign of the development of the regiment. Where there had been silence and constraint when Kinnaird and I first joined, now there was a comforting sense of companionship, an air of purpose and energetic industry. I was particularly glad to see the way the young subalterns had settled down and made themselves fully part of the family without any undue restraint in the presence of senior officers, but also without any show of lack of respect. In the conditions in which we were now all living each officer had to prove by his own worth that he was entitled to the respect due to his position or rank. Gone was the tradition of the other regiments I had known, where even in their own home, the Mess, the younger men only spoke when they were spoken to and remained at other times unnaturally silent.

After two months Fox was posted away to another job and, being the senior captain, I was given command of 'C' Squadron. I was surprised and a little put out at this sudden elevation and regretted leaving the duties I was just beginning to understand. But once I had taken over and the first anxiety had been overcome, I found that I was glad. It was not a new role really, and I enjoyed having a command of my own. I had had many months of training for just this moment, months during which I had watched and unconsciously absorbed the lessons of Kinnaird's technique of command. Now it seemed no great step to take command myself. I was awed a little by the thought that I was now responsible for some 140 men and sixteen tanks and about the same number of trucks and lorries. But after the initial tension I realized that I already knew a great deal of my job. I felt as if I was living a dream I could still remember clearly.

A month later we got our orders to move back to the desert. The tanks were to be loaded on to the train at Gizeh station, and would detrain the following day in the desert south of Sidi Barrani. From here they were to move to a concentration area farther south, where they would join the wheeled vehicles, which were to move separately from Cairo.

Before leaving I went into Cairo for a final celebration with Peters and Drummond, two of the troop leaders of my squadron. We went to the 'Nocturne', a small but lively night club, where we met other officers of the Brigade, and the party developed, as so many parties did, into a noisy and boisterous rag, only quietened for a short time by the cabaret. The last act was a dance of the 'Seven Veils' by a dusky and very shapely half-caste who called herself, since her parents could not have known the word or its meaning, 'Caresse'! When the lights were lowered and her dance had begun, Peters whispered urgently to those of us round him, 'Let's cordon the lights and stop 'em being put out.'

This we did, and when, with a roll of drums and a clash of cymbals, Caresse, with a movement of fine abandon, discarded the last of her veils, expecting the lights to be put out simultaneously, instead they were switched on to full brilliance. The 'battle for the switches' had been short and hectic, but victorious. The confusion was worth all our efforts. Caresse, with such a look of cold fury as I would not have believed possible, fought her way through the throng, mocking her with feigned indignation at the sight of the thin strip of flesh-coloured material on her loins. The manager screamed and shouted and phoned for the military police, but before their arrival the night club had emptied and we were all well on our way back to camp.

In a sense our next battles were to be different. We were now one of the three armoured regiments of the newly formed 4th Armoured Brigade Group, a title it had been given to denote the fact that it included its own regiment of field-guns, battalion of motorized infantry, an anti-tank and an anti-aircraft battery, as well as its own engineers, field hospital and supply train. The guns were to work in close co-operation with the tanks, and the infantry were to protect the guns by day and the tank leaguers by night. Each of the tank regiments would move and fight in concert with a proportion of the guns and infantry. Kinnaird's task in the forthcoming battles would therefore be complicated by the need to manoeuvre many more men and vehicles than in the past.

Our new tanks were essentially no better in battle than those we had before, and the proportion of Mark IIIs and IVs would certainly have increased in the German tank units. And with them, almost more dangerous than the tanks, would be the more powerful 50-mm. anti-tank guns and the 88s. At least we would have near parity in numbers, but the disparity of the guns and armour remained.

In September we were given a new title – the Eighth Army – and with it a new Commander. The announcement of these changes to the world at large early in October and the daily increasing evidence of the assembly of a great and growing army could mean one of two things. Either we were due to make an advance or we were being mustered to meet the threat of a new German attack. Everywhere I drove about the desert I had come to know so well there were signs of the great preparations being made. The railway had been extended and the railhead for supplies of all kinds was now not far from the position of the derelict Italian camps at Sofafi. New divisional and brigade signs blossomed like spring flowers all over the frontier areas. The 4th Indian Division we already knew. Now we saw the New Zealanders, the South Africans and the 1st Army Tank Brigade.

As the weeks passed we moved ever nearer to the frontier. From our first concentration area we moved south-west to a saucer-shaped depression ringed with sharp-edged cliffs. From here we went west again and finally, early in November, to an area even closer to the frontier. Here we made our final arrangements, checked our maps and orders and prepared handy summaries of the wireless codes and pennant recognition signals.

By now I had reached a stage in learning the function of command when I was confident that I could handle the tanks of my squadron as a closely-knit and effective tactical unit. By much practice and the equally important discussion and development of clear and well-known and understood battle drills, I had acquired a degree of control of my troop-leaders and they an awareness of my intentions and ideas which meant that only the briefest of wireless orders or a short wave of my arm were sufficient to initiate the execution of all but the most complicated manoeuvres. In the process I had come to know each of my officers well and to understand the qualities and weaknesses peculiar to each.

Clayton, my second-in-command, was two or three years older than myself and always conscious that he was the eldest of the officers in the squadron. He was amusing and efficient, with a gift of sordid repartee and a fund of pornographic anecdotes which reminded me of Egerton.

Seagrim, the second-captain, and Mills and Elliott, the two youngest troop leaders, were the most recently arrived and the least sure of themselves. They were pleasant and willing, though requiring supervision and guidance. Mills and Elliott had only recently reached the stage where I felt that I could give them complete control of their troops, which up to that time had been commanded by their respective troop sergeants.

Drummond and Peters, the two remaining troop leaders, were the ones with whom I found I had most in common. Of the same age – a year or two older than myself – they were both seasoned troop commanders of the campaigns of the spring and early summer. They were inseparable companions, quiet, good-tempered and determined in the ordinary course of their duties, but energetic and boisterous at a party.

3

Into Battle Again

DURING 17 November we received the final orders for the offensive, and at last light moved forward to our assembly positions, which were still some seventy miles east of the wire which we were to cross at a point about twenty miles south of Sheferzen. At 0600 hours the next day, after a night of torrential rain, the advance started. Preceded by armoured cars, the three armoured brigades of 7th Armoured Division moved in a wide fan due west to the wire. We were on the right, with 7th Armoured Brigade in the centre and the newly arrived 22nd Armoured Brigade on the left. Once through the wire the whole Division turned north-west. We were directed on Gabr Saleh, 7th Armoured on Bir Berraneb and 22nd Armoured on Bir el Gubi.

The orders for the advance were clear and simple. The object was the destruction of the Axis Army in Libya and, as a result, the relief of Tobruk. I wondered, as I glanced round at the familiar sight of the Brigade in battle formation, whether others really believed any more than I did that this was a feasible proposition. It was true that including the garrison of Tobruk we had a superiority in tanks of almost two to one. But without exception they were armed with guns of 37-mm. calibre firing a two-pound shot, whereas a large proportion of the German tanks were Mark IIIs armed with a 50-mm. gun firing a four and a half-pound shot.

Of the rest there were bound to be a few of the light Mark IIs and more of the Mark IVs, whose 75-mm. guns fired a good high-explosive shell which could on occasion do no small damage even to a tank. The Italian Ariete Armoured Division would be equipped with M13s, which we knew well. But now there would be two German Panzer Divisions, since the 15th had been joined by the 21st.

Late in the afternoon we crossed the line of the Trigh El Abd, and soon afterwards received the signal which we had been expecting all day. We had not moved in wireless silence, as no one had believed that the massive advance would pass undetected, but wireless messages, with no enemy in sight, had been few and brief. As I listened to Kinnaird's first orders for battle it seemed for an instant as though all the intervening weeks of rest and training had been only a dream. I heard:

'Hello, NUMO; NUMO calling. Figures two zero enemy tanks and some armoured cars reported stationary facing south about figures twelve miles north-east of us now. Change direction figures five degrees right. We are to engage. Report as soon as you see them. Over.'

We acknowledged our orders, swung on to the new line and the advance continued. In the last half-hour of fighting light we met up with the enemy, who, after a brief exchange of shots, withdrew to the north. There were no casualties on either side, and the sight of the myriad lights of the tracers winging their ways toward the enemy did much to revive my optimism. We leaguered where the battle ended. The first day had gone according to plan, and there had been no casualties to mar the high spirits of all in the leaguer, where we were busy with the evening meal and with the business of refuelling. Cairo radio, which we picked up on the tank set, broadcast an inspiring message from the Prime Minister which seemed a fitting climax to the day. It said:

'I have it in command from the King to express to all ranks of the Army and Royal Air Force in the Western Desert, and to the Mediterranean Fleet, His Majesty's confidence that they will do their duty with exemplary devotion in the supremely important battle which lies before them. For the first time British and Empire troops will meet the Germans with an ample equipment in modern weapons of all kinds. The battle itself will affect the whole course of the war. Now is the time to strike the hardest blow yet struck for final victory, home and freedom. The Desert Army may add a page in history which will rank with Blenheim and with Waterloo. The eyes of all nations are upon you. All our hearts are with you. May God uphold the right!'

At dawn, before the first streaks of light lit the eastern sky, the leaguer woke to life. As the atmospherics pipped and wheezed in the head-phones and the rigmarole of the morning net was played out, each tank moved farther and farther away from the Regimental Headquarters until, as the sun topped the horizon, we were dispersed and ready for battle.

There was no pause before the battle started. Before I felt that I was even fully awake, the first battle orders came from Kinnaird:

' ... Concentration of enemy tanks and vehicles reported three miles north-west of here. Move now on a bearing of figures four five degrees. Off.'

While I manoeuvred my headquarters into the correct position in relation to Kinnaird and checked that the troop leaders had taken station on me, I pondered that however early we had woken up and broken leaguer, the armoured cars had been before us, searching and probing for the enemy. The early morning air was chill and crisp. The cold whip of the wind made my eyes water, and as I brushed the wet away from my cheek I could feel the first uncomfortable stubble on my face. By now I was wide awake, all my senses alert and keyed up with the first twinges of apprehension and with excitement.

We had moved for not more than three miles when the first reports came in from the leading troops of the centre squadron:

' ... Enemy concentration of MT and tanks stationary at a range of figures one five zero zero yards. Over.'

Kinnaird answered, ' ... O.K. Advance and engage. Report as soon as you can the exact numbers of the enemy. Off to you.' He then called the two flanking squadrons, mine being on the right, ' ... Move now into battle-line right and left, and engage as soon as you can. See if you can find the flanks of the enemy's position. Off.'

I slipped automatically back into the habits learned before:

165

'Driver, close down,' I called down the intercom. 'Gunner – 37-mm. action. Loader, get a stack of shells handy.'

I looked to right and left to check the dispositions of my troops and then settled back in my cupola to scan the ground before me. Already to my left front I could make out the solid mass of the enemy's concentration and the occasional flash of the enemy field-guns as they ranged on our approaching tanks.

Before I realized what had happened I found that I was over-hauling the tank immediately to my front, and that all along the regimental line the other tanks were coming to an abrupt halt. To my right I could see the crew of one tank tumbling out of the turret as the first thin wisps of smoke came from the engine-covers. I drew level with the centre of my squadron and looked in vain to discover what had happened. Away to my left front I could still see the mass of the German tanks, stationary, menacing and, to all appearances, silent.

'What's the trouble, Hickson?' I called to the gunner. 'Can you see why they've all halted?'

'Can't be sure, sir, but I think there's anti-tank guns in front of them tanks. Look, sir. See that flash over to the left?'

'By God, you're right!' I answered, but before I could report to Kinnaird I heard Stendall's voice in the head-phones saying, ' ... Enemy anti-tank guns in position about figures eight zero zero yards forward of the enemy tanks. I am withdrawing out of range to try to locate their exact positions. Can you send the O.P. to me? Over.'

' ... O.K., he'll be coming soon. Make sure you don't let him go too far forward and get into trouble. Off to you,' was Kinnaird's reply. To me and Chesham he called, 'Probe outwards and try to locate the flanks of these guns. Off.'

The enemy position had been too cleverly sited for either Chesham's or my squadron to be able to see the flanks without going far enough forward to draw the enemy's fire. Invariably this courted disaster, as the enemy guns held their fire without giving away their positions until they knew that we were within lethal range. Four more tanks were lost before Kinnaird called a halt to this expensive practice and signalled, ' ... Pick out the enemy positions and I'll send the O.P. to you in turn to deal with them.'

For the rest of the morning and the early afternoon we lay in watch, the gunner O.P. moving from squadron to squadron to direct the guns on to the anti-tank positions which had been located.

'It's too bloody easy,' I could not help remarking to my crew. 'Their tanks know we can't deal with them until we get within eight hundred yards, so they sit a few hundred yards behind a screen of anti-tank guns. And we can't deal with the anti-tank guns quickly because we've only got the field-guns to fire H.E., and they're not designed to hit pin-point targets. Wish to God all the brigades were together, then one of them could do a worthwhile out-flanking move on these positions and come in from an unexpected direction while the others occupied the Jerries' attention.'

But it was no use wishing, and all I could do was to watch the laborious process of the supporting battery trying to deal with each enemy position in turn.

When the midday haze started to clear at about 1500 hours, peering through my binoculars at the ground before me in search of the enemy guns, I became aware of a larger dust-cloud behind and beyond the German main positions, approaching from a north-easterly direction. At first I paid no particular attention to it, thinking vaguely that perhaps it was merely the dust of other actions being borne on the wind. As the cloud came nearer I began to suspect that my first idea was wrong, and it was with a growing apprehension that I distinguished the squat black shapes of a large number of tanks, looking somewhat like the tree-trunks of the forest of dust and sand. In my ear-phones I heard Peters confirm my sudden discovery, ' ... About figures one zero zero tanks moving towards us now. I can see them at a range of about figures two zero zero zero yards coming fast.'

' 'ere we go again,' I heard Jones, my operator, say.

'Look at the bastards,' Hickson muttered.

' ... No move unless I order it,' Kinnaird's voice came over the wireless. 'We'll fight here and only give ground if we have to.'

To my surprise, I heard Clayton ask, ' ... Where do you want me to be?'

Glancing round and seeing his tank just behind, I answered briefly and irritably, ' ... Where you are, of course. And keep off the air unless you have something more important to say.'

167

Almost immediately Mills reported, ' ... Enemy tanks now only figures one zero zero zero yards from me and still moving fast.'

And Peters, on the right flank, added the disquieting news, ' ... More enemy tanks now visible to my flank and moving in fast.'

I was about to answer when I realized that Peters, quite rightly, had reported this news development direct to Kinnaird, missing me out.

Kinnaird answered immediately, ' ... O.K. Keep an eye on them, and I'll get our elders to move somebody else up to deal with that.'

So we joined battle again. As before, I found that I failed to measure the passage of time in the heat of battle, and when I looked at my watch in a lull in the firing I was staggered to discover it was already well past 1600 hours. To my front the scene was exactly like the many other battles in which I had taken part. Mills' tank lay derelict and smoking, and I wondered how many of the crew had escaped. I had not seen any. One of Peters' tanks was on fire, but I remembered seeing at least two of the crew bale out. Beyond Peters, another regiment had come into action, and they too had had casualties. To my left I knew that at least one tank of my squadron was knocked out, and I had seen another withdrawing slowly, in reverse, out of battle. The Germans had not gone unscathed. There was a satisfying black pall of smoke lying over their positions and in the gathering gloom I could pick out, on my immediate front alone, the flicker of about a dozen fires. Occasionally one of these flared momentarily, or another exploded with a shower of sparks. Darkness brought an end to the battle, and we moved away into leaguer.

When I had given a hand with the disposal of the empty cases which cluttered the turret floor and had helped to fill up with a new supply of ammunition, I walked round my squadron to see how they had fared. Mills had died, as so many tank commanders would, from a shot through the head. It was impossible to see accurately the fall or strike of shot without using binoculars. To do this each tank commander had to keep his head sufficiently far out of the turret so that his eyes were above the level of the cupola, leaving six or more inches vulnerable to any bullet or shell

168

splinter and courting death from any 50-mm. shot which passed within inches of the top of the tank. Before the rest of Mills' crew had recovered from this disaster, the tank was penetrated, killing the driver and mortally wounding the gunner just behind him. Only the operator, who climbed over the dead and dying, had escaped. Four other tanks had been hit, three being total losses. In each case at least one of the crew had died.

I reported to Kinnaird, who answered soberly, 'That makes fourteen tanks we've lost and thirty good chaps killed or wounded. Not bad for a start. But Brigade say that the Jerries have lost over sixty tanks, which is more than we have, and so they say honour is satisfied. Seventh Armoured Brigade have captured the airfield at Sidi Rezegh. From the guarded reports about 22nd Armoured, I reckon they've had a pretty good knock from Ariete. Ah, well, make sure all your men get a good night's sleep – this is just the beginning. Good night.'

Early on the following morning we joined battle again. Before my squadron had spread out to our battle positions from the night leaguer, and when the first rays of the rising sun still blinded any vision to he east, Sergeant Storney, who had taken over Mills' troop, reported, ' . . . Enemy tanks moving round my right flank out of the sun.'

All through he morning the running fight continued. From ur night positions we were forced gradually south. The relentless German pressure continued, searching always for the right flank, so that by the early afternoon we had been forced to swing farther and farther to the right, until we faced due east. Still the Germans came on. Their determination to advance led them to take risks, with the result that the balance of the losses was, at first, against them. At noon visibility was reduced to so low a level by the heat haze that a mutual truce was called.

' . . . Take advantage of this lull to get something to eat and replenish,' Kinnaird ordered.

'I'm so bloody 'ungry I could eat a couple of filthy bloody camels,' my driver announced as he busied himself first with the refill of petrol, and then with the brew.

At othe times and places we would have been celebrating this day, the anniversary of the first great tank-won victory of the first war, with good food and games and merriment. Memories flooded back to me of gay and enjoyable days, when my operator, as if reading my thoughts, remarked, 'Bloody awful Cambrai day, I calls it.'

The cold bully beef and hot tea were nevertheless welcome.

During the afternoon the German tank attack was renewed, and from then on I was reminded of the battles of the early summer. All afternoon we were harried and threatened with envelopment. I lost another two tanks and re-organized my squadron into two troops and my own headquarters. One of the casualties was Elliott and his crew, and their deaths brought a new and sinister development to desert fighting. I had seen Elliott's tank crippled by a shot that severed the track, had watched him and the crew bale out. And then with horror and impotent rage I saw them stumble and fall, shot down by German machine-gun fire. Previously each side had respected the crew who were forced to abandon their tanks.

Shocked and angry, I reported, ' ... The bloody Huns have taken to shooting up crews who bale out.'

Kinnaird answered, ' ... Yours is not the only case. Give no quarter from now on.'

We were driven gradually farther and farther west, until by last light, though contesting every yard of the way, we were almost back to the leaguer position we had occupied at the end of the first day of the advance.

The battle continued until it was so dark that we were only shooting at each other's gun-flashes. At last Kinnaird decided that it was a fruitless waste of ammunition and ordered, ' ... Cease fire and rally on me for leaguer.' Dispersed as we all were, and with each tank commander more concerned until that moment with the position of the enemy than with his own immediately superior headquarters, it was a slow and painstaking business to concentrate.

The delays were so long that Kinnaird, exasperated at length by the non-appearance of A Squadron, inquired irritably, '... Where are you? It'll be dawn, if we don't hurry up. For God's sake get a move on.' But still there was no reply.

At last, after he had called both Stendall and me to his tank to discuss what might have happened, the weary and despondent voice of Chesham was heard saying, ' . . . I have been brewed up twice and my two IC has disappeared. I have five of us with me, but we don't know where to go. Can you put up a light?'

With relief Kinnaird replied, ' . . . O.K. I will put up a green light in figures five. Meantime see if you can collect any others. If not, come in with what you've got.'

After five minutes he fired the Very light, which lit the desert all round our huddled group of tanks. At last what remained of A Squadron appeared and Chesham reported to Kinnaird, 'We were just collecting together when about six Jerry Mark IIIs appeared out of the dark and shot us up. There was all Hell for about five minutes, and we dispersed madly to get out of the fire. My tank was completely shot up, and we lost two others almost as quickly. I think the five of us are all that's left. We got three of them, though.'

With this last sobering piece of news, we moved back into leaguer. I felt weary beyond belief. For three days now we had been in almost constant action for many hours a day. Food had been intermittent and scanty, sleep been brief and very disturbed. Fear had been our constant companion, sapping our strength, and taking a toll of our supplies of courage and determination which only the utmost will-power would replace. Physical exhaustion was at the acutest stage before our bodies had become adapted to the strain of the endurance demanded of them.

4

Surrounded in Leaguer

I HAD not been asleep for more than two hours when I felt a hand shaking my shoulder and a voice whispering urgently in my ear, 'Stand to, sir. C.O.'s orders, and he wants to see you in his tank.'

I rubbed the last vestige of sleep from my eyes and scrambled out of my blankets. While I pulled my boots on and climbed into my overcoat, I became fully awake, my mind searching frantically for the cause of this unexpected order. At Kinnaird's tank I found a small group of figures gathered, nervously silent, as if expecting some disaster.

Kinnaird counted us to make sure we were all present, and then, indicating the infantry company commander who was standing beside him, said in a low voice, 'Clive here has sent out two separate patrols, who both report the enemy digging in about five hundred yards away. Judging by the noise, they're moving anti-tank guns into position. Another patrol is out checking up the position to our south-west, but I think we can take it as certain we've been surrounded. It's clear we can't stay here. As soon as it's light they'll open fire. We'll move directly we get the last patrol's report.'

There was silence for a few moments as the news sank in and while we waited for the return of the patrol. Stendall broke it at length, his voice seeming alarmingly loud to each of us in the eerie quiet which held the lurking menace of a hidden enemy preparing our destruction. He said, 'Don't you think it would be better, sir, if we waited until nearer dawn before we move? If we go now, while it's dark, like as not we'll lose some of the vehicles. If we go, say, about a quarter of an hour before first light, we can all make off in the same direction, and when it's light we will have more chance of collecting again.'

Kinnaird did not answer at once, but eventually he replied, 'Yes, I agree. Good idea, Ian. Right, we'll do that. First light will be about 0530 hours. Stand to till 0445 hours. Then report to me for final orders and we'll start up and move off at 0500 hours prompt. As we're all facing east, we'll move off in that direction and swing round to the south and then south-west. There must be absolute quiet in the leaguer, so that the enemy does not realize that we know his plans. O.K. Make sure every man knows what's happening, and that they're all alert.'

I looked at my watch. It was just after 0200 hours – almost three hours to wait before we could be on the move. I walked quietly round my squadron and told each of the crews of the enemy trap and of the plan to escape. I checked with my fitter sergeant that the tanks were all fit to move; I made certain that they were all refilled; I did anything and everything to spin out the minutes of waiting. And when I looked at my watch again it was still only 0245 hours. I couldn't believe it, and listened to satisfy myself it had not stopped and tested to see if I had remembered to wind it. The minutes and hours dragged by – more slowly than I could

172

ever remember before. I looked at my watch so frequently that the hands never seemed to have moved, until I finally made a mental resolution not to look again until at least half an hour had passed. But when I looked again only twenty minutes had gone.

At last it was time to report to Kinnaird, and I joined the small group of figures who had quietly and stealthily climbed down from their tanks and were now gathered round him. There wasn't much to be said. 'Make sure every man knows his orders and don't start up until you hear me. Any questions? Right. Well, get back to your vehicles.'

I passed the orders on to my own tank commanders and watched them disperse into the black night back to their tanks. I climbed into the turret, adjusted my head-phones and made myself comfortable in the cupola. These last few minutes were the most nerve-racking of them all. Through my mind passed all the disasters that might occur. Perhaps at the last moment my tank wouldn't start up; or perhaps the one in front of me would fail to start and block my way; or another tank might run into mine in the darkness.

With a roar Kinnaird's tank started, and was followed immediately by all the rest. Without pause we moved off, each column fanning out slightly as it went, to avoid crashing into its neighbour. For a few hundred yards our progress was without incident and unimpeded. Then from the ground before us we saw the shadowy shapes of men leaping out of the way. Here and there one or more Germans, wider awake than the rest, opened fire with rifles and pistols. To my front I saw the figure of a man outlined by the flashes behind him. Then we were over him and the roar of the engines and the crack of the tracks muffled all but the first notes of his piercing screams as he was swept under the tracks. After that we were through and into the safety of the empty desert beyond the thin screen of the German anti-tank guns. In the clouds of dust that shrouded the whole mass of tanks and vehicles it was impossible to see more than a few yards ahead or to the sides. More by luck than judgement I sensed that the leading vehicles had started their swing to the right and, praying that I would not become entangled with any other tank or gun-limber, I gradually conformed. The first hectic rush to clear the enemy was now checked and we were moving at a more even,

173

slower speed. As pale streaks of dawn appeared in the sky to our left, Kinnaird ordered, 'Halt now. Stay where you are until it's light, and then we'll sort ourselves out. That was good. I think we got away without a scratch.'

Dawn brought no period in which we were free to sort ourselves out, for, hard on the heels of the early rays of the sun, the German tanks moved in to attack. There was a wild scramble of tanks and vehicles, out of which Kinnaird gradually sorted some kind of order and got us all facing north-east towards the enemy attack. Vehicles were lost in the process, some of the lorries, finding themselves between the fire of the two sides, being crippled or set on fire before their wild progress could get them away from the danger.

For some time I was completely lost in the chaos of the battle, bewildered by the fog of war. Friend and foe were almost indistinguishable in the early light, their outlines blurred by the clouds of dust and the black smoke of the shell-bursts.

At last there was a pause. Our frenzied though determined resistance had been sufficiently effective to bring the German tanks to a halt, and Kinnaird could say with satisfaction, ' ... Stay where you are now and don't move until I order you back to refill. Friends are about to attack on our right and left to keep the enemy occupied.'

I watched with relief the advance of one of the other regiments of the Brigade on my right, and saw that the mass of German tanks before me was being thinned out to meet the new menaces to their flanks. By mid-morning the Brigade was in battle line facing north-east, ready to meet any new attack. The shell-fire on both sides grew in intensity as the morning passed, until the heat-haze reduced visibility and any further shelling was a waste of ammunition.

With a sigh of satisfaction, I heard Kinnaird's first orders for the replenishment, and called down into the turret, 'Let's have something to eat. Anything will do me – bully-beef and biscuits. And hand me up my water-bottle.'

Kinnaird took advantage of the refill to sort the regiment out. Ruefully we counted the few tanks that now remained of the regiment that had moved into battle three days before. Twenty-five tanks were all that were left of the fifty-two that was the regiment's full strength. Not all those which were lost had been entirely knocked out, but in each case one or more of the crew had died, and where the survivors had not brought their tanks back to safety, these now lay in areas dominated by the enemy.

But even the replenishment was not to be undisturbed. Just when I was counting on the midday haze to give us time and opportunity for a brew, Kinnaird gave further orders:

' ... Enemy now reported to be thinning out and moving off north-west. Follow up as soon as you see any sign of movement in front of us. We are to give chase and do all the damage we can. Off.'

I acknowledged the orders in my turn and gave the orders to my crew, disgusted by the change of plans. All along the battle line I could see the spurts of white smoke from the exhausts as each tank started up and began to move forward. In the haze it was difficult to distinguish the German tanks and impossible to estimate the range to them. As we advanced Kinnaird warned us, ' ... Keep your eyes skinned for anti-tank guns. This is just the sort of chance they will be waiting for.'

And so it happened. To my front I caught a glimpse of a flash and saw the tank immediately ahead of me jerk to a standstill. Another flash from the sand and scrub 800 yards away and the crew of the tank baled out in confusion and huddled at the rear of their tank. Seeing their plight, I ordered, 'Driver advance up to that tank. We'll have a go at rescuing the crew.' Knowing the urgency of speed, the driver covered the intervening distance as fast as possible, and when we came to a halt I shouted to the four men in front of us, 'Come on, jump up, and look sharp about it.' There was an answering shout, 'Both the driver's legs are broken, and he can't move. We'll have to wait for the doc.'

'O.K.,' I shouted back; 'I'll get him up to you.' To the driver I said. 'Driver, back the way we came,' and I bent to the microphone to give Kinnaird news of the wounded crew and to ask for the doctor.

In so doing I failed to watch where the driver was going. After reversing a few yards to clear the crippled tank, he moved forward again, swinging to the left to turn round to the way we had come. As we moved clear of the shelter afforded by the hulk, I felt the sharp jar of a hit, and with a clang of broken metal the engine

175

ground to a stop. 'You bloody fool,' I shouted down the inter-com, 'We're hit. Bale out.'

And when we were all gathered by the side of the tank, the driver said contritely, 'Sorry, sir. I didn't think about that enemy gun.'

Ashamed of my outburst, I answered, 'That's all right, Dunney. My fault. I ought to have warned you. Well, we'd better see if we can get away.'

Stopping and starting, stumbling and running, I eventually reached the nearest tank, which I found to be Clayton's. The thought crossed my mind, 'He might have come to our rescue,' but I dismissed it immediately, crediting him with the sense to have seen what had just happened and not wishing to repeat it. But the enthusiasm with which Clayton answered my order, 'Come on, Reggie, out you get; I'll take over,' renewed my doubts, and I answered with more than a touch of anger his complaint that he would not be able to take his bedding, 'Well, I've lost mine too – unless you'd like to fetch it off that tank.'

As usual, the German tanks attacked to cover the withdrawal of the anti-tank guns, but thereafter, throughout the afternoon and early evening, the battle moved farther and farther north, while we did our best to harry the German rear-guards.

At about 1630 hours, when the right flank of the regiment had successfully attacked the undefended supply lorries of 21 Panzer Division some miles to the east, Kinnaird passed on new orders which he had just received from Brigade, ' ... Orders. Friends who captured the airfield have had serious losses against large numbers of enemy tanks. Other friends who were with us this morning have run into trouble east of Sidi Rezegh. We will move now as fast as possible to attack enemy now reported south-east of the airfield. Off.'

Kinnaird stressed the urgency of the desperate situation of the forces on the airfield. The advance continued, now in a north-westerly direction, but soon we were forced to halt to refuel with petrol. With all their advantages of reliability and speed, the Honeys had one major defect: their endurance. There was only capacity for enough petrol to cover about forty-five miles in battle conditions. Refuelling had to be frequent, and was often required

176

just when the situation was least opportune. There was delay while the supply lorries came forward, after being left some miles behind by the speed of the advance and the reluctance of the column commanders to become embroiled in the wayward unpredictable movements of the battle. There was further delay while the lorries did their round of the tanks, delivering the cans of petrol. There was even further delay because so many of the cans on examination proved to be empty. The cans were the thin tin, four-gallon type, known as '*safiyha*' in Egypt, which when packed two to a wooden crate had been fairly satisfactory. By the winter of 1941, due to the shortage of wood, they were packed in cardboard boxes or thin plywood cases. In either case the tins were soon dented or holed and the wastage of petrol was immense. We looked with admiration at the strong German-made type, so eminently suitable for war and soon named 'jerricans', which already littered the desert in large numbers.

The refuelling was at last completed and we moved forward again. Rain had begun to fall by this time, and when this and the gathering dusk made visibility so bad that the leading tanks ran unwittingly into another anti-tank gun ambush, we halted and then went into leaguer.

5

Sidi Rezegh

WHILE we in 4th Armoured Brigade were fighting on the inner flank of the Division's wide wheel behind the German frontier positions, the other two armoured brigades, the 7th and 22nd, had had hard battles also. Indeed, the former had by the morning of 22 November almost ceased to exist.

Twenty-second Armoured had attacked the Italian Ariete Armoured Division at Gubi, but the threat to us just east of Gabr Saleh had been such that they had been ordered east to our support. They had had a stiff battle on the way and had joined the battles of the morning of the 21st on our left flank. From here they had moved north to the support of 7th Armoured at Sidi Rezegh, and while we had been cursing at the delays of the refuelling they had joined in the hard fight for the landing-field and the tomb and had suffered severe casualties.

On 19 November 7th Armoured Brigade had seized the small airfield at Sidi Rezegh and, aided by the Support Group, had held back the few minor attacks launched during the following day. That night the garrison of Tobruk were ordered to break out, and chose, by an ill chance, the precise sector of the front to which the Germans had posted troops with the intention of breaking in. This sector was just to the north-west of Sidi Rezegh. During the 21st the battle in this area had become more and more intense. The Tobruk garrison were trying desperately to make contact with 8th Army at Sidi Rezegh, where in turn 7th Armoured Division were striving to clear the enemy from the short dividing distance. Equally determined to prevent this junction of forces, which would have sealed the only good escape route to the west for all their forces east of Tobruk, the Germans threw in the whole weight of their armour.

By the evening of 21 November, 7th Armoured Brigade had been reduced to a total of thirty tanks and 22nd Armoured to almost the same number.

I woke the next morning to the certain knowledge that there would be fierce and desperate battles all day. Without my own bedding, with a crew who were not yet used to my ways and fads, almost smothered by the fug under the tarpaulin which had been necessary to keep off the rain which beat down all night, I could not have been less ready for instant and exhausting action. My beard was at the most uncomfortable stage of its growth, my clothes were damp and foul-smelling, my face and hands cold and numb. I left the operator to complete the net and walked over to Kinnaird's tank. I was such a picture of misery and despondence that Kinnaird, despite his many anxieties, grinned and said, 'Cheer up, Tony. You're still alive. It could be worse. But you've come just at the right moment. Here are the others, and these are the orders. Seventh Armoured and the Support Group are already being attacked from the north-west. We have got to get to them. But as far as is known both 15 and 21 Panzer are between us and them. So we shall have a bloody battle before we can even give them any help. Right – we move off in five minutes.'

Within a few minutes of starting, the reports began to come in, all telling the same story of tanks and anti-tank guns on the escarpments to the east and south-west of Sidi Rezegh, preventing us from moving to join the desperate battle on the airfield.

All morning the battles swayed forwards and backwards round the airfield and the high ground to the north. While 7th Armoured and the Support Group beat off the first attacks, we and 22nd Armoured fought to get through to them.

I lost all count of time, and only the growing aches of my empty stomach and the parched dryness of my mouth indicated the passage of the hours. I lost, too, all count of the casualties in my squadron and the losses which each tank claimed to have inflicted on the enemy. The early battles were fought in the mist of the damp of the sodden ground evaporating in the sun. Later a dark pall of smoke and dust overhung the whole battlefield, hiding friend and foe alike. In the turmoil and confusion it was miraculous that more mistakes were not made in shooting against friends. Gradually we pushed the Germans farther and farther back, with the loss of many tanks on both sides. My own tank was penetrated by a shot which spent itself in the effort of piercing the armour and only fell to the floor at my driver's feet, doing no damage. There was a momentary relief of the tension, when, referring to the many rumours of the desperate methods the Germans were reputed to be resorting to in their search for metals he remarked, 'Not bad for bloody church railings, I calls it.'

Peters' tank was hit and set on fire. He and his crew, the driver and gunner torn and shattered and with the pallor of imminent death already marking their features, were brought out by another tank. I felt a lifting of my spirits at the sight of Peters and the knowledge that he still lived. Drummond announced laconically, ' . . . Had a spot of bother. Am withdrawing. Off.' A few moments, later I saw his tank limping slowly back in reverse: this was a trick we had now all learnt – it kept the thickest armour facing the enemy, and the withdrawal was so imperceptible that it did not invite the hail of shot which a stricken tank always attracted.

I stopped Drummond when his tank was parallel to mine and only a few yards away and asked, 'Where did you get to?'

'Another push and I think we're over. I believe I saw the air-field before I was hit. Couldn't see much – but the noise and the people you meet!' Drummond answered with a grin, and then his tank moved on.

At midday and for an hour afterwards there was a lull, except for the shelling by the field-guns of both sides. I took this, my first chance of the day, to get something to eat. My crew and I chewed ravenously at the bully-beef and biscuits as if they were the most delicate feast. A 'brew' was impossible, and the plain water, cold though it was, tasted sickly and oily with the disinfectant with which it had been treated, and did little to assuage our thirst.

At 1400 hours I was abruptly woken from the day-dreams I had been allowing myself, by Kinnaird's voice in the head-phones, ' ... Orders. Enemy tanks are reported to be forming up to attack Sidi Rezegh from the west and north-west. We must break through the enemy holding us up and get to the aerodrome. There is to be a concentrated attack on our part of the front, which we will lead. When I give the order we will advance as fast as we can and crash through whatever is in front of us.'

I acknowledged, and noted that it was not Chesham's voice who replied in his turn, but that of his second-in-command. I was so preoccupied with my thoughts about Chesham's possible fate that I only half heard the acknowledgments of the gunner battery and the infantry company, and was startled to hear Kinnaird's brief order, 'Advance – conform with my movements.'

So much happened within the next fifteen minutes that I found it impossible to register, let alone take the required action for, each event. My vision was obscured by the smoke and dust, my field of view confined to the area within a radius of about 200 yards from my tank. At times I lost sight of the leading tanks of my own squadron and at others could not see in the surrounding murk either Kinnaird's or the navigator's tank. Only the gun-flashes of the enemy tanks were an adequate guide to direction, and soon these disappeared as the tanks were either knocked out or were left behind to be dealt with by the following waves of our tanks.

In the relatively calm area behind the German line through which we had now broken, I was appalled at the extent of the devastation and carnage, which seemed to spread as far as the eye could see. It was a frightening and awesome spectacle – the dead and dying strewn over the battlefield, in trucks and Bren-carriers, in trenches and toppled over the trails of their guns, some silent and grey in death, others vocal with pain and stained by red gashes of flowing blood or the dark marks of old congealed wounds. Trucks, guns, ammunition, odd bits of clothing were smouldering or burning with bright tongues of fire. Here and there ammunition had caught fire and was exploding with spurts of flame and black smoke. Tanks of all kinds – Italian, German and British – littered the whole area. There was no plan or logic in the positions in which they lay – facing all directions, inter-mingled, crippled, blackened with fire or distorted with the explo-sion of their ammunition. And round them, lying or sitting or sprawled in the positions in which death had overtaken them, were the crews. Some appeared to be untouched, and it was only their unnatural pallor and the eerie intentness of their gaze that stopped me calling out to them. Others had lost a limb or limbs, the white stumps of bone showing brightly against the dark brown of the dried blood. Even so, they might have been alive. About others there could be no doubt – heads crushed beyond recognition, bodies severed or contorted, lying in the dark pools of their spilled blood – they could not possibly be alive, and I averted my eyes from these scenes, the horror of which brought a feeling of sickness and nameless distaste and nausea.

Beyond this area of death and decay we entered once more into the battle in all its fury. Waved on by the gesticulations of a large man standing unprotected in an open car flying a brigadier's pennant on the bonnet, I led my squadron over the airfield and up to the high ground beyond – wondering as I went whether our intervention would not have been of more value if the whole Brigade had halted for sufficient time to be able to strike a co-ordinated blow. The situation before me was obviously so desperate that my doubts were only momentary as we moved on again to engage the enemy tanks which were clearly visible on the crest-line.

All through the afternoon, under a gathering pall of dust and smoke, the battle continued. Gradually, fighting every yard of the way, we were first dislodged from the high ground north of the aerodrome and then from the airfield itself. Each pace of the retreat was marked by a burning tank, a crippled gun or the broken body of a man. But each tank and gun and man took a toll of the enemy which, mounting with each moment and hour, held back and slowed their advance.

On the northern edge of the airfield, with the bare expanse of flat ground behind me affording no cover or protection from fire, my tank was hit and the driver killed instantly. Further shots hit us, severing the tracks, setting alight the bedding stowed on the running-boards, smashing the glass vision-blocks and jamming the machine-gun. At last the tank was reduced to such a shambles that I ordered, 'Bale out,' and leapt from the cupola to the engine-covers, and so to the small area of shelter behind the tank. The gunner and operator followed, and I mentally echoed their incredulous shout of, 'Christ! we've made it – it's a bloody miracle we weren't all killed getting out.'

Our elation was damped by the thought, voiced by the gunner, ' 'ow the 'ell are we going to get out of 'ere, though? There's not much future in trying to cross this airfield with all this muck flying about. We wouldn't stand a chance.'

'Let's 'ang on 'ere, sir,' the operator said. 'Things might take a turn for the better – yer never know.'

'You're — 'opeful, you are, I reckon,' the gunner snorted. 'We might as well say our prayers now or give ourselves up to them bloody Jerries. But anyway, I votes we 'ang on for a bit an' see what 'appens, like you said. What do you think, sir?'

I answered after a pause: 'Yes, I think that's all we can do. If something doesn't turn up soon, maybe we can get away when it's dark.'

We continued to peer anxiously at the situation around us, occasionally taking a hasty look towards the enemy, but our chances did not appear to improve. We were so preoccupied that only the loud wail of the klaxon with which each 'Honey' was fitted drew our attention to the rear, where, ten yards away, a tank was halted with the commander waving frantically to us. We clambered aboard and squatted on the engine-covers behind the turret. I had not had time to see who the commander was, and it was the gunner's exclamation, 'Blimey, it's the C.O.,' which told me that Kinnaird had come to our rescue.

It was in this fashion that we moved back across the airfield, Kinnaird being careful to reverse the whole way, so protecting himself from direct shots and giving some cover to us, huddled behind his turret.

When darkness began to shroud the gloomy scene even

further, Kinnaird started to collect what remained of the regiment. In twos and threes, and even singly, from all directions we rallied to the burning tank which Kinnaird had chosen as his landmark. More and more arrived, and I was amazed when the total reached thirty and remarked, 'Where did they all come from, sir? I thought we started the day with about twenty.'

'Yes, but just as we were moving off to get through to the airfield, Clayton arrived with fifteen more which had been found all over the desert and into which he had put the spare crews. Thank God he did. All the same, we seem to have lost half a dozen or so since then.'

No one knew what had happened to Chesham and his crew. Of Stendall we heard from members of his squadron that he had been killed on the airfield, hit by a shell-splinter while he was climbing out of his burning tank. The other four tanks were manned by scratch crews. We had no idea who was in them, let alone what had happened to them.

Soon afterwards we moved into leaguer. Kinnaird took the regiment south-west from the airfield into what seemed a relatively quiet area. The long, slow, tedious march, with the billowing clouds of dust and the acrid fumes of the exhausts clogging our eyes and scorching our throats, was the usual last, trying ordeal to be endured. When at length we were settled and had sorted the crews and rearranged the squadrons for the morrow, we waited for the supply echelon to reach us with the evening stew and replenishment of fuel and ammunition. My crew and I, and the others who had lost their tanks, waited with special anxiety to get more blankets.

In the peculiar conditions in which we spent the days cooped up in the close confines of our tanks in the limited company of our crews, and the nights eating, refilling, reorganizing, on guard or asleep, there were few moments when the officers could meet and exchange news and comments. In these circumstances it was natural that certain men – the doctor, the padre, the technical adjutant – who during the day ranged far and wide over the battle area in the course of their duties, should in leaguer become the clearing-houses of news and views and each in his own way a focus for certain other officers. After Kinnaird, with whom I felt more and more in tune and to whom I went first each night to report and receive orders and stayed to gossip over a drink of whisky, I preferred the company of Henderson, the doctor. A middle-aged man, tall, thin, grizzled, and wise with a wisdom gained by half a life-time in the service of a country practice, he was calm under all emergencies, with an underlying sly wit which appealed to my own sense of humour. In battle the doctor's first-aid post was an oasis of reason and sanity whatever the scale of the casualties or the nature of the wounds he had to treat. He never appeared to be flustered, and only the tragedy which lurked behind the look in his eyes showed the depths to which his feelings had been bruised by the endless stream of torn and tortured bodies which it was his duty to tend. I had watched on occasions, with the deepest fellow feeling, when I saw the sad, resigned look on the doctor's face as he brought what comfort he could to a man who he knew had no hope of life. So this night, as on many others, while we waited for the supplies to arrive, I went in search of him, from whose influence I could gather strength.

It was while I was with him that I became aware of a growing sense of unease. As usual, the leaguer seemed to be ringed with enemy, whose presence was always marked by an astonishing display of coloured Very lights. But it was not these nor the failure of the supply column to arrive that caused my worry. For no accountable reason I felt that something was wrong somewhere. Henderson noticed my nervousness and remarked, 'Tony, you're on edge. What's the matter?'

All I could say in answer was, 'I don't know. Just that I feel something's going to happen. I think I'll go and see the C.O.'

With Kinnaird I was no nearer finding a solution, except that I heard that the Brigade was still not fully accounted for and that tanks, some in fairly large numbers, appeared to be wandering aimlessly about the area in which the units had leaguered. While I stood by Kinnaird's tank and listened to the flurry of orders and information being passed on the Brigade forward control, I suddenly heard, quite distinctly, at no great distance, the muffled note of the engines of a column of tanks and the accompanying clank and creak of tracks. For a moment I nearly shouted to Kinnaird to ask whether we should attract the attention of the tanks moving by. But some instinct restrained me, and I listened to the column move past without even disturbing Kinnaird, whose attention was still fully occupied with Brigade Headquarters.

In the next instant I knew what had caused my anxiety and recognized the mistake I had made in not warning Kinnaird. From the direction in which the column of tanks had gone there was suddenly a holocaust of firing and the crash and stutter of all sorts and sizes of guns. The sky was lit by flying tracer, Very lights, cascades of exploding ammunition and the bright flames of several petrol fires. Kinnaird appeared out of his cupola shouting, 'Brigade say they're being attacked. Good God! look at that. I should think they bloody well are! Tony – tell everyone to get into their tanks and switch on their sets again. We'll have to be ready to move.'

It was the work of a few moments to warn the leaguer, already alert as the result of the noise and lights to the east. We got no sleep that night. When Brigade Headquarters had determined the scale and direction of the attack against them, we and the other two regiments were ordered to move to their support. But before we had moved more than a mile, another furious battle broke out just to our south, where one of the other regiments had run into an enemy leaguer. This battle lasted a good hour, and when it gradually fizzled out we waited while Brigade Headquarters tried to restore some sort of order out of the chaos around them. To do so they fired a succession of Very light signals to indicate their position. This invited further attention from the Germans, who soon afterwards surrounded the headquarters and one regiment and then attacked. Over the Brigade Forward Control wireless set we heard of the sudden turn of events. There was nothing we could do to help. In the complete darkness and the confusion of the many individual actions, any attempt to help might well have resulted in further losses to our own side. It was impossible to distinguish friend from foe. All we could and did do was to sit waiting for any opportunity that might present itself. All night long we stayed at the alert in our vehicles. To begin with there was enough noise and sufficient light from the fires to keep us awake. And when, towards dawn, these died away, there was still the threat of a surprise attack to prevent us falling asleep or relaxing our vigilance.

With considerable apprehension we watched the approach of

dawn. It was an anxious time for all. Since the final attack of the previous night Kinnaird had lost all touch with Brigade Headquarters. For all we knew, the Brigadier and all his staff were either dead or prisoners, the codes compromised, the plans captured. Nor did we know the frequency on which Divisional Headquarters were working. There was no one to whom Kinnaird could report or from whom he could get information or orders. All this he made plain to us, and stressed the vital need for extreme vigilance. So as we moved farther in search of either friend or foe we were keyed to the utmost pitch of alertness. The sleepless night just passed, the weariness caused by days in action, the exhaustion induced by alternate periods of fear, excitement and boredom – all were momentarily forgotten.

It was my squadron, moving out to the north-west of the night's leaguer area, who made first contact with other British forces. I heaved a sigh of relief as I listened to Peters' information, ' . . . Have made contact with the people who were on our left the first day.' [That must be 22nd Brigade, I thought.] 'They have no news of our elders and say we had better join them until they get orders for us from their elders. They are with men from the deep south' ['Must be the South Africans,' I muttered], 'and have been attacked twice already to-day. There is another German attack forming up now, so it is urgent that we join them. Over.'

' . . . We will move now,' Kinnaird ordered. 'Tell them the direction from which we shall be coming and get exact orders as to where I am to go. Tell them again that I am anxious to get in touch with my proper elders as soon as possible. Off.'

During the morning we fought shoulder to shoulder with the South Africans, beating back the incessant tank and infantry attacks which were being launched against them from north, north-west, west and south-west. At about midday Kinnaird was ordered to withdraw east to rejoin 4th Armoured Brigade, the Brigadier and some of his staff having escaped and made contact with Division. On our way we passed through the tattered remnants of the Support Group, moving south to rest and reorganize after being reduced further in strength by a heavy attack early that morning. From them I learnt that no contact had yet been made with the garrison of Tobruk, but that the leading elements of the New Zealand Division were established about six miles east of Sidi Rezegh. This was some consolation for the loss of Sidi Rezegh itself and for the severe casualties suffered in trying to hold it. I was impressed by the bearing and steady discipline of these remnants. They looked as if they had suffered no defeat but rather that they had won a great victory. And so in a sense I supposed they had. They had proved that their prowess matched that of the enemy, and they had taken a severe toll of his strength.

Unknown to us during our move eastwards, a large force of German tanks moved parallel to our course, but some miles to the south, in the opposite direction. By 1500 hours they were formed up to the south-west ready to attack the 5th South African Brigade, with whom we had been all morning. Despite the urgent need to move to help, not a tank in the Brigade could do so immediately, as none had been refilled since the previous day.

When at last we reached the battle, we were confronted with a scene which almost exactly matched that of Sidi Rezegh the day before. The German tanks had broken through the anti-tank defence line and had knocked out all but a few of the handful of tanks belonging to the 7th and 22nd Brigades which had tried to hold up the attack. They had swept on through the gun lines and the defenceless infantry and had overrun the Brigade's Head-quarters itself. Burning vehicles, exploding ammunition and all the macabre paraphernalia of death were all that we could see. Kinnaird moved us into the midst of the destruction and, where we could, we rescued the few remaining dazed men who were not dead or mortally wounded. Under cover of our tanks others appeared and drove away in the few vehicles which had escaped damage.

As darkness fell we withdrew from the battlefield to leaguer. It was a grim, oppressively gloomy scene at which I occasionally glanced back as we moved east. Through the clouds of dust and smoke which overhung the flickering or exploding fires I could see the blood-red orb of the sun, like some fantastic backcloth.

We moved ten miles before we went into leaguer. Every nerve and sinew in my body was crying out for rest. But I discovered, as we were all to discover many times again, that we possessed immense reserves of strength and resilience we had never before suspected – only we must not give in. Kinnaird added the final touch which kept us going, ' ... I have just been told that to-morrow will be a day for rest and reorganization.'

6

Alarms and Excursions

AT dawn, before we broke leaguer, Kinnaird issued instructions which he had received from Brigade during the night. Since all wireless codes and recognition signals had been captured, the regiment was in future to be known as 'Peter' – his own christian name – and each squadron similarly. The recognition pennants would no longer be used. These had been a mixed blessing, in any case. At long ranges they were invisible, and at the shorter ranges they had only served to indicate clearly to the enemy the identity of our tanks. In trying to take up a hull or turret-down position they had been merely another item to consider, as each tank commander had to remember to lower his aerial unless he wanted to give his position away.

Perhaps most important of all, as a means of avoiding a recurrence of the disasters of the night of 22 November, Very lights were not to be used in future to indicate the position of any leaguer. Instead whoever was trying to find the leaguer would, after a warning wireless message, fire a tracer bullet. The leaguer would take the bearing to this marker, and the outlying tank or column would move in on the back bearing, which was passed to him.

There was an air of holiday abandon about the regiment as we moved south-east that morning for the rest we had been promised. The wireless messages had an unnatural tone of informality about them with the use of christian names in each message. Even the rigmarole of the morning wireless net sounded amusing with the outstations answering as 'Tony One' or 'Buster Three' instead of with the usual formless, phonetic jumble of letters.

It was a bright, sunlit day, the dew glistening on the desert and the stunted shrubs of scrub. The damp kept down the dust which later would plume and surround each tank. Food and a 'brew' were uppermost in each of our minds – a longing for a quiet, leisurely breakfast at last, with time to cook something more than the interminable bully and biscuits which had been the staple breakfast fare for so many days.

Kinnaird's next wireless message shattered all our fond daydreams. ' ... Orders,' he announced, and I could almost imagine what he was about to say by the tone of his voice. 'We are to move north on a bearing of figures one two degrees to attack an enemy concentration reported to be forming up south of friends who are advancing west along the escarpment.'

We wheeled left through 115 degrees and set off on the new course to the north. It was a small, depleted force compared to the strength that it should have had. Our regiment was in the lead with two weak squadrons – all that was left. My squadron consisted of three troops of three tanks and my own. Tapson, who had taken over when Stendall was killed on the airfield, had only two troops and his own tank. These, with Kinnaird's tank and that of Hutchins, the second-in-command, were the full strength of the regiment. The other regiment was no stronger, made up to the few numbers it had by the remnants of the third regiment, which had been overrun with Brigade Headquarters two nights before.

Two young officers had joined my squadron, but rather than risk disaster due to their inexperience I put Sergeant Storney in command of the third of my three troops, for, in all our earlier battles, he had shown an alertness and imaginative battle-sense which was remarkable. He, Peters and Drummond made a very strong and reliable combination.

After moving ten miles, Peters reported a number of vehicles to his front. On further investigation he found these to be the New Zealanders, who were unaware of any enemy near them or of the purpose of our Brigade. Peters reported this to Kinnaird, who answered, 'O.K. Halt and wait while I report and find out what we are to do.'

I toyed with the idea of a 'brew', hoping that whatever pause there might be before a further move would be a long one. I asked Kinnaird, 'Is there time for a quick "brew"?' but the only answer I got was, 'I've no idea. Our elders say that their elders are in a flap about something but that we ought to get orders soon. You can risk a "brew" if you want one, though personally I think it'll be a waste of effort.'

His guess was accurate, and when a few minutes later he gave out his further orders, there was a note of urgency in his voice which immediately made each of us alert to catch each word he said.

'Hello, all stations Peter; Peter calling. Orders. A large force of enemy tanks is reported moving south-east from the area of Sidi Rezegh towards the Trigh el Abd. They have engaged and driven back the remains of Jock's and Davy's parties. We are to move on a bearing of figures one seven four degrees. Conform to me in the present formation. Over.'

'Tony O.K. Off,' I answered followed by Tapson's, 'Buster O.K. Off.'

Knowing that the Support Group and 7th Armoured Brigade had been withdrawn to rest and refit the previous day, I was more than startled to hear Kinnaird's information that they had been met and attacked by a German column. If that were so, then the Germans must be well among the various Divisional and Corps headquarters, and that would be like putting the cat among the pigeons. I could imagine the feathers flying in all directions and the squawk and cackle on the various wireless nets. But where, I wondered, were the Germans off to? Could they be after the massive supplies in the dumps some fifteen miles south of the Trigh el Abd? Or were they on the way to help the frontier garrisons of the Omars, Capuzzo and Sollum which the Indians were attacking? Or were they perhaps intent on objectives farther east: Sidi Barrani, Matruh – Alexandria, perhaps?

There was little time for speculation, however. First there was a halt to refill with petrol. During the twenty minutes it took for the supply lorries to catch up and do their round of the tanks, my crew managed to get a 'brew' and cook a few mouthfuls of bully-beef. They had got the whole proceedings down to a split-second drill. There was even time to eat the meal before we moved off again.

Moving at the best possible speed over the bumpy, broken ground, we were fully occupied in preventing any physical harm to ourselves from the constant jolting and jarring. The tank commanders were particularly susceptible to injury. The 'Honeys' were not fitted with any commander's seat, and the best that the overtaxed resources of the base workshops could do was to fit hooks at each side of the lower edges of the cupola on to which a crude narrow canvas sling-seat was hung. There was no convenient place on which we could put our feet to get sufficient purchase to stop a sudden jolt. If I slipped, I knew that I would either bang my face on the cupola in front of me or bark my shins or cut my legs on some projection inside the turret.

At twenty miles an hour and over, the cold, in the winter months, caused acute discomfort. The wind lashed our eyes until they poured with tears. Even if we wore goggles the air still seemed to get under or round them. Our cheeks and forehead became numb and ached with a dull throb. We took to wearing balaclava helmets and swathed ourselves with scarves. Some men did not remove theirs for days on end, sleeping in them at night as well.

By early evening Peters and Drummond, still in the lead, found our easy progress impeded by a motley selection of vehicles, driving fast, apparently aimlessly, in all directions except south. From them we heard tales of the panic and chaos which the sudden advance of the German armour had caused.

Peters summarized it neatly when he reported, 'Hello, Peter; Tony One calling. I can't get any sense out of anyone I've met so far. It's as if a rake has got into Roedean and all the girls are dashing madly away from a fate worse than death.'

By the time we had eventually picked our way carefully through the mass of stray vehicles, each of which had to be approached with some caution in case it turned out to be enemy, darkness had almost overtaken us. In the last half-hour of light we made contact with a thin screen of enemy anti-tank guns a few miles north of the Trigh el Abd. We could do nothing in the time, and as soon as it was dark we moved north a mile or two and into leaguer.

From here we watched the incredible sight to the south. My driver remarked, 'It's like a bloody Brock's benefit at Blackpool.' As far as the eye could see, to east and west, along the line of the Trigh el Abd, and presumably between us and the Divisional and Corps headquarters and the supply dumps, the Very lights of the German leaguers flashed and exploded.

I reported as usual to Kinnaird, and heard from him more of the day's events.

'As far as I can gather, one of the Panzer Divisions with Ariete

Division in tow drove down the Trigh to the frontier and are now trying to mop up the Indians and anything else they can find there. Div. H.Q. are somewhere east of us. By the mercy of heaven the Jerries missed the two supply dumps, though they passed through the top edge of one. I must say I give whoever was responsible full marks for dispersing them so well and keeping their presence hidden. To-morrow we are to go south to protect them. Well, I'm off to bed. I'm bloody tired. Good night.'

I felt restless and in need of company. I failed to find Henderson, and so went in search of Davidson, the padre, who in his way had made a considerable impression on the regiment. He had been somewhat retiring and quiet during the short time he had been with us before we moved out from Beni Yusef. Unaware of the mettle of the man, I had mistakenly remarked to him on the second night of the battle: 'Hello, Padre. Afraid this isn't your cup of tea, is it?', only to be answered, 'That's where you're wrong. I think I can do quite a lot to help some of the men in leaguer at night by a talk or a short gossip. I never did like all the forms and formalism of conventional churchianity, as I call it, though I hope my Bishop never gets to hear of it. I think there's a deal too much time spent in explaining why the Church does this or that or doesn't at various times of the year. This is more the religion I believe in. I try to be a mind-and-soul doctor, and pretty rewarding I find it, too. There's more Christian feeling and comradeship in one leaguer in one night than there is in many parishes during a whole week.'

It was so direct and honest that I was greatly attracted to the padre. So much of the religion I had seen before was old-maidish and stilted, narrow and uncharitable. On many other evenings I searched him out for a talk.

At dawn we advanced to defend the supply dumps. We expected to find opposition, but crossed Trigh el Abd without seeing any enemy, and were well on our way when we were ordered to move west to the support of the 1st South African Brigade, who were being attacked by tanks some twenty-five miles away.

At about midday we saw unmistakable signs of battle on the western horizon. A dark cloud of smoke and dust hung menacingly in the air. Soon afterwards we were among the South

192

African lines, and Kinnaird ordered, ' ... Halt now. There are guides to show us where to go. Do not move until you have met them. Off.'

An xcited captain climbed on to my tank and explained, 'You're just in time, Major. We're all but out of ammo, and we'd have had it without you. You just get on with beating the Jerries and we'll look after you.'

The first impact with the German tanks was a hard battle. Not until both they and we had had some casualties did they with-draw to a range from which they could no longer harass the South African positions. Seagrim's tank was lost, and Seagrim died soon after being taken out of the turret. I was with him until he died. Never before had I sat and watched cold-bloodedly as death came to a man. It was an unnerving experience, made worse by the evident efforts that Seagrim made to say something, all of which was incomprehensible, as he had his lower jaw shot away. When he died I climbed back into my tank. Somehow the many losses of tanks and men, of friends and companions, had not affected me so much as this one death.

At last light the South Africans withdrew to the south, and when they were clear and there was no further threat of a German attack, Kinnaird rallied us, and we moved south also and into leaguer.

I found it difficult to shake off the depression which was affect-ing me after Seagrim's death, and I brooded on the losses we had suffered since we marched from Beni Yusef only two months ago. Three of my squadron had now been killed – Mills and Elliott, so young and so new to the desert, and now Seagrim: and of the original squadron commanders only Williams of H.Q. and myself were now left. It was a sobering thought. I ate my evening meal alone, made my round of the squadron, reported to Kinnaird and returned to my tank. This was the time at which, each night, I had to make my choice of the hours for my turn of guard. The squadron was so short of officers that I felt it my duty to take a share. I always found it difficult to decide when I would do it. The first two hours had the advantage that when they were over I could sleep the rest of the night undisturbed. But we had to mount the guards soon after the leaguer was formed, and if I did this period I was prevented from doing my rounds or making the visits I wanted to. On this night, though, I selected these hours and settled myself in the turret.

I found that it was no use staring too hard into the night, as I invariably imagined shapes and movements, which further peering proved to be illusory. The vast expanse of the cloudless sky enthralled me: always I was reminded of the line I had read somewhere – 'the soldier stars that pace the beats of heaven'. The silence and the chance to sort out my thoughts and emotions calmed my troubled spirit, and when I rolled into my blankets I slept soundly.

On the morning of 26 November we moved south to the supply dump. Here we refilled with the food, water, ammunition and petrol which we had not had for two days. Here, too, we received the first major reinforcements. The regiment was made up to a total of forty tanks, and the other remaining original regiment of the Brigade to about the same number. I heard for the first time of the grave losses which both 7th and 22nd Armoured Brigades had suffered. The former, I was told, had been withdrawn to Base to re-equip, leaving only a few tanks and crews to help make up the third regiment of our Brigade, who were to refit as quickly as possible and rejoin us.

In the afternoon we moved twenty-five miles north, where we leaguered for the night. There was an air of optimism about, engendered partly by the survival and recovery from the unforeseen lunge by the German tanks and partly by the estimate of enemy tank losses put out by 8th Army. The Germans were said to have only sixty left, and those were short of ammunition and fuel.

We were all able to relax for the first time since the offensive started. No one knew precisely where or when the German armour would reappear, so orders for the morning were merely that we should disperse and wait for instructions. I had a few worries as to the safety of the leaguer to occupy me; the crews had already been reorganized that morning and there was nothing more to be done. I determined to sleep early. I had noticed an increasing irritability in myself in the last few days, an inability to relax or see things calmly. This did not worry me so much as the thought of what the next symptom of tension might be. So far my judgement was not noticeably impaired, but there was no knowing whether it would not soon be affected, too, by an increasing nervous disorder. Sleep, I felt, was the main cure – sleep and some rest from worry and the exhaustion of constant battles. But sleep so earnestly desired did not come quickly, nor was it always complete.

I knew I was more morose and unapproachable than I had ever been. I had caught the surprised look in the eyes of my troop leaders when I had made an abrupt remark. They did not expect it of me, and must have supposed that I was growing hard and restless under the stress of the daily battles and the mounting losses of men and tanks. This estimate could not have been farther from the truth. The thing that worried me more than anything else was the realization that I had a growing morbid anxiety about the safety of Peters, Drummond and Sergeant Storney. It was as if, having lost so many men, these – the three I knew best of the survivors – had grown peculiarly valuable. To me their death or loss loomed now as an irreparable disaster. During each action I watched anxiously to see that they came to no harm, and after each battle I took exceptional steps to find out if any harm had come to them.

The following morning was shrouded with thick mist, which gradually dispersed as the sun mounted. There was a threat of hidden danger behind the thick white blanket. For all we knew, the last Panzer Divisions might have moved overnight. But when the mist cleared there were no signs of the enemy, and breakfast and the first wash for almost a week took up the rest of the morning. We all began to feel more human again, and when one of the ammunition lorry drivers produced a football out of his cab, there were two almost complete sides playing before I had shaved.

At noon the growing activity round Kinnaird's tank attracted my attention, so I walked over to discover what it was all about.

'Hello, Tony,' Kinnaird greeted me. 'How did you know anything was up?'

'I didn't,' I answered. 'But is there? I wondered if there was when I saw you grab the head-phones.'

'Well, as a matter of fact Brigade have just given out the latest aircraft tac R. report, and have told everyone to stand by for a move. The Panzer Divs. have turned west and are moving now along the Trigh Capuzzo. It's a pound to a pinch of snuff we shall be told to intercept or they will get behind the New Zealanders without any hindrance. You'd better go back to your tank. We'll be getting orders any moment now, I expect.'

Before I had reached my tank I saw my operator grab the headphones and wave frantically to me. I broke into a run and clambered on to the turret as Kinnaird finished his orders. My operator acknowledged and turned to me saying, 'Orders, sir. Move now on a bearing of four eight degrees. Enemy armoured column reported moving west along the Trigh Capuzzo.'

By this time it was a day of brilliant sunshine. Well fed, washed and shaved, I felt better equipped to go into battle once again. But it seemed incongruous that I should be required to do so on a day when so many other things had hinted of more pleasant times.

I knew that the Trigh Capuzzo was twenty-five miles away – a good two hours' marching time. I settled myself more comfortably in the turret, adjusted my goggles and balaclava to exclude every possible whisper of wind, braced myself in my sling-seat and said to the driver, 'You can see the general direction – pick your own route to avoid the worst bumps.'

For an hour we moved at good speed, with only the wheezing and crackling in the otherwise silent head-phones to keep the commanders awake and alert. Then, as we crossed to the northern edge of a ridge of high ground, Peters reported excitedly, 'Hello, Tony; Tony One calling. Enemy column of vehicles moving west about figures seven zero zero yards to my left front. There are no tanks, I say again no tanks. Now's our chance. Shall I move to engage? Over.'

'Hello, Tony One; Tony answering,' I replied. 'Wait until I join you. Don't expose yourself meanwhile. Now I see them. They don't seem to know we are here. Off to you. Hello, all stations, Tony; conform to me. Off to you. Hello, Peter; Tony calling. Am engaging enemy column of figures two five lorries. Over.'

'Hello, Tony; Peter answering,' Kinnaird immediately replied. 'You will not engage – I say again you will not engage. Return to your original position. Over.'

I was aghast, and for an instant entirely undecided what I should do. Then I leant down into the turret and shouted to the operator, 'Don't answer. We'll pretend we didn't hear.'

Again Kinnaird called: 'Hello, Tony; hello, Tony. Peter calling – return to me now – do not engage. Over.'

Still I did not answer, and followed in the wake of my three troops who by now had almost closed the distance to the enemy. In front of me I noticed three or four lorries detach themselves from the southern edge of the column, and saw that they were towing anti-tank guns. Unable to use my wireless without giving away my deception of not having heard Kinnaird's order, I could only use my arms to convey to the troop leaders what I wanted them to do. Peters and Drummond I waved on to the south of the column, hoping they would understand my signals to get into line ahead. Sergeant Storney's troop I waved round to the north, indicating that he was to fall behind a bit, so as to be out of the line of fire of the other two troops. With relief I saw my orders obeyed, and at the same moment heard the stutter of Peter's machine-gun as he opened fire on the first of the anti-tank gun crews.

Simultaneously Kinnaird called again, 'Hello, any station Tony; acknowledge and return to me. Over.'

Peters answered, 'Hello, Peter; Tony One answering. Am now engaging enemy, who are entirely unprepared. Cannot withdraw at present. Will return as soon as possible. Off.'

In five minutes the action was over. All but one of the lorries were burning or crippled, and the entire crew of the four anti-tank guns killed or wounded round their guns. The remaining Germans had fled into any place of hiding they could find. One lorry escaped to the west, and we last saw it bumping and careering over the rough ground at a mad pace.

I circled my arm over my head as the signal to withdraw, and waved to each troop leader as he passed me. Peters pointed inquiringly at his head and microphone and threw his head back with a roar of laughter when I raised my hands despondently, a picture of innocence, to indicate that I didn't know what was wrong.

Ten minutes later we rejoined the regiment and moved into our correct position. I thought the moment was opportune to report and said:

'Hello, Peter; Tony calling. We destroyed about figures two five lorries and four anti-tank guns. My set now appears to be O.K., but went dis. for a bit. Over.'

197

'Hello, Tony; Peter answering,' Kinnaird replied slowly and with unusual emphasis. 'Don't go off like that again without my permission. Our orders are to get to the main enemy without delay and without diversions. Most extraordinary about your set. I hope it doesn't happen again, or you'd better get a new operator. Off.'

I grinned guiltily at my operator, who grinned broadly back at me.

Soon afterwards we met the main body of the German Panzer Divisions and an inconclusive battle continued to last light – serving at least to delay the enemy move to the west.

Throughout the next three days we fought along the Trigh Capuzzo, gradually moving farther and farther west. Each day we were encouraged in leaguer at night by the news that the Germans had lost large numbers of tanks, and on each following day they appeared with not less than sixty or seventy again. Kinnaird passed his driver's disgusted comment on to Brigade: 'Hell, they must 'ave a bloody tank breeding ground somewhere.' Thereafter we received fewer optimistic reports of the enemy casualties, which caused us satisfaction for two reasons: first, that we were no longer daily disillusioned, and, second, that we hoped that the higher headquarters were now making more realistic appreciations of the enemy.

Each day's fighting took a mounting toll in killed and wounded. New tanks and new crews arrived and were lost almost before the men were known by name. With growing dismay I wondered how much longer the old members of my squadron would last. As each night we saw them again in leaguer I began to hope that their skill and experience would keep them always out of trouble. Some, though still alive and unwounded, were reaching almost the end of their reserves and nervous courage. They were irritable and jumpy, slow to obey orders and lagging always a little behind the battle-line when action was joined. Clayton was one of these, and daily I saw further confirmation of the doubts I had first had during the early days of fighting.

On 30 November the fighting took us over the scene of the battles of Sidi Rezegh. There was a brooding air of death over the whole area. I found it a grimly nerve-racking experience to be in position all day beside a crippled tank with the dead crew lying

198

round it. At midday, when I knew the haze hid me from the enemy, I walked over to see who the crew were. They were too far decayed to be recognizable, and it was only as I turned away that I noticed a few letters of the officer's name on his bedroll. I read – ESH – and instantly, like a crossword expert, the letters fell into place. I felt certain, with growing horror, that it was CHESHAM. I cut the bedroll loose, and as it fell to the ground, displaying the full name, my fears were realized. I searched more closely, and found Chesham at last, with no clearly visible sign of the cause of death. I and my driver buried the crew. I kept Chesham's few valuable belongings – his watch, his lighter and cigarette case – to give to Angela when I next saw her. The thought of the interview appalled me.

In the afternoon we moved farther west, and I found myself among the broken lines of the 5th South African Brigade position. Here, where the carnage was more concentrated, I became more aware of the dry, musty smell of death and ash which I had first noticed in the morning and had failed to define.

At last the light faded and the moment for which each day I longed more came for us to move back into leaguer and to sleep.

Before dawn I was woken by the duty operator who slept each night at Regimental H.Q. It was the time I disliked most each day. Only in sleep could I escape the tensions and responsibilities of command and renew the depleted and hard-tried stocks of nervous energy.

'Orders, sir, in a few minutes. The C.O. wants you at his tank. I've told him I'm fetching you, sir.'

'All right,' I mumbled sleepily as I reluctantly left the warmth of my blankets and dragged on my boots and overcoat. I was awake and alert, though, when a few minutes later I stood by Kinnaird's tank and listened to his news.

'Our battles during the last few days have been fought to prevent the Germans from severing the junction made by the New Zealand Division with the garrison of Tobruk. During the last two days the New Zealanders have been under continuous and intense attack. To relieve them the 1st South African Brigade were to attack during last night in an effort to join them. This attack has failed – in fact the South Africans have been counter-attacked and driven back. It is now clear that few, if any, units of the New Zealanders remain as formed bodies. We are to move at first light to rescue as many of them as we can. Go back to your tanks and wait till my next orders.'

At daybreak, in concert with the rest of the Brigade, Kinnaird ordered, ' ... Advance now to a point on the escarpment just east of Sidi Rezegh. From there we will move north and rescue as many men as we can find there.'

Under fire from the two flanking escarpments to the north and south, both still held by the enemy, we moved up the valley until we were placed between the bulk of the New Zealand Division and the German tanks. Behind us, the survivors, the wounded, the lost were rescued and taken to safety. Throughout the morning and early afternoon our vigil lasted, made bearable only by the knowledge that many valuable men and lives were being saved. It was an oppressive scene, blanketed with smoke and dust, and scarred with dead men and destroyed equipment. When we withdrew finally, each tank carried a quota of the last handful of men who were the rearguard. They were marvellously grateful and showered us with praise and thanks. We liked their grim, business-like attitude to war and felt that our troubles of the day had been well worth while.

In the clear, sunlit afternoon we moved twenty miles south and leaguered in peace.

7

Followed into Leaguer

HERE we stayed for two days, sleeping and eating and, in the intervals, repairing the tanks and cleaning ourselves. A wash and a change of underclothes worked wonders.

In the meantime the armoured cars had established that there were enemy positions on a line south of El Adem to Bir Gubi which blocked our further advance to the west. So, while the 4th Indian Division attacked Gubi itself, for five days we watched the desert to the north, to protect the flank of the Indian attack and if possible to intercept any reinforcements moving south from El Adem.

It was an exhausting battle. At dawn each day we moved out to make contact again with the enemy, and throughout each day we fought a duel of nerves and stratagems against their anti-tank guns backed by tanks. For the more pressure we could exert the easier would be the task of the Indian Division at Gubi.

The endless tension and strain took their toll of all of us. Kinnaird, on whom the major responsibility rested each day, now showed clear signs of the ravages of the stress of battle. Even in the brief space of a fortnight his hair had grown perceptibly greyer. The lines round his eyes and mouth were etched deep, accentuated by the dust and dirt which covered his face and the daily longer stubble of his beard. His eyes were red-rimmed, the usual alertness dimmed and their normal calm scrutiny replaced by a nervous, tense, darting look which was so completely out of character that I was aghast at the change.

On the air his orders were still as precise and firm, his voice still edged with authority and decision, though there was more than a hint of utter weariness. But it was his appearance that gave us all cause for anxiety on his behalf, though we were all changed in some degree or respect.

My anxiety for Kinnaird gradually changed into a fellow feeling for all who had survived the holocaust of the first weeks. For Kinnaird, Peters, Drummond, Sergeant Storney, my crew and the many others who had been through the worst days, I felt a close bond in which none of the more recent arrivals could be admitted.

In the main we were all silent and morose, withdrawn, tired, dejected. I had reached the lowest ebb of my endurance and felt that anything would break my self-control.

The disturbed nights, the useless and endless slaughter, the mounting level of exhaustion continued day after day. It was during this time that one of our nights was disturbed in a very unusual way.

All through the day our duel south and west of Gubi had continued. Behind the screen of their anti-tank guns the German tanks refused to give battle. We did all we could to lure them out, but with little success.

At last light, with the low sun behind them blinding our eyes, the Germans launched a strong attack. Until the light had completely gone the battle continued, neither side sure of the targets at which they were shooting. Gradually the firing died away. An occasional flash of a gun or the thin stream of tracer bullets showed that a tank here and there was still alert and ready to fire. The remainder of us were trying to rally to return to leaguer to replenish, to eat and to sleep.

Peering into the night, I was trying to locate all my outlying tanks and to guide them on to me. No directions seemed to be of any avail, so at last in desperation I called, 'Hello, all stations Tony; Toffee apple going up in figures three. Off.'

I bent to my gunner and shouted, 'Give me the Bren and one tracer, Rogers.' I loaded the gun carefully and, pointing it straight upwards, waited till my watch showed that the appointed time had passed. Then I fired, and the flash seemed to illuminate the desert for yards round me.

All my tanks saw the signal, and soon they were gathered behind me in line ahead ready to follow to the rendezvous with Kinnaird. I congratulated myself as we moved off that I was no longer required to be anywhere but in the lead, where there were no fumes nor dust to clog my eyes and nose and to cake my mouth.

We had been moving for a few minutes when a voice which I recognized as that of Drummond called, 'Hello, Tony. Don't look now, but I think we're being followed. When we moved off I was the last in line, and now there's somebody behind me. I can't make out who it is, but I think it's a Mark Three. Over.'

'Hello, Tony Two,' I answered. 'Are you quite sure, or are you trying to be funny? If so, I'm not amused. This is no time for fun and games. Over.'

'Hello, Tony. No, I'm not trying to be funny,' he answered. 'I can't see yet what it is behind me, and if I'm too inquisitive and give the show away and it is a Mark Three and they decide to do something – well, that'll be that if you see what I mean – as far as I'm concerned, anyhow. Over.'

'Hello, Tony Two. O.K. Off to you. We'll have a call over to make sure who is where. All stations Tony will report where they are in the column, starting with whoever is behind me and working backwards. Over.'

When this was completed it still showed that Drummond should have been the last in the column, and yet he still confidently asserted that he was being followed. Kinnaird now took a hand.

'Hello Tony; Peter calling. I've heard what's been going on. Move on now as if nothing has happened. As soon as I can hear you we will join in on your flank and deal with the last one in your column, and let's hope it's a Jerry, and not just some bloody fool whose wireless set is not working. Over.'

I acknowledged, and moved steadily on the bearing which would bring us to Kinnaird. Each minute seemed an age. Though I was safe enough, my thoughts were constantly with Drummond and the suddenness and violence of his fate if the German tank commander awoke to the situation. Drummond reported at frequent intervals, 'Hello, Tony. Still being followed. I'm practically certain it's a Jerry. A light went on a moment ago in the turret and I caught a glimpse inside. Over.' And later he said, 'Hello, Tony. This is getting a bit much. Any sign of help yet? I feel I'm on a powder barrel which might go up. Over.'

Ten minutes passed in this way and still no message from Kinnaird that he had heard our movement. At last he said, 'Hello, Tony; Peter calling. I can hear you now. You're just passing us on my right. Go as you are, and we'll close in on you. Off.'

The minutes ticked by, and I peered into the night on my left to see if I could make out the shapes of any approaching tanks. The strain was beginning to tell on us all now, except apparently Kinnaird. His voice on the air was almost jaunty, and he kept repeating, 'We'll soon be ready to get this one. He must not get away. If we can't get them by day we'll get 'em by night.' Later he added, 'We'll have to work out the details carefully, or there will be an accident. Tony, shine a light – not too bright – out to your left. When I see this I'll know I'm level with you, and the tail of the column will be ready to cope. Hello, Tony Two. When I give the word you will also shine a light – as bright as you like – to your left. On that signal we'll fire just behind you, and hope we hit whatever is there. Off.'

I continued to move forward, and except for the knowledge that there would soon be battle, I might have been deluded into thinking that I was moving quietly into leaguer, enjoying the moments of the day which were always the most pleasant, coloured as they were by the thoughts of food, companionship, and sleep.

'Hello, all stations Peter,' Kinnaird called. 'I can now see

Tony's light. When I give Tony Two the word to light up, the last six in my column will open fire behind him. If there is any sign of anything being hit, they will halt and engage. If not, they will continue to move with us. There must be no indiscriminate shooting. Right. Stand by now. Hello, Tony Two. Light up. Off.'

I twisted myself round in the cupola the better to see behind me. As I did the darkness to my left was studded with the flash of guns and I could feel the concussion of the explosions. Perhaps ten shots had been fired when behind the tail of my column the night was lit by a brilliant flash, and flames showed up the outlines of what was clearly a German Mark III. Ammunition and fuel were burning fiercely, sparks flying in all directions, and I could clearly hear the thin crackle of the exploding machine-gun rounds. I wondered what had happened to the crew and whether any had escaped or would escape. Their chances of survival were getting smaller each moment. Kinnaird had stopped any further shooting, and our columns had moved on for about a quarter of a mile when the German tank finally blew up. The flames and black smoke seemed to hesitate for a moment. Then, at the base of the turret, there suddenly appeared what seemed to be a ball of fire, intensely hot and brilliant. I stared as with uncanny deliberation this ball rose, slowly expanding as it lifted the turret and shattered the sides of the tank. Up and up, out and out the flames spread – showering the desert for yards around with sparks and burning fragments and reaching higher and higher into the night sky. The whole desert was lit with the brilliant light, so that each tank was plainly visible, still moving steadily away from the fire. As suddenly as they had flared up, the flames died away, leaving only a pall of black smoke lit by the sputtering remains of the tank and the burning fragments which strewed the desert in all directions.

Awed into silence by the vividness of the sudden disaster which had overtaken the German, we moved on into leaguer. Many times we had seen tanks go up in flames and explode, but somehow there had been little of the fury and terror we had just witnessed when the same thing happened by day and was seen at a longer range.

Trials and Tribulations

I AWOKE the next morning feeling tensed almost to breaking point. My head ached, my eyes hurt and each and every action of my crew jarred my overwrought nerves. I noticed with sadistic bitterness the effect of my sharp words on them. They were no less exhausted. The realization of this fact influenced me not at all. I was in no mood or condition to concern myself with the welfare of others. It was only by the greatest effort that I was keeping myself under control. I could only stand my fellow men if they stayed clear of me and my frayed nerves. Neither Peters nor Drummond, searching for the consolation and encouragement which I should have been able to give them, was able to extract more than surly word or two from me. They also were worn and exhausted and unwilling to spend any of their slender reserves on reviving me. Kinnaird, too, had only a shadow of the inspiration which he normally displayed and no energy to exert himself to give encouragement. This was the inevitable result of endless days of fighting at the high tempo of armoured operations. There was bound to come a time when the human frame could stand no more without cracking. Mentally and physically we had been reduced to a condition where we all hovered on the edge of breaking point, and only the determination not to break kept us in battle. It was often so easy to be brave for a short time, but so difficult to produce the same level of courage for days on end.

I watched while my driver turned over the engine with the starting-handle to avoid any chance of damage by a hydrostatic lock to the bottom cylinder of the radial engine, listened to the tick-tick of the ratchet, which sounded like the winding of an enormous clock, saw the driver stow the handle and check the stowage of the bedding, and together we climbed into our places in the tank.

Once in the cupola I bent to find my headset and microphone and to adjust the setting of my sling-seat. As I bent down, the cupola lid, which I had carelessly propped only half open, fell with a sickening crash on to the finger-tips of my right hand. Weakened with exhaustion, and with nerves frayed to almost breaking point, the stinging agony of the pain took my breath away completely. Furious at my own stupidity and the pain, I cursed and swore against my crew. I beat the turret in impotent rage until the fury of my blows made my unhurt hand sore and bruised. Gradually my anger subsided, and shamefacedly I sucked the tips of my bruised fingers, the numbness of which was beginning to wear off, giving place to a dull, deep throb of pain.

This was a bad enough beginning to the day, which had further trials and tribulations in store. The enemy had moved north-west from his positions of the previous day and had to be found and exactly located anew. Throughout the morning and afternoon we were switched from point to point in search of a flank or gap. There was no time for food except for cold bully and biscuits, which were impregnated with petrol. There was no pause for rest, no period when we could relax the constant alertness. Prodded by Brigade, who had been told to expect a general enemy withdrawal, Kinnaird was relentless and inexhaustible. He seemed to have gained a new supply of energy and determination.

At midday another incident occurred which was a further test of my exhausted condition. In the course of our energetic search for a weakness in the German defences, my squadron came across a small group of dejected Italians who had been hiding among an outcrop of rocks. Once flushed by the leading tanks they were directed back towards my headquarters. There were fourteen of these men, bedraggled, weary and apprehensive, yet with an air of hope that perhaps their troubles were nearly at an end. When they were no more than thirty yards from my tank, I was startled and horrified by the sudden chatter of my machine-gun. Dazed with incredulous surprise, I watched the Italians collapse one by one under the hail of bullets, to lie writhing or starkly still. The first ingratiating grins were wiped ludicrously from their faces, which were now twisted in agony. It was over before I could move to stop the slaughter. Sickened and furious, I bent to Rogers, my gunner, who was sitting, collapsed at my feet, his head in his hands.

'Why the bloody hell did you do that, you silly bastard?' I yelled at him.

He stared vacantly back at me and answered slowly, 'They killed me Mum and Dad with a bomb. They deserved it.'

'They didn't do anything of the sort, you fool,' I answered sharply. 'In any case, these were Ities – couldn't you see?'

'Ities or Jerries, it's just the same – they're as bad as each other. They didn't have to kill me Mum and Dad. They wasn't doing nobody any 'arm. I'm glad I killed 'em, sir. It's done me good. Do what you like, sir.'

My cold anger was only increased by the knowledge that there was nothing I could do, so I said instead, 'Get out and see if there's any way you can help them.' I sat in the turret and watched while the driver and gunner searched among the bodies for any signs of life. There were none, and when we moved on the array of corpses was left as grim evidence of the state of our nerves. We hardly talked to each other for the rest of the day, and I frequently caught myself looking in wonder at Rogers or intercepting the puzzled glances of the other two crew members.

Late in the evening, when there was only a short period left of battle light, my tank was halted temporarily next to an abandoned Italian M13. Loot, such as we had found in the first campaign, had so far not come our way. The sight of the well-known outlines of the M13 revived memories of the past, and I jumped to the ground and clambered on to the derelict tank. It was discoloured but otherwise appeared to have suffered little damage, and the cupola lid lifted easily when I prised it open. For a moment the sight that met my eyes held me transfixed. Then I dropped the lid and jumped hurriedly to the ground. The interior of the tank was blackened and scorched with flame and, peering upwards, as if waiting for salvation, was all that remained of the head of the tank commander, the black recesses of the empty eye-sockets staring malevolently upwards, the white teeth, bared by the lips, which had been burnt away, grinning hideously at me. Trembling with the shock of the surprise, I threw myself into my turret and moved the tank hurriedly away. All that night my sleep was made fitful by the memory of the ghastly sight.

On the following morning, when we were all set for another day of our duel with the enemy dug-in positions, the armoured cars reported soon after first light that the positions were deserted, and that they had made no contact. I, for one, breathed a sigh of relief and felt calmer at the mere knowledge that the inevitable battle had been postponed for a few hours. We prepared breakfast and ate it peacefully and leisurely, while the sun grew hotter and hotter as it rose, and sanity and a tinge of cheerfulness crept back into the marrow of our bones. I walked over to Kinnaird's tank for a talk, in the hope that his determination would revive my spirits even further. But Kinnaird was asleep and the Adjutant busy bringing his lists of killed and wounded up to date. I felt no inclination to watch or help in this morbid task, and returned to my tank, where throughout the rest of the morning I dozed and slept fitfully.

At about midday Kinnaird warned us that we were to move in half an hour's time against new enemy positions which had been located by the armoured cars some twenty miles to the north-west. We took the chance to prepare a meal. Rested, fed and refreshed by a quick wash, I felt almost my normal self and ready, if not willing, for whatever lay in store.

The fast, uneventful move north-west, the refuelling halt during which we managed a 'brew', were further stimulants to all. When at last the enemy tanks were seen and we manoeuvred to discover their exact positions, there was a zest and energy about the movements which had been lacking for some days. The Germans, caught without a defensive screen of anti-tank guns, were unwilling to give battle, and slowly withdrew, until at length we realized that they were falling back on to anti-tank defences being hurriedly prepared farther back. It was fruitless to attempt any further advance. We halted, leaving the gun battery to continue the duel so far as they were able.

Meanwhile behind us the Indian Division moved north to El Adem. Late in the afternoon their leading elements were counter-attacked by German tanks. We were promptly ordered north to engage this threat.

As the light was fading and while the Germans had the considerable advantage of the low sun behind them, hiding their movements and spotlighting our tanks, I swung my squadron through ninety degrees from the line of advance north to face west. On each side of us Kinnaird ranged the other two squadrons. Behind this battle line the other regiment of the Brigade continued to move north and then swung back into position on our right. In the fading light and the glare of the low sun the battle was confused. Using their favourable position, the German tanks became more aggressive than they had been recently and the battle grew in intensity as the range closed. To my left I saw one of my squadron go up in flames, but I was myself too closely engaged to give it more than a moment's thought. To my front the German tanks had moved to within 800 yards, and I knew that any strike at that range by their 50-mm. guns was liable to be fatal.

Kinnaird was well aware of the pressure being exerted against us and of our chances of successful resistance, and had already asked Brigade whether he could withdraw to positions which were more favourable. The Indians, however, had not yet moved clear of the threat, and so Kinnaird was told we would have to stay where we were.

Closer and closer the German tanks came, and miraculously our line held. Again, somehow, the enemy had been able to muster almost fifty tanks. Against the inferior armour and gun-power of our only slightly more numerous Honeys it was almost enough to give victory.

I was by now forced to watch my supply of ammunition care-fully, and warned my squadron to do likewise. There would be no time to arrange any sort of gradual refill before darkness fell, but equally there was still some fifteen minutes before it would become so dark that the Germans could be expected to call off the battle. They too, however, were probably suffering the same difficulties, so that it was only as the last vestige of fighting light lingered that they launched another determined assault. It was too late to carry them far, but this last fling gave them isolated successes here and there.

Suddenly my own tank was struck twice on the front, without apparent serious damage, until I ordered the driver to reverse slowly to confuse the Germans by an alteration of range. Then the grinding and crunching of metal along the side of the tank showed that the track had been hit and distorted.

At the instant that I realized that we were immobilized Kinnaird ordered, 'Hello, all stations Peter; Peter calling, with-draw now. Do not wait and invite further casualties. Withdraw out of range, and in figures five, when it is dark, we will rally. Over.'

Before I could acknowledge in my turn, the tank was hit again and penetrated. The shot entered the lower part of the front plate of the turret on the loader's side, missed Turner, the loader, by inches and crashed into the wireless set, which was left a tangled mass of broken valves and wiring.

Perched in the cupola, intent on the enemy and the need to tell Kinnaird of the state to which my tank had been reduced, I was not immediately aware of what had happened in the turret. Only when I heard no side-tone in my ear-phones did I realize that something was wrong. When I heard no other acknowledgements of Kinnaird's orders, I bent to shout at Turner, 'What the hell's happened? My mike is dis.,' and was surprised and startled at the reply:

'Shot 'it the set, sir, and proper mucked it up. Not a 'ope of mending it.'

This was indeed disaster. A crippled tank, no wireless, the squadron out of sight and the Germans so close as to be still visible. My heart sank at the apparent hopelessness of the situation.

9

Crippled and Deserted

I SAT upright and scanned the scene around us. To our front the German tanks were halted and silent, their dark, menacing shapes silhouetted by the crimson backdrop of the last minutes of daylight which clung to the western horizon. On each side of us the ground was deserted. Ordered to withdraw while still in contact with the enemy, the tank commanders of my squadron had been too intent on their own battles to notice that I had not moved with them. Behind us the sky was already so dark that it effectively hid our tanks, though they were probably by now rallied in squadron columns. A further glance round the whole area surrounding my tank confirmed that we were alone, with only the enemy still just visible a few hundred yards away. I could only hope that the darkness hid our presence and that the last rays of the sun did not glint on any surface of the tank.

A sombre, deathly silence had now settled on the battlefield. With the wireless stilled, the quiet was so intense that it seemed to press on the eardrums. When I spoke I did so quite naturally in a whisper, and equally naturally I was answered in hoarse whispers by the crew.

'We've been left behind – I could hear our tanks moving away not long ago, but they've gone too far now for us to contact them. I don't fancy a walk at night, so we'll have to stay here. We'll probably be picked up in the morning.'

'As long as we don't get picked up by them bloody Jerries, I'm cushy,' Rogers replied.

'Same 'ere,' added Norton, the driver. 'Let's have a bloody good feed. I got some cheese and marmalade off the quarter-bloke yesterday. What do you say, sir?'

I was busy turning over in my mind the various courses of action open to us and answered absently, 'O.K. – we can't do anything else, so let's eat.'

While the food was being prepared I continued to ruminate on our predicament and the various courses of action we could take. We could remain in the tank all night and hope to be rescued at dawn. But this entailed the risk of being found first by the Germans or of not being found at all. We could work on the damage during the night, move away from the immediate vicinity of the German leaguers, and be ready to move to join any friendly forces who passed near us the next day. But this would mean a risk of attracting enemy attention during the repairs, and we could not be sure of meeting friends the next day before we ran out of fuel or broke down again if the repair was not complete. Then I remembered that we had not yet seen the extent of the damage and could not therefore decide whether this last plan was feasible. If only, I thought, the wireless was still working. Then we could tell Kinnaird of what had happened and might even have help sent to us. However, it was of no use hoping for the impossible. I would have to face the fact that I had to make my own decision, but I was in no mood to make up my mind there and then.

I welcomed Rogers' hoarse whisper, "Ere you are, sir. Nice tasty meal. Bit of a change from bully.'

I ducked down into the close, warm confines of the turret, blinked as the petrol, oil and cordite-fume-laden air stung my eyes, peered round in the dim light of the shaded torch and took the bulky sandwich being offered to me. I could feel the eyes of the crew upon me, trusting, honest and faithful, but expecting me

211

to have a plan, to have reached a decision about our actions. Guiltily aware that I had not, I took refuge in eating the sandwich, stuffing my mouth so full that no word could be expected of me. We all ate in silence for some minutes until Norton suddenly said in an exaggerated whisper:

'Reckon we ought to clear off from 'ere, sir. 'Tain't 'ealthy, with all them Jerries so close. I reckon we won't take long to fix the track. We've a couple of spare links. With them in we'll be as right as rain.'

I saw that really this was our only chance and answered, 'Yes; good idea. We'll finish our food, and then we'll have a look at the damage. If we can mend it we will, and then move off a couple of miles to get out of the way.'

We finished the food in silence, washed down the crumbs with the water remaining in the water-bottles, and then Norton, Turner and I climbed to the ground, leaving Rogers in the cupola on guard against any enemy. By the light of a carefully shaded torch we examined the damage. Two track-links and the connecting pin had been broken and twisted out of all recognition. The jagged end had been carried forward and upward over the sprocket until they had bent and twisted and become embedded in the sand-shields, so that there was a mass of jagged iron which looked hopelessly tangled. In silence the three of us surveyed the wreckage.

Turner at last broke the silence, 'God! what a mess,' and turning to Norton he added, 'Any chance of sorting that lot out, Bert?' There was a silence while Norton examined the damage more carefully, then he straightened, pushing his beret farther back on his head with the back of his hand. I wished I could see his face, to gauge from his expression his actual thoughts, for his voice was flat and non-committal.

'Reckon we've a chance, sir; but there'll be a bloody lot of noise. Will that matter?'

'It won't have to,' I answered briefly and added, 'Come on, let's get to work.'

For a time we worked in silence, except for the involuntary grunts and gasps as we exerted all our energy to disentangle the mess. But to no avail. We took it in turns to hold the torch while two did the work, and after a time I put Turner on guard, in the hope that the fresh energy of Rogers would do the trick. It became clear that the metal was too twisted and tangled for us to be able to achieve any result with the limited tools at our disposal. A mood of desperation seized us all and we worked with a frenzy of energy, exhausting ourselves in the hopeless task. All the time, too, there was the anxious thought that the enemy might be creeping nearer to us in the surrounding darkness.

At last I stood back, wiped away the sweat on my face with my sleeve and said, 'There's only one thing to do. We'll have to start up and move the tank forward a yard until the broken track is pulled away from the sand-shields. It's our only hope. If we are quick the engine needn't run more than fifteen seconds. It's our only chance. Agree?'

There was a mumble from Norton and Rogers, which I accepted, if not as agreement, certainly as showing no sign of violent disagreement. 'O.K. Hop in, and when I give the word, start up and move forward – as soon as I stop you, switch off again, and after that we'd better all keep bloody quiet for a bit.'

It was the work of half a minute. When the roar of the engine had died away again there was a deathly silence. I felt sure that the engine and the rending crash of tearing metal must have been heard for miles. In the distance, at a range I found impossible to estimate, two white Very lights soared lethargically into the sky. Closer at hand I thought I heard the crackle of camel-thorn, being trodden down, and every nerve in my body tensed for the shock of sudden discovery or of being fired on. For minutes afterwards I imagined new sounds all round in the darkness. I could picture dark, stealthy shadows stalking ever closer to us. Slowly we relaxed.

The tense silence was at last broken by Rogers saying, 'Think it's O.K., sir? I don't reckon anyone heard us. We'll 'ave it done in a jiffy now, sir.'

A few expert blows with the pin and sledgehammer and one track-pin shot out of its position and landed with a tinkle of metal on the pebbles beneath the tank. The other track-pin was more obstinate. Bent by the distortion of the two broken links, it had become firmly wedged in its position, and no amount of hammering or coaxing would dislodge it. By now I was more than a little concerned about the sustained level of noise which we were

213

inevitably making. I felt that a spasmodic disturbance with intervals of silence was less likely to attract attention than the continuous clatter which any work on the tracks entailed. The periods of rest were only of physical relaxation, as during these moments my nerves and mind were tensely aware of the risks and dangers we courted. The noise we made and the light we used, however carefully screened, made us sitting targets for any wandering enemy patrol. For the man on guard in the turret – a duty which we took it in turn to perform – the nervous strain was increased. Divorced from the close struggle with the track and its pins, he was a prey to every sort of terror and trick of the imagination. Shapes which had been marked as bushes or clumps of camel-thorn seemed suddenly to have moved or disappeared. New shapes or shadows appeared momentarily where none had been before. The light of the stars, appearing fitfully through scudding clouds, created all sorts of phantoms.

At length, exhausted and covered in sweat, we stopped work on the track, and for a time sat in silence. I was weary with physical exertion and the mental strain of the long hours of responsibility, extended by now beyond the normal daily limits to which my mind and body had become accustomed. The struggle seemed hopeless, and only the thought that there was no alternative course of action stopped me from admitting defeat and suggesting a policy of inaction and a trust that all would turn out well with the first light of day. Norton's voice, when he at last spoke, contained a note of thoughtful hope which immediately roused both Rogers and I:

'There's one thing we could do, sir. These are new tracks, an' I expect there's a link to spare on the other side. We could take that an' dump this 'ere one with the bent pin. What d'you say, sir?'

The solution seemed so simple and obvious that for a few moments I remained silent, afraid that there was some snag, hidden temporarily but so insurmountable that our growing hopes would again be dashed. At last I said:

'Can't see any snags. Let's get going.'

First we disposed of the offending link which had caused us so much trouble. It was exasperating that, separated by only a few inches, the next track-pin should move so easily. I cursed myself inwardly that so simple a solution had not occurred to me earlier.

Next we loosened the idler wheel adjustment, which gave more slack to the track, removed the necessary track-plate from the right track, and then reconnected the broken ends. With the spare plate the damaged left-hand track was itself soon mended. It was with a considerable sigh of relief that I helped to stow away the tools and with the shaded torch to make a last inspection of each track to be sure that all was secure. Behind me I thought that I could already see a faint lightening of the sky in the east, the first hint of another day of battle already drawing upon us after a night of no rest or sleep. It was a groundless apprehension, though, as I proved by a quick glance at my watch. Though our struggle had seemed endless, in fact there were still three hours of night left to us.

'O.K. Start up and swing round wide to your right,' I said. 'We don't want the bloody track to break again, by making too tight a turn.'

When we had moved in a wide semicircle and I had picked out the star on which I had already determined to set our course, we drove on at a steady speed, gradually putting more and more safe distance between us and the enemy leaguers marked intermittently by coloured flares and lights.

After half an hour we halted. To Norton, who had worked without relief and had had the added strain of our recent march, however short, I gave the privilege of an uninterrupted sleep during what remained of the night. The guard duties I then divided among the three of us, putting myself last, both because I felt that every nerve in my body was clamouring for rest, and also because I wanted to be on duty at daylight to meet whatever alarms or crises might occur.

10

False Alarm

IN contrast to my dark mood of the previous night, the first rays of the sun glistening on the dew-covered pebbles and scrub gave me new life and hope. The tensions and anxieties of the night were forgotten and I was revived despite the length of the previous day's trials and the lack of sleep. The new day seemed to hold some sort of promise, an indefinable hope of better times to come. I dismissed these ideas as stupid in view of the fact that we were still alone and had no idea where the Regiment had gone.

As soon as the light was sufficient to give adequate visibility to ensure that we were not surprised, we moved off due east. For a time complete emptiness around us caused me some disquiet. At length, to the north-east, I detected a plume of dust, lit by the low rays of the sun so that it hung like a golden cloud in the sky. This could only be made by a fair-sized force on the move. We changed direction to meet it. Ten minutes later, after being challenged by the flank screen of the Brigade, I was moving behind and slightly to the left of the Brigade H.Q. A.C.V. Here I stayed until at last the whole force came to a halt and I was directed to the north-west, where the Regiment was in position looking north towards the perimeter of Tobruk.

Kinnaird greeted me with barely concealed signs of emotion, 'Tony, I am glad to see you. When we got no answer from you, I really thought you'd had it. Thank God you're all right. We've been through too much for you to come to any harm at this stage. Well, you'd better go off and join your squadron. Peters and Drummond will be glad to see you. Change into another tank. You'll have time, I think. I believe we shall be here for the day. I'm expecting orders any time now – and mind you get some sleep.'

I could only answer rather lamely, 'Gosh! I'm glad to be back. I thought we were lost yesterday.'

I rejoined my squadron and was a bit taken aback by the warmth of the welcome from all the crews that I passed. Until then I hadn't realized that I had instilled any sort of personal feeling for myself, which was voiced simply but wholly adequately by the S.S.M., who said, 'We're all glad you're all right, sir. The men were proper miserable last night when you were missing. Didn't sleep a wink, sir, what with them all coming and asking if there was any news of you, sir.'

I changed my tank and watched my old crew sadly as they drove off to get the crippled hull mended. My new crew were keen and willing enough, but somehow, try as they did, they were not the same as the old friends I knew. A tank crew was always a particularly close companionship, like no other in any arm or service. The links of discipline, though strong, were tempered as nowhere else by a degree of tolerance, compassion or mutual esteem which bound the crew together as a small but complete family. There were liberties which I expected and accepted from my crew which I would not have countenanced from any other man, except perhaps my batman. Equally I knew I could make demands of or treat my crew in a way I would not have dared to treat other men of my squadron, in case there was misunderstanding or disapproval. The close affinity of an established crew was a plant which had to be carefully tended and nurtured. Its growth in a new crew could not be hurried or presumed on. It was this period of critical, calm scrutiny which I disliked whenever I changed a crew. It was seldom that the close bonds failed to grow, but the period of growth was a time of mental discomfort and even nervous tension.

For three days we lay at rest. There was a shortage of fuel, so that while the Indian Division moved forward to close contact with the new enemy line stretching from Gazala in a semicircle centred on Bir Temrod, we were immobilized and fully content to be so. The period of peaceful rest was almost a necessity. It gave time for our bruised morale to revive and for the battered tanks and vehicles to be tended and overhauled. The days passed quietly with long periods of sleep and ingeniously contrived meals. The only excitements were on the first morning, when news of two events served to drag the mind of each of us beyond the limited confines of our own personal experience, which had been for so long the only preoccupation, and to make us aware not only of the larger issues of the campaign in which we were involved, but also of the conduct of the war as a whole.

Early in the morning, soon after we had settled down to rest, Kinnaird called on the wireless:

'Hello, all stations Peter; Peter calling. You can close down except for one station, which will remain on wireless watch until this time to-morrow, when we will net.' Then after a pause: 'You will be interested to know that the Tobruk garrison report that they are no longer in contact with any enemy on any front. That is all. Off.'

Later, when the Indian Division lorries were driving through our area, I heard vaguely, since I was half asleep, a lorry draw to a halt near my tank and a cheerful voice call out:

217

'Wot you think of the news of the Nips, chum?'

'Wot news?' I heard my driver answer, slowly and a little suspiciously.

''aven't you 'eard? They bombed the Yank Navy, and the Yanks are in the war now.'

'And about bloody time too,' was the brief reply. And then: 'You sure that's true? You ain't pulling me winkle, are you?'

As the lorry drove on again the cheerful voice shouted back, 'It's the truth all right, mate. We've got friends besides them twisty Ruskies now.'

A moment later the driver appeared before me saying, 'Did you hear that, sir? Do you think it's true? How long'll the war last now?'

I was too weary to pay all the attention demanded of me and answered, 'I don't know if it's true – but if the Yanks are as ready for war as we were in 1939, it'll be some time before they can do anything.'

Nevertheless throughout the day, while I dozed fitfully, at the back of my mind I turned over the implications of the news, and when evening came I walked over to Kinnaird to discuss its importance. By then the attacks on Hong Kong and Malaya had been announced, and the thought that reinforcements would be sent from the Middle East brought home to each of us the possible impact that this new development would have in our struggle. The need to go to the help of Greece had left us dangerously denuded earlier in the year, with the result that the Germans had been able to sweep across Cyrenaica. Would this new danger again mean that we would be greatly weakened, and so afford the Germans another chance to regain the ground won at so desperate a cost in men and material?

We were not left long to brood over this eventuality. An hour after first light on 13 December we were swept back into the turmoil of our own war. I was about to eat my breakfast when the operator called out:

'You're wanted on the set, sir. C.O.'s on the air calling all squadron leaders.'

'Blast,' I said – 'and damn,' I added as I put down my plate of sausages and bacon. Breakfast was a meal I always enjoyed, particularly now that the supplies had caught up and the meals consisted of several variants from the evolting porridge concoction which my crew had produced on so many days from powdered biscuits and which they had proudly named 'biscuit burgoo'.

I climbed on to the tank, answered the call, waited while the other squadron leaders answered, too, and tried to guess what was impending. At length, when all were ready, Kinnaird called:

'Hello, all stations Peter; Peter calling. Information – figures five zero enemy tanks reported stationary figures one zero miles to our south-west. Orders. We move in figures one five minutes. We shall be leading. I will give you the exact bearing on which we are to march when we move. Off.'

With a pang I realized that the days of rest were over and that once more we were to go to war, and yet again opposed by the inevitable figure of fifty German tanks. We moved off at length on a bearing of 250 degrees. The brisk morning air, the dew which lay on the desert and kept down the dust churned up by our tracks, the threat of an enemy moving round the open flank, all combined to encourage a swift advance. The cool air whipped the moisture out of the corners of my eyes and froze my chin and lips so that speech was difficult. The move took on the character of a mad chase, an effect which was increased by a terror-stricken gazelle which somehow appeared in the middle of our formation, frantically trying to get clear of the surrounding tanks, yet finding each way barred, as wherever it turned there was another roaring monster bearing down on it. At last, in desperation, it turned and ran back the way we had come, and so disappeared into the bright sunlight behind us.

Soon afterwards Peters, who was on the left of my squadron and well in the lead, reported:

'Hello, Tony; Tony One calling. On a bearing of figures two four five at a range from me of figures five zero zero yards there are, quite distinctly visible, figures five zero approximately stationary. ...' There was a pause, and I listened with bated breath to the thrumming of the carrier wave and then, ' ... camels. I say again camels. There is no sign of any tanks, and I imagine these are what were mistaken for tanks. Over.'

And so it turned out to be. After a long delay, when our plans were in doubt after so abrupt an anti-climax, we were ordered to stay for the day where we had halted. Revived by the move and by the first alarm after a period of inaction, I found that when night fell sleep did not come as quickly as it had done in the past few days. Instead of going to bed soon after my evening meal, I climbed into the turret and tuned the wireless set to all the stations I could receive in turn. The programmes were much the same. The favourite music of all nationalities, friend or foe, was a brand of sentimental melancholy which appealed to me no less than to the other men and women separated from their homes. The B.B.C. programmes relayed by Cairo had the Forces' sweetheart singing 'Yours'; the French programmes played 'Tristesse' and 'J'Attendrai'; the Axis programmes played 'Lili Marlene'. Soaked in nostalgia and peculiarly inspired by the thought that life seemed to continue so normally behind the battle-fronts, I at length switched off, climbed sleepily out of the turret and into my blankets, where I was soon asleep.

At dawn we broke leaguer and spread out into open formation. We breakfasted. Then, as so often happened, the alarm that came was urgent, demanding an immediate, hectic move. From behind the bastion of their newly occupied line at Gazala, German tanks had swept forward to deal a heavy blow at the Indian Division, who were gradually closing in on them. The attack had met with some success, and we were ordered to move north in all haste in case a further attack succeeded in breaking through.

The cold, chilling chase of the day before was repeated. Fifteen miles at a speed of about twenty miles an hour brought us at last to our battle positions. By then the German attack had been held, and we lay all afternoon under spasmodic shell-fire, in wait in case the Germans should try again.

As the sun lit the western sky-line like a crimson backcloth, we were ordered to withdraw. Behind the reserve lines of infantry, behind the gun areas and headquarters, we re-formed into battle formation facing south, and when the light began to fade we moved at the same speed as that of our morning's dash, past our previous night's location, on south, for twenty miles in all. At length we came to a halt, moved into leaguer, refilled, cooked our evening meal. Over the steaming stew we discussed and guessed at the cause of our new move and retired to bed none the wiser, but sure that something more unusual even than our recent experiences was in store.

11

We Visit Rommel's H.Q.

HALF an hour before first light, before the crews had been roused and the daily bustle of an awakening leaguer had started, Kinnaird sent for all the officers and senior N.C.O.s. In a campaign which had been harsh and ruthless and which had already taught us to regard nothing with surprise, this was so novel a procedure that each of us was filled with curiosity and the event assumed even more of an air of drama.

When we were all gathered, Kinnaird switched on his torch and directed the carefully shaded beam on to a piece of paper held in his hand. Only the light reflected dimly off the white surface lit his head and shoulders, outlining the strong, determined line of his jaw and etching into even deeper shadow the dark hollows of his eyes. In a quiet voice he said:

'I have got you here because I think if things are to go right to-day, you should know at least the main details of the planned operations. We lie now south and east of the enemy defensive line at Gazala. We are some twenty miles from its nearest point. From here we are to move due west for about fifty miles. Then we shall turn north for fifty miles and advance to cut the main coastal road to the west somewhere near the enemy landing-ground at Tmimi. We shall have to move if we are to cover the one hundred miles before darkness. Some of the going is known to be bad – steep-sided, deep wadis, boulders, rocks, rain-sodden mudpans. We shall have to pick our route. We are going to lead the Brigade. Get back to your crews and tell them all I've told you so that they will understand the need for extra exertion to-day. If we succeed we may bounce the enemy out of his present line and make him withdraw a long way farther back.'

While the first rays of the morning sun lit the sky to the east, we moved off due west. As the sky brightened and gradually wider areas of desert became suffused in golden light, we spread farther and farther apart. In front as my tank topped each crest on the line of march I could see my squadron stretching 500 yards on each side of me. I could see the three troop leaders, flanked by their tanks, scanning the ground before them for enemy and carefully picking a route through the broken country. Beyond my troops I occasionally caught sight of an armoured car, probing and searching perhaps two miles ahead. When I looked behind, I saw that the desert was covered with an array of vehicles of all kinds. Beyond the small group of Kinnaird's headquarters' tanks, the sandy-coloured A.C.V. waddled slowly, like a mother hen. To all in the Brigade it was now affectionately known as the 'Gin Palace'. To right and left of Brigade headquarters were the guns and infantry, the northern flank protected by the other regiment of tanks, strung out in extended line stretching from our outer flank well to the rear. It was an inspiring sight. The more so because we were all bent on fulfilling one of the traditional roles of armoured formations: turning the enemy's open flank and attacking him in the rear. It reminded me of the march to Beda Fomm, and I only wished that the results could be as definite.

All morning our march continued, with only one halt to refill with fuel. During the brief twenty-minute pause while the petrol lorries did their round of deliveries we managed a quick brew of tea and a hurried meal of bully-beef and biscuits. Then we were off again. The route lay south of the areas that any of us had seen before. After the relatively unbroken desert south of Tobruk, we were surprised and disgusted, since it slowed our progress, to have to negotiate the steep sides of wadis, down which it was difficult to find possible routes. Then we had to find paths up again on the other side not only for the fairly agile tanks but also for the less mobile and heavily leaden fuel and ammunition lorries, the gun tractors and, not least, for the 'Gin Palace'.

Just before midday our route was barred by a large expanse of water. The presence of water at all was a surprise, but the size of the area covered was even more surprising. In dry weather it was a mud-pan, but the heavy rains of November had not yet had time to seep away into the almost waterproof, sun-baked crust of fine mud.

Kinnaird reported the obstacle to Brigade, and there was a momentary halt until we received new orders. At length he said:
' ... We turn north here. Move now. We will turn right and move in the same formation on the new line. Be as quick as you

can, as we are holding up everyone behind us until we are in position. As soon as we are all on the new line we will halt and refill again. Off.'

The manoeuvre was not so complicated as it sounded, but the broken nature of the ground caused some delay. At length it was completed and we moved forward with increased speed over an area which was suddenly flat and free of obstacles.

The frustration of the slowness and difficulty of our recent progress disappeared in the speed and freedom of our advance. Here we stopped again to refill.

Just before midday we moved on, and soon struck the southern fringe of an area which was covered with rocks and huge boulders. Progress for a time was slow and on occasions was barely perceptible as the leading tanks searched for routes which were passable. Thinking back to the advance to Beda Fomm, I realized that this was probably the eastern end of the same rough belt which had so delayed our advance on that occasion. Slowly as we were forced to move, progress was steady, and eventually, some two hours later, Peters announced triumphantly:

'I'm through. It's smooth but hilly where I am now. No boulders, thank God.'

Even then we were unable to move on at the speed we wished, as we had to conform to the movements of the mass of vehicles behind us, some of which, particularly the supply lorries, heavily laden and by no means in the first flush of youth, were finding the going almost impossible. At length, after further delays, we were told to push on, leaving the vehicles to catch up as best and as soon as they could.

By early evening, still minus most of our supply lorries, which were struggling through the rocks, we reached a point some twenty miles due west of the coastal road at Tmimi. I was surprised to recognize two fairly high peaks about five miles away to the north-west and for a time could not place them. Only when we were ordered to move forward to the road and the two peaks slowly merged into one as we drew level with them, did I remember when I had seen them before. I realized with a start that I was crossing the very route on which my troop had been chased by the Germans after the fall of Machili and searched the ground even more carefully than usual in case I could catch a glimpse of the tank I lost that day, and perhaps some indication of Tomkins' fate.

The ground was too broken, however, and soon I had to put my mind to other matters as we came closer to the coast road. We could see a fairly constant stream of traffic moving in both directions, and beyond, to the delight of us all, the evening sun glinting on the crests of the waves of the Mediterranean.

Before darkness finally closed in we were able to move in on the road in extended line and were rewarded by the destruction of twelve lorries which were left blazing merrily when we eventually withdrew.

The journey back to the leaguer area was slow, tedious and exhausting. After refilling, with the small amount of fuel available, and a meal, my troop leaders and I assembled in my car, mentally invigorated by the day's actions and unwilling, despite our physical tiredness, to go to bed. Discussion, as usually happened on these infrequent occasions, ranged far and wide, stimulated by whisky and also by the strong sense of fellow feeling which had grown between us during each day of the trials and dangers which we had all survived. At length we found ourselves clearly divided on one topic. Peters backed by Sergeant Storney argued:

'I reckon that if you see another of your tanks being badly battered you should not go and try to rescue the crew. You're far more likely to get yourself brewed up than to rescue the others. It's much better to leave them to bale out as best they can and make their escape on foot. That's what I think. . . .'

'And I agree,' added Sergeant Storney. 'I saw one chap rescue another crew once and then the tank was brewed up and both crews went with it. Now, if the second chap had done no rescuing, like as not some of the crew he went to rescue, if you see what I mean, would have got away with it on their feet.'

'That's all very well,' Drummond answered; 'but supposing one of the crew to be rescued was wounded and could not make it on foot. Then what do you do? Leave him? Or do you go and get him? I say you get him – and as you will never know if one is wounded or not, you must go to the rescue as soon as you see a crew bale out.'

'And have your own tank knocked out too?' Peters asked.

'Yes, you've got to take that risk. After all, there are always more tanks where that one came from,' Drummond retorted hotly.

'More tanks – yes,' Peters answered; 'but what if your crew are killed and wounded? Then you've lost twice the number of lives necessary by trying to rescue one or perhaps two of the crew who are alive but so badly wounded that they can't help themselves.'

At this point I put an end to the argument by saying, 'Off to bed now – this could go on all night and you'd never agree. We must get some sleep. Turn the lights off, somebody, before you open the door. Good night.'

An hour later I was disturbed by a hand on my shoulder and woke to hear, 'C O. wants you, sir. Soon as you can.'

I mumbled sleepily and crawled out of bed. I put on my boots and battle-dress tunic, swung my greatcoat over my shoulders and picked my way carefully through the silent leaguer. I saw a glimmer of light at one of the windows of Kinnaird's staff car, tapped on the window, was greeted by a voice shouting, 'Wait a moment while I turn the light off,' then the door opened and I climbed in, closing it behind me. The sudden glare of light was blinding. Kinnaird said:

'Sorry to wake you, but I've got a job for you. The Brigadier has just told me to send a squadron off to-morrow to beat up what is suspected to be Rommel's H.Q.' He spread the map before him and went on, 'We're here. Twenty miles east is Bir Temrod. Just south of it in a wide depression we believe Rommel has his headquarters. You are to take your squadron and do what you can to beat it up. The object of our coming round here was to try to dislodge the enemy from their Gazala line. The Brigadier feels that our attack on the road last night probably did not create a big enough impression. Only one or two of our supply lorries have caught up, so he can't move the whole Brigade to Tmimi, as he would like to do. A squadron is about the largest force that we can refill. So he wants to create the greatest impression he can with so small a force. That's why you are to go to Temrod. You will completely refill at first light and move off as soon as there is any light to see. Any questions?'

I thought for a moment and then said, 'What frequency do you want us to net on?'

'Stay as you are,' Kinnaird answered. 'We shall be moving back to meet the lorries, so there should be no interference. Anything else?'

'Ammo,' I answered. 'We used some against the road, and I should like to refill.'

'O.K. I'll have what you want taken out of my H.Q. tanks – let me know in good time. If that's all, you go and get some sleep, and I'll have your squadron woken an hour before first light. The R.S.M. has already taken all your men off guard. Good night, Tony.'

When we were woken I passed on my orders to the troop commanders, who dispersed to supervise the replenishment. In a moment Peters was back again, and the tone of his voice was the only indication, in the darkness of the early morning, of the tension of his feelings.

'Would you look after some things for me and send them home to Rosemary if anything happens to me?'

'Of course,' I answered; 'but what in the world should make you think anything will happen? It will be a pretty hectic swan to-day, but there's no reason to suppose we shall have much hard fighting.'

'I know,' was Peters' calm reply; 'but for some reason I feel I am going to die to-day. It may be silly and sound melodramatic, but I've the strongest conviction that I'm going to be killed. So will you take these things and send them off if necessary? If I'm O.K. I'll get 'em off you in leaguer to-night.'

'O.K.,' I answered quietly. 'Of course I will do what you want. But I hope to God it won't be necessary.'

When all was ready I went to Kinnaird.

'All set, sir,' I reported.

'Good,' said Kinnaird. 'The best of luck; and don't hang about too long when you've made your presence felt.'

As a line of dark shadows we swung out of the leaguer, turned east and moved into the first light of the rising sun. I knew we were being watched by Kinnaird. In the weeks since the opening of the campaign he had aged perceptibly. Under the edge of his beret the hair at his temples and behind his ears had grown distinctly greyer. His movements were slower, more precise, more consciously made. For a sensitive man the continual loss of men had been a constant reproach of his efficiency. Only the clear results measured in the losses inflicted on the enemy and the geographical gains could balance the personal loss he felt with the death of each man.

12

Peters is Killed

WE moved on a course a little south of east. I increased speed as it grew lighter and spread out farther and farther, so that we covered and could see over the widest possible frontage. The country was unremarkable, undulating, smooth and lacking any obvious ridges which could be used for observation or battle positions, except away to the south, where it was more broken.

There were no signs of the enemy for some time. Not only did we not see any groups of static vehicles, but we did not make contact with any column, supply or otherwise. After about an hour Drummond, who was on the right flank, reported a large group of vehicles and what appeared to be tents immediately to his front at a range of about 2,000 yards. We reduced speed and slowly closed in on the enemy. It seemed that we were still unobserved, and I was intent on making our attack from the best possible direction, the north, so that afterwards we could sweep south and west and so away in the direction we had come.

I gave my orders, 'Hello, all stations Tony; Tony calling. Tony Three will bear slightly left, followed by Tony One. Tony Two will halt where they are now and continue to report on the enemy. Off.'

Before we completed this manoeuvre, Drummond reported, 'Hello, Tony; Tony Two calling. Figures five enemy tanks moving now to engage me from the east. To my south there are two tanks – I think they are only Mark Twos – which are moving west parallel with our line of advance, presumably trying to see if there is anything behind us. Over.'

'Hello, Tony Two; Tony answering. O.K. Stay where you are unless you can move to a better battle position. Off to you. Hello, Tony One and Tony Three. Cancel my last orders. Move now instead in the order Tony One, Tony Three to positions on the right of Tony Two in the order left to right Tony Two, One,

Three. Tony Three will watch carefully for any further signs of enemy tanks moving round our right flank. Over.'

The acknowledgements were prompt:

'Tony One, O.K. Off.'

'Tony Two, O.K. Off.'

'Tony Three, O.K. Off.'

Drummond was then engaged by the enemy tanks to his front, which had meanwhile closed to about 1,500 yards. While two Mark IVs halted and engaged his troop with inaccurate and ineffective H.E. fire, three Mark IIIs moved in closer, picking their way carefully from crest to crest, hesitating before each further move, as if they were uncertain of the extent or exact position of the opposition against them. Drummond had done his best to find a position, but except for a prominent ridge to the south, about 2,000 yards on our right flank, there were no crests which afforded any worthwhile protection. The moves of the rest of us were, by this time, distracting the attention of the enemy. As yet I could see no indication whether they would move into position north or south of Drummond's troop.

After the initial surprise at Drummond's report of the enemy tanks, I found that I was calm. Events which occurred with split-second speed I was able to register, consider and counter. Like a cricketer who had batted long enough to be able to see the ball large and clear, I had now seen enough of tank battles for my mental reactions to be accelerated so that I was aware of all that happened and could plan in time and with certainty. It gave me a sense of power to realize that I did not feel hurried or in doubt. I felt elated almost by the excitement of the swift moves and the mental stimulation of impending battle. Whereas in the past the fear of things not fully comprehended had served only to distract me, now, when I knew exactly the extent and nature of the dangers to be met, my mind was quickened and made clear, so that each problem seemed small and the answer obvious.

In swift order I saw and measured the next sequence of events. The three Mark IIIs halted and engaged Drummond at about 1,000 yards. The two Mark IVs ceased fire and moved in to join the Mark IIIs. I moved into position just behind Drummond's right flank and noted that there were now three Mark II tanks on the high crest 2,000 yards to the south. They seemed to be stationary. From behind the vehicles and tents to the east more tanks appeared and made for a position to the right of the five we were already engaging. There seemed to be at least another five, but whether they were Mark IIIs or IVs I could not yet tell, as the frontal silhouette at that range was so similar. Nevertheless, whatever they were I could not ignore them, and ordered:

'Hello, Tony Three; Tony calling. Do not move to the right of Tony Two. Take up a position on his left and engage the figures five enemy tanks which are now moving into position on the right of the first five. Over.'

Sergeant Storney and his troop were at that moment passing behind my headquarters, making for their place on the right flank. As I completed my orders I saw Sergeant Storney's tank heel over to an acute angle with the violence of his wheel and his two tanks conformed to his move. As they passed, fifty yards to my left, I heard the acknowledgement, 'Tony Three, O.K. Off,' and now Sergeant Storney waved a gloved hand in salutation.

To my front the fire had increased in intensity. Mingled with the muffled explosions of the fire of the guns, I could hear also the sharp crack of the enemy shot which were passing over both mine and Drummond's tanks. Peters was just moving into position with his troop. Before this could produce any dispersion of the fire against Drummond, the right-hand tank of his troop started to reverse slowly out of battle and I heard:

'Hello, Tony Two Ack; I am wounded and the gun is jammed. Moving out now. Off.'

Beyond the crippled tank I could see the first five enemy tanks shuffling their positions to meet the new threat of Peters' troop. Farther off I detected two more tanks which were moving south, making for a position wide of Peters' right flank. We were now outnumbered by one, or two if I took account of the tank which was just out of the battle. I decided that we had made as big an impression on the enemy as we could and that any further delay would be unwise. Already we were being outflanked and had suffered one casualty. We were so far from help that any other casualties would be a considerable burden and would be without adequate medical attention for hours.

I gave my orders. 'Hello, all stations Tony. Start to withdraw now. I am moving south against two more enemy tanks. As soon as you are out of range, move west as fast as possible. I will join you. Off.'

As I moved off, I saw out of the corner of my eye, a figure leap from the turret of Drummond's tank, followed a moment or two later by another. They huddled for a time behind the tank and one ran, stumbling, towards Peters' tank. As he did so a third figure climbed slowly and painfully from Drummond's tank and huddled at the rear. I was passing just behind Peters' tank, which I saw was moving slowly towards the running figure. Before I could question this action, Peters came on the air saying, 'Hello, Tony; Tony One calling. Am going to see if I can pick up any survivors. Off.'

I drove on and took up a position facing south, as a threat to the flank of the two German tanks which were still moving slowly west probing for our flank. A shot or two warned them that they were observed and they turned to face me. Satisfied that my move had achieved what I wanted, I turned to see what had become of Peters and Drummond. For some unaccountable reason my confidence seemed to have evaporated and I was filled with dread. I remembered the argument of the previous night and Peters' sombre forecast of the early morning, and sensed that I was now to witness some disaster which I would be powerless to prevent.

I saw Peters' tank stop near Drummond's, watched the two figures climb slowly on to the engine-covers, and with relief saw Peters' tank begin to reverse. As it moved the rate of enemy fire against it increased. To the normal quota of armour-piercing shot they now added an intense concentration of H.E. from the Mark IVs. Surrounded by the black smoke of exploding shells the tank appeared momentarily in gaps still reversing slowly backwards.

When it had gone back about 300 yards I saw it halt and then move convulsively forward, swinging right-handed in a tight turn to bring it round facing west. As it turned, the red flash of an exploding shell appeared directly behind the cupola, squarely on top of the engine-covers. All the German tanks were now on the move, swinging to their left to join the two tanks which faced me, so that they could prevent our withdrawal to the south. I could afford to watch Peters no longer. It was to be a desperate race if we were to avoid the trap, and I gave orders at once.

'Hello, all stations Tony. Withdraw now and move south-west at all speed to avoid the enemy tanks. Off.'

The remaining two tanks of Peters' troop swung into line with mine. We would have to hold the hinge of the enemy wheel for as long as possible to allow Sergeant Storney's troop, Drummond's remaining tank, the cripple and Peters' now almost certainly damaged tank to escape.

When the Germans were south of my position in force I saw that I could not delay my move any longer. Behind me the rest of the squadron were already streaming away to the west. It was still possible that the superior speed of the Honeys might just enable me to outpace the Germans sufficiently to leave at least 800 yards between us when I eventually swung south across their front into the more hospitable broken ground where we could hope to rejoin Kinnaird and the rest of the Brigade.

For a time we moved parallel, gradually drawing away until I could order the leading tanks to start swinging south ahead of the foremost tanks of the German column. With relief I saw them gain the high ridge I had noticed earlier in the day. I saw them turn and move into position, and sensed a slight slackening of the pace of the German tanks as they became aware of this new development. As I turned gradually south also I noticed that the German tanks were now halted and that, as a last desperate measure, they had again opened fire, though the range was at least 1,200 yards. Despite the extreme range, I felt the thump of a hit, followed by the crack and groan of the suspension and a frightening jarring which seemed to indicate that the left track was in imminent danger of disintegrating or falling off. The driver did not slacken pace, and a moment or two later we reached the top of the crest, safe at last and out of range of the German tanks, which lay sullenly in the valley below.

Here, when I turned in my cupola to survey the desert to the north through my binoculars, I saw a sight which convinced me that our task had been accomplished. As far as the eye could see, across the whole northern and eastern horizon, the desert seemed alive with vehicles, all moving north and west, away from Gazala positions.

I tried to call Kinnaird to tell him the news, but could get no reply. I had no idea where the remainder of the Brigade had got to, and assumed that they must be out of range of wireless as the rocky, broken ground lay between us.

We moved down the slope to join the rest of the squadron, which had assembled in a ragged group round the supply lorries. It was only when we had halted and I had climbed to the ground and was walking towards this central group that I sensed that something was wrong and remembered the shell falling on Peters' tank. Sergeant Storney detached himself from the group of silent figures and walked to me, saying:

'Don't come, sir. You've no need to. There's nothing we can do. Mr Peters – he's dead – it must have happened as quick as a flash. Mr Drummond is very bad, sir – wounded in the head and shoulders and only just alive. It'll be a miracle if he lives, sir.'

My right hand moved automatically to my coat pocket, where I had put the few belongings which Peter had entrusted to me. I remembered his words so clearly. Dazed by the shock of this loss coming so soon after the elation caused by the clear evidence of the success of our attack, I mumbled:

'It was the shell, wasn't it? I saw it land, and never thought what it might have done. Thank you, Sergeant. Where is Mr Drummond? Make him as comfortable as you can.'

'He's in the lorry, sir, lying on all the coats and blankets we can find. He's as comfortable as we can make him.'

'And Mr Peters?'

'He's in an empty ammo lorry, sir. Shall we bury him now or take him with us?'

'We'll take him with us, Sergeant Storney. And we'll go now – there's nothing we need wait for.'

'No, sir; that's true,' Sergeant Storney answered quietly. 'The lads wanted me to say how sorry we all are about Mr Peters and Mr Drummond, sir, 'specially as they knew you was particular friendly with them, sir.' He paused, and I could not answer, so he went on wonderingly, 'And only last night Mr Peters was saying how he wouldn't go to rescue anyone, and he died doing just that.'

We moved south through the broken, fantastic area of deep ravines and steep-sided cliffs, halting at intervals to try to make contact with Kinnaird. At midday we halted for our first meal of the day. There was no conversation or laughter, and we moved on again immediately afterwards. All through the afternoon, dejected

232

and silent, we continued our slow progress. I performed my duties in a daze. I managed to do what little was required of me, but only half my mind was at work. The other half was thinking of Peters and Drummond, of Egerton, who had died six months before, of all the other friends and brief acquaintances who had gone in the past year.

In the late evening I at last made contact by wireless with Kinnaird, reported the moves of the enemy and to Kinnaird's cheerful inquiry, 'Are you all right?' could only give the literal answer, 'Yes'. I moved my squadron into a leaguer already formed and shrouded by the darkness of a moonless night. I recounted briefly the day's events to Kinnaird, who understandingly let me go without demanding too detailed a report.

Back at my tank, still numb from the shock of Peters' death and in no way encouraged by the M.O.'s first report on Drummond's condition, I climbed into the turret and switched on the wireless for consolation. From Cairo I heard the voice of the announcer say, 'You are listening to a programme of messages and request tunes from the families at home of the men who are fighting in the desert. And next we have Mrs Rosemary Peters ...' Rooted to the spot with horror, I could only gaze in fascination at the set as I heard Peters' wife say, 'Hello, darling. I hope you are well and getting all my letters. I've asked for our favourite tune: "I'll walk beside you".'

Released suddenly from the tension which had held me, I switched off the set with desperate haste, tore the head-phones from my ears and sat, crumpled, dejected and dazed. I remained in the turret all night, sleeping fitfully, dreaming grotesque nightmares, on the verge of overwhelming sorrow, until sleep at last claimed me an hour or so before dawn.

Just as there was a point beyond which physical exhaustion mounted no further, so there came a time when the mind became attuned to the emotional crises and stresses with which it was daily inflicted. When I awoke my brain seemed cleared of the worries and ceaseless anxieties with which it had been burdened when the safety of Peters and Drummond had weighed so heavily with me. I felt as if I had undergone a spiritual spring-cleaning – a hundred-and-one details and concerns had been swept away and, however much I may have regretted their going, my mind was now clear and fresh. All my worrying had not saved Peters, who would have died in the same fashion if he had not been so carefully watched over. Drummond, too, I would probably never see again, so maimed was he that he would inevitably be given a quiet and safe job elsewhere. They were gone, and I was uplifted with the thought that I had done all I could to safeguard them, but that, in the end, a power greater than mine had taken them. The full realization of this was the main cause of my sense of release from a responsibility which I had assumed in ignorance and error. I would continue to do my best to safeguard the men under me, but not again would I allow the inevitable losses to create a sense of guilt within myself.

So released of care that I was almost refreshed, I set to with a will to transfer my kit to the new tank I had been allotted. The crew were already engaged in refilling, with ammunition and fuel. There were new names to learn, new faces to remember, new personalities to probe and befriend. The war would not stop for me, whatever I had suffered. I had to catch up or be left behind. I watched, almost impersonally, as the small cortège escorting the body of Peters moved out from the leaguer. From time to time as I worked on the preparation of my tank I glanced to the point below the sharp edge of the cliffs to the west where the still, small group showed where the burial was taking place. I could not go till I was ready, since at any moment Brigade might issue the orders for which Kinnaird was now waiting. When all was done and still no orders had come, I asked and obtained permission to visit the grave. The burial party had long since gone, so that I was alone as I stood, beret in hand, in silent homage to the dead. I felt no sorrow. I knew that Peters had died in a just cause, as many more would die. Rather, his death had steeled my determination for ever.

Before midday we moved north through the lines which the enemy had held so tenaciously until the day before. At dawn the next day we moved west for sixty miles until, by the early evening, we had reached a point fifteen miles south-west of Machili. It had been an almost uneventful day, marred only by the sudden surprise of being bombed by the R.A.F. during the early afternoon. A formation of light bombers had appeared suddenly from out of the sky to the east, had dropped its bombs and flown on, leaving

234

behind the smoking wreckage of two burning lorries and the horribly mangled bodies of the four men who had been their crew.

For almost two days we lay at rest at Machili. Here the Headquarters of 4th Armoured Brigade, with the other remaining armoured regiment, left us to return to the Delta. We came under the command of the re-formed and re-equipped 22nd Armoured Brigade and resigned ourselves to further battles instead of the rest, good food and enjoyment to which we saw our friends depart with such joy and newly found high spirits.

Late on the morning of the 21st, Kinnaird was ordered to move independently to Agedabia. By nightfall we had all but reached Msus. Next morning the early rays of the sun lit up the sand-coloured walls of the ruined fort, making of it so romantic and picturesque a scene that I for one found that my spirits were raised. The rest had worked wonders on Kinnaird, too, who ordered, 'We'll halt here and have breakfast and enjoy the view.'

By nightfall we reached Antelat, and found at last, after a search, the site of the well we were looking for. It was set in a valley surrounded by hills on all sides but the north. The sky had clouded and some rain fell as we moved into leaguer. We all felt somehow awed and oppressed by the gloomy evening and glowering sombreness of the surround-hills. I was oddly aware of a sense of foreboding which I felt was unjustified, since there was no report of any enemy.

13

Wounded

THE next morning dawned bright and clear, however, and after spreading out into open leaguer we settled down thankfully to preparing breakfast. The squadrons were ranged in a wide arc to north, west and south of the well where Kinnaird's headquarters were located. My squadron was watching the flat ground of the break in the hills to the north.

Rations and water for the past week had been short and meals had been meagre and monotonous. During the previous day new supplies had caught up, and we had been given delicacies almost forgotten – tinned sausages, baked beans, cheese and jam. All the ingredients for a good breakfast were to hand, and the experts of each crew were using their full ingenuity and artistry to produce an appetizing meal.

I was sitting on my turret folding the maps which we would require for the day and placing them carefully on my map-board. It was a task which engrossed me, as I liked to have my maps well set. The light wind was no help, so I called the operator, who seemed to be at a loose end, to help me. The task was nearly completed when the operator suddenly said:

'Look, sir. Over there. Looks like about a dozen Honeys coming towards us flat out.'

I looked up towards the flat ground to the north. There, sure enough, were a number of Honeys moving fast towards us, and from beyond them I could hear intermittently the crack of shots. Occasionally among the approaching tanks there appeared the black cloud of a shell-burst, mushrooming slowly upwards as the sound of the explosion reached our ears.

I just had time hurriedly to complete the arrangement of my maps and to jump to the ground when the leading Honey came to an abrupt halt near me and a figure shouted from the turret:

'There's fifty or sixty Jerry tanks chasing us. You'd better bloody well get organized or you'll have had it too. Overran us in leaguer at first light, they did. The O.C. has been killed.'

I turned quietly to my crew and said, 'Scrub the "brew" and pack up. Get on to the C.O. and tell him that there are enemy tanks coming towards us.'

Then, turning back to the other tank, I asked:

'But who are you? And where were you last night?'

'We're an independent squadron attached to one of the Support Group's columns. We were leaguered about five miles north of here last night,' was the answer.

'O.K. You'd better report to that tank there,' I said, pointing to Kinnaird's tank, 'and get your orders from our C.O. He'll tell you what frequency we're on and where he wants you to go.'

As I climbed into my cupola I could see that already the squadron was almost packed up and ready to move. To the north I could see the dust-cloud thrown up by the enemy tanks some 2,000 yards away. I grabbed the microphone:

'Hello, all stations Tony. Conform to me now and face north

on the ridge on which I am sitting. Figures five zero to six zero mixed Mark Threes and Fours reported moving towards us. Off to you. Hello, Peter; Tony calling. I am taking up position here. Will this do? Over.'

There was no immediate reply. I could see Kinnaird finish his conversation with the tank which had reached him. Then he answered:

'Hello, Tony; Peter answering. Hold on as long as you can while we move into position beside you. If you find you are too hard pressed move slowly back up the hill to the south. We'll all try to get there in the end. Off to you. Hello, Archie, hello Buster; Peter calling. Archie will move into line on the left of Tony and Buster on his right. Move now, at once. Enemy tanks are nearly on to Tony's position. Off.'

My squadron was almost immediately engaged. The enemy force seemed to consist of a majority of Mark IIIs with about one-third Mark IVs. The new and glistening paint on them all showed that they were either reconditioned or new tanks recently arrived at Benghazi.

The lie of the ground favoured us to some extent. The narrow northern extreme to the valley was blocked by my squadron, and the high ground to our right and left masked the moves of the other two squadrons. This caused the Germans to hesitate. They clearly had orders to push on, and did not delay for long. We were engaged at shorter and shorter range, the fire of the 50-mm. guns becoming more and more effective as the range closed, taking a growing toll in destroyed and crippled tanks. Even when the other two squadrons had got into position and had brought their fire to bear on the enemy, the enemy pressure on my squadron was such that I was forced to report:

' ... Can hold on no longer, and will have to withdraw. Over.'

' ... O.K. Go now,' was Kinnaird's reply. 'And as fast as you like. We may trap a few into following you and be able to knock them out from our positions on the high ground. Take up a position with Roger, our new friends, half-way up the hill due south of you now. Off.'

I gave the signal to withdraw, and when we were out of range of the enemy, turned and moved at speed to the new position.

237

Behind us we left the hulks of four burning tanks, but knew that we had done all we could. In the new positions we had a brief period of rest while we watched the battle of the other two squadrons. At length these, too, were outnumbered and forced to withdraw, leaving behind their quota of dead and crippled, among whom was Tapson, who was taken prisoner in full view of his squadron when his tank was immobilized and he and his crew had to bale out.

Across the floor of the valley, which the previous evening had seemed to me gloomy and overcast with an atmosphere of foreboding, the German tanks moved to engage us again. Hidden in the shadows of the hollows of the hillside on which we had now taken up position, we were difficult to find and fight. In places the ground was so steep and undulating that at the best battle ranges some of the German tanks were unable to elevate their guns to a high enough angle to engage us. We had the considerable advantage of both being able clearly to see the enemy tanks and also of being able to direct a plunging fire on to their vulnerable top armour. Baulked and frustrated by these tactics, the German tanks withdrew slightly, leaving the Mark IVs to engage at long range with the high-explosive shells of the 75-mm. guns.

I had heard of the phenomenon of being able to see a shell in flight if the focus of the eye at the precise fraction of a second happened to coincide with the path of the shell. I was watching the movements of a particular Mark IV and happened to see for an instant the shell from its gun coming towards us. The next moment my tank was struck on the front. In the dust and smoke and flame I was not surprised that I was unable to see. I ducked into the turret and found that my head-phones had gone and that I was still blinded. I shouted to the gunner:

'What's happened in here? I can't see a thing.'

I was astonished to hear an answering shout of:

'Christ! you're 'it, sir. Your face an' goggles are covered in blood. Are you all right, sir? Sit down 'ere, sir.'

Dazedly I slipped off my sling-seat and sank to the bottom of the turret. The gunner took charge.

''Arry, reverse out of 'ere,' he shouted to the driver. 'Get the first-aid box, Kim,' he said to the operator. 'Now, sir, you just sit still and we'll 'ave you as right as rain in no time. We can't do anything if we stay. The sight's bust, the M.G. is jammed and I reckon the gun ain't in too good shape neither.'

I was in no mind to argue or take any responsibility. I experienced no pain, and was surprised that I only felt dazed and a bit sleepy. As in a dream I heard the high-pitched whine of the engine as the driver gave it all the power he could to take us out at the best speed in reverse. Every now and then I could hear the dull crump of the exploding shells around us.

All that happened afterwards seemed to me, in my dazed state, to pass with remarkable speed. The doctor saw me and replaced the shell-dressing hurriedly put on by my crew. I was put into an ambulance with other wounded, fussed over by an attentive orderly and driven away over the bumpy desert, with the sound of the battle dying away behind. I tried hard to keep awake in order to be alert for any new danger which threatened. The effort exhausted me, so that when, at nightfall, we reached the tents and marquees of a field hospital near Machili, I ate my meal in a state of semi-consciousness and fell into a deep sleep when my head touched the pillow of the luxurious-seeming hospital bed.

Of the next day – Christmas Day, as I gathered from the hilarious conversation – I was only partly aware. Still I desperately tried to stay awake and alert, not comprehending that I was already miles from any threat or danger and still, after so many weeks of ceaseless vigilance, unable to rest and relax, despite the blow on my head which had left me fuddled. By evening I had begun partly to realize that I was out of the battle.

That night I spent in the bomb-shattered wreck of the hospital in Tobruk, tended to my surprise by a neat and lovely nurse. At dawn I was put on a hospital ship. This final sign of my complete release from battle assured me at last that my vigilance was no longer needed, and I fell into a restful coma, half-way between sleep and complete awakeness, only vaguely aware of the sights and sounds of the preparations for sea and of the voyage. I was going back to Alexandria. There would be sleep and rest. I wondered how Kinnaird was and how the battle had gone. I felt I ought to care, but somehow I didn't.

PART FIVE

1942: EIGHTH ARMY AT BAY

1

Cairo Again

FOR six weeks I was in hospital in Cairo. It was a solid concrete building with wide verandas, cool wards and long passages, set among lawns and trees on the edge of the river. Though I had managed to stay if not alert, at least awake until the moment I got into bed, thereafter I slept like the dead for most hours of the day, waking only for a morning and evening meal. Exhaustion, loss of blood and concussion had taken their toll and only sleep could restore the sinews of my being. My wound was not serious in itself, but my continued torpor at length caused the doctors some concern lest my brain had been bruised or damaged. I was X-rayed, and it was found that my skull was fractured, though only slightly. I had indeed had a miraculous escape. A piece of the shell, large enough to wipe my beret and head-phones off my head, had grazed my skull and scraped off a patch of skin down to the bare, clean bone. The area of broken flesh accounted for my loss of blood, the weight and size of the piece of metal for the fracture and concussion. It was apparently not unusual that the effects of the blow had been delayed for the five days it had taken for me to get back to the hospital. The duration of the effects was the disturbing factor, for I was semi-conscious for about fourteen days, only gradually becoming more and more awake each day after that.

When I was at length more aware of my surroundings I settled down to enjoy myself. Except for very brief periods, this was the first time that I had lived in a proper building since I had left England almost eighteen months ago. Tents and bivouacs could be made comfortable and become almost like homes, but there was still, I felt, a great deal to be said for solid walls and a roof.

Though I was not allowed to walk far to begin with, another thing which gave me some pleasure was the smooth, solid floor – no stones nor soft sand to impede my footsteps. Most of all it was the modern sanitation which I enjoyed – the abundance of water, cool and with no trace of salt nor disinfectant, the baths and the clean-smelling lavatories. It was a relief not to have to take my spade for a walk each day! Clean sheets, too, were a pleasant change, and decent crockery and cutlery.

About the middle of January, Celia and Peter Kinnaird paid me a visit. I had fully regained consciousness by this time and found the afternoons and evenings interminably dull after the bustle of cleaning and inspections each morning. So it was indeed a pleasant surprise when I first saw Kinnaird peer round the door of the ward, followed by Celia.

They came and sat on each side of my bed, and it was Celia who spoke first.

'Tony, we are glad to see you sitting up and taking notice at last. I came to see you soon after you first got here and we both came about ten days ago. But each time you were sound asleep, so we left without disturbing you. You do look better now – still a little pale and interesting! How do you feel?'

'Fine,' I answered. 'In fact I am fed-up with the place – but how nice of you both to bother to come –'

'It's no bother, Tony; you know that,' Celia answered. 'And now that you've come to life again you must let us know anything you want, and we can bring it to you. Now I am going to leave you – I have got some shopping to do and I am sure you want to have a gossip to Peter about things. Bye-bye. Write and tell us what you want, and when you are allowed out, come and stay with us. Oh, before I forget, you've got some things for Angela Chesham, haven't you?' I nodded and she went on, 'She knows that and she asked me to ask you to go and see her when you can. She doesn't want to come here to talk about it. She is being marvellous about it – how she can be so cheerful I don't know. She talks about Bill as if he was still alive. Well, I must go.'

After she had gone we sat for a while in silence. I took the chance to have a good look at Kinnaird and was relieved to see the vast change that even so short a leave had made in him. Gone was the look of utter exhaustion, the expression in his eyes that told how he felt at the loss and death of so many of his men. He was grey still, but he was alert and alive again, though he gave me the impression that he was still in need of a rest. He spoke at last.

'Let's see, Tony – it was Christmas Eve when you were wounded, wasn't it? It was touch and go, that battle, but we only lost another one or two tanks after you had gone, and the Germans didn't try to advance any farther. The next day we went on to Agedabia, where we sat for two days looking at the defences which Jerry had built there. We hadn't enough tanks or infantry to do anything – and a day or so later we were relieved and came back to Beni Yusef and on leave.'

He paused for a moment or two, staring out of the window and then went on. 'We're back in our old camp, and sometimes I think that none of all the past has really happened and that it's only a nightmare. Funny, isn't it? While it was on I thought I should never forget it – but now a lot of the horror seems to have faded already.'

'It was the hell of a battle,' I answered inadequately.

'It was,' said Kinnaird thoughtfully, 'and I hope no one will ever belittle the victory we gained. In the main our equipment was inadequate and the plans made seldom resulted in our being superior in numbers where the battle was being fought – the Germans somehow always managed to have most of their armour working closely together, but we always seemed to be spread about in small groups all over the battle-field. I hope to goodness we do better in the next battle – but I don't know that we shall. When we left Agedabia there were damned few troops up forward and those that were there were dotted about just as we were before the German advance last year – why we don't move down to the Wadi Faregh and form a decent defence line, I don't know. Well, don't let me depress you, Tony. Buck up and get well and come back to us soon. I'll keep C Squadron for you – Clayton has got H.Q. now, but I've put a good chap called Irving in as your second-in-command.'

We chatted on for a bit after this, talking of many things, but mainly of the future; the new officers who had already come, the new equipment we would get – there was talk of a really powerful tank at last – of the parties we would have before we went back again to the desert. Of the past we spoke hardly at all – how quickly did memory fade, or could be made to fade, with a conscious effort to ignore the unpleasant.

A week later we began to get hints of just what Kinnaird had feared would happen in the desert. His words had been cause enough for worry, but I heard, too, from others in the ward of units and ships and aircraft which had been sent to the Far East to meet the threat of the Japanese advance. It looked as if the tragedy of the previous year would be played out again and for the same reasons – an unsound disposition of the forces available and a weakening of these forces by the need to reinforce other theatres of the war. We had suffered once before the bitter disappointment and testing trials of a withdrawal, and I waited now anxiously lest the fruits of our recent success, so hardly won, would be lost again.

By the end of the first week in February the front had again been stabilized on a line from Gazala on the coast to Bir Hakeim in the desert to the south. At least the isolation of Tobruk had not been repeated, but the race back was in danger of becoming an annual event – this time it became known as the 'Msus Stakes'.

In the middle of February I rejoined the regiment after a week's leave which I spent in the Kinnairds' flat. It had been all peace and enjoyment except for a brief visit I had paid to Angela Chesham to return the few belongings which I had found on Bill Chesham's body at Sidi Rezegh. It was a heart-rending experience. Young and lovely, but still distrait as the result of her loss and grief, she was a tragic figure. We were both at a loss for words, and it was with a feeling of thankfulness that I eventually left, with a promise that I would see her again.

I arrived in the mess at Beni Yusef on the day that the fall of Singapore was announced. So close on the heels of the loss of our own recent gains, this was a heavy blow to those of us who had been in the winter fighting. But we noticed that the new officers – and there were many to fill the gaps – did not take it in the same way. Less aware, perhaps, than we were of the trials which must have led up to the loss of so vital an area, they regarded it as a spur to them, an added incentive to get into battle to win back some of the losses. This was an inspiration. But what was a goad to our depressed spirits was the corollary of this attitude: that

243

they would teach us where we had gone wrong and that disasters would not occur in future. We were told of 'Bumper' and other names of massive exercises which had been held in England, during which all the lessons of all the wars had been taught and learnt!

I had to start again the uncomfortable process of learning many new names and faces, for except for a very few, most of the officers were new or had belonged to other squadrons during the battle and had therefore become known to only their immediate companions. Kinnaird, Henderson the doctor, Davidson the padre, and the Quartermaster were the only ones who remained at Regimental Headquarters. We had a new second-in-command and a new adjutant. Williams, who had commanded H.Q. Squadron, now had A Squadron – Clayton had left me to take over H.Q. Squadron and a new officer – Richards – had arrived to command B.

In my own squadron all except one of the officers was new. The only old hand was Storney, who, at Kinnaird's recommendation, had been given an immediate commission. He left the regiment one Friday morning as a sergeant, and returned for tea the following Sunday as an officer. We had all done our best to make the process of transition as easy as possible for him, but it was Ben himself who had made the unusual course the success it was. Despite the lack of experience, both in his private and in his previous Army service, despite the new surroundings, the new customs and the suddenness of it all, he was an instant success, and a success in a mess where the atmosphere was still a little strained and difficult with so many newcomers.

Of the men of the squadron little more than a tenth remained of those who had lived and worked in this same camp not six months earlier. Not all of those missing, but a very large number, had been killed, and of the remainder some were so badly wounded that they would never live a full life again. Among those who had survived, many had been wounded and recovered to return as I had done.

'The surviving tenth', as I always thought of them, gave me much food for thought. Most of them were newly joined only the previous year, when we had the few hectic weeks in which to learn the Honeys and to prepare for battle. In the circumstances we had had little time for the accepted method of making good soldiers, drill. And yet they were now smart and soldierly in appearance, self-confident, self-reliant, reliable. They worked hard and gave no trouble, there was a wealth of mutual respect and fellow-feeling between them and their officers and N.C.O.s. I wondered whether good drill was really the way to make soldiers, or whether it wasn't that good soldiers drilled well, as they did all other things well.

Just before we were due to leave for the desert again, towards the end of March, Kinnaird sent for all the squadron commanders and the R.S.M. We seated ourselves on the chairs in his office. He looked up at us and then said:

'I really want your advice. I have here a – a – document, shall I say, which I am going to read to you, and then I want your opinion. It's addressed to all commanders and chiefs of staff, and it's from H.Q. B.T.E. and M.E.F. It reads as follows: "There exists a real danger that our friend Rommel is becoming a kind of magician or bogey-man to our troops, who are talking far too much about him. He is by no means a superman, although he is undoubtedly very energetic and able. Even if he were a superman, it would still be highly undesirable that our men should credit him with supernatural powers. I wish you to dispel by all possible means the idea that Rommel represents something more than an ordinary German general. The important thing now is to see to it that we do not always talk of Rommel when we mean the enemy in Libya. We must refer to 'the Germans' or 'the Axis Powers' or 'the enemy', and not always keep harping on Rommel. Please ensure that this order is put into immediate effect and impress upon all commanders that, from a psychological point of view, it is a matter of the highest importance."' Kinnaird paused and looked at us and then added, 'Now I will tell you what I think and I want you to tell me if I am right. I see no reason whatever to say any more about this order. I am quite clear, and I think all the tank crews know damned well, that the reason why the Germans have had their successes and why we found them so difficult to beat recently was that their tanks are about twice as good as any of ours except the Grant tank we have now. He damned well ought to have won with that advantage, and I for one have no great respect for him because he has had one or two successes. He knocked us back first when some of us had Italian tanks and all the other troops were ill prepared and ill equipped. He has had another success, but again against troops new to the desert. No – I don't think we want to blind ourselves to the fact that he has good tanks and good crews to fight them. It's the Panzer Divisions we have always worried about, and let's go on doing so. But I wish others would blame the worth of our equipment and not have funny ideas about Rommel.'

We all agreed whole-heartedly with his views. But the incident gave us all cause for anxiety. We were quite clear that the German successes were due to their superior equipment, but the order Kinnaird had read to us more than implied that some of our commanders and staffs were unaware of this, and, as a result, were developing an inferiority complex about Rommel.

2

Waiting for Battle Again

A FEW days later we moved up again to the desert. At dawn the cars and lorries left by the well-known desert road and the desert tracks beyond for an area just west of Capuzzo. At the same time we went in our tanks to the railway station at Gizeh, on the outskirts of Cairo. There we loaded the tanks on to the flat-topped railway cars specially built to carry them. Each train carried a squadron and had, too, one passenger coach and a luggage van at the front just behind the engine. Each crew lashed their tank to the flat and then, with whatever materials they could find in the station and the tank tarpaulin sheet, they built a bivouac either at the front or the rear. The passenger coach I kept as my office and the officers' mess – it was an ancient type of coach with no compartments, the interior rather like that of a large bus with wooden seats ranged down each side and a gangway down the middle.

We spent the day in the already unpleasantly hot, fly-ridden station yard, and moved off only as darkness fell, so that our progress through the many towns of the Delta should not be observed by any lurking enemy agents. It was an uncomfortable and dirty journey. We were disturbed frequently during the night, as whenever the train halted we had immediately to guard the whole length against the swarms of thieves and pilferers who emerged mysteriously from the shadows and greeted us with bland smiles when they saw we were ready to receive them.

At dawn the train was slowly climbing the escarpment south of Mersa Matruh, and by midday we had reached our destination, a few miles short of the frontier near Capuzzo. Here we detrained and were met by Kinnaird in his staff car, and the petrol and fitters' lorries, which accompanied us to our new concentration area.

Late spring in the desert was the best time of the year. I had failed to appreciate this fact the previous year while I was walking along the coast into Tobruk, but now I saw it in its quite remarkable beauty. There was a week of heavy rainfall when we first arrived in the desert, and afterwards we found it covered with a wonderful variety of grasses and flowers, particularly in the shallow valleys where the water collected. On our schemes and manoeuvres we avoided these places when we could. The hot, blistering sun would soon put an end to these pastoral stretches and we were reluctant to destroy or damage them before their time.

Everywhere we went we saw the litter and evidence of the winter's fighting – the ever criss-crossing marks of the tank tracks, the piles of empty shell-cases, the occasional rusty solid shot, the derelict vehicles and tanks, the lonely graves – mute testimony of the struggle there had been and a sobering reminder, amid all the beauty of the spring, of the trials that lay ahead.

April gave way to May and we moved south to Gubi for further training and to be nearer the battle-front. The fresh flowers and green grasses were daily being burnt to browner shades and withering under the increasing heat of the merciless summer sun. There was a mounting feeling of expectation of battle and our labours took on a more urgent note so that we would be completely ready.

All this time we were learning our new tanks, the Grants, which had also come from America. Twice the size and weight of any tank we had ever had before, they were armed, at last, with a gun which could fire H.E., a counter to the dug-in anti-tank guns which had been the cause of so many of our troubles hitherto.

247

But there were disadvantages too. This gun, a 75-mm., was housed in a mounting beside the driver which allowed only a small angle of traverse to each side of the centre position and meant that to engage the enemy almost the whole tank had to be exposed. In a turret mounted to one side of the hull was a 37-mm. gun, the same as that of the Honeys. Only two squadrons – mine and Richards' – were equipped with Grants, Williams' squadron retaining the Honeys to act as a fast reconnaissance squadron for our essentially more ponderous tanks.

The 75-mm. gun had its own crew of gunner and loader, so that each tank had a total complement of six – a commander, a driver, gunner and loader for the 75 and gunner and loader, who was also the wireless operator, for the 37. I picked my crew carefully from the men in the squadron whom I had known and liked. Chandler, who had walked with me to Tobruk, had joined the regiment, and him I made a corporal in charge of the wireless of the squadron and my own operator. Norton, who had been so ingenious with the broken track, I had as my driver. Rogers, who had been my gunner in the winter battles, was the gunner of the 75. The other two crew members – Harden, the 75 loader and Larkin, the 37 gunner – were new men, recently arrived from training regiments in England.

In our small mess bivouac, built on to the side of the three-ton mess lorry, I often looked round at the officers of the squadron and wondered how many would live to see another year. In here we spent the days when we were not training and the evenings when we had not been invited to other similar squadron messes. We grew ever closer as each day we knew that the battle was drawing nearer. The longer we stayed together, the better we got on, learning to make allowances for the habits which were annoying.

Tom Irving, my new second-in-command, was tall and large, big in everything he did, with a huge laugh, a huge appetite and an overgrown sense of humour which showed itself in schoolboy practical jokes. Jim Beck, the second captain, we saw little of, as I had sent him to live with the supply lorries a few miles behind us, so that the lorry drivers would realize their importance to the squadron and feel that they belonged to the fighting team.

Three of the troop leaders were new from England, Joe Carless,

248

Frank Groves and Edward Parry; and last but by no means least, there was Ben Storney. Joe Carless was almost as large as Tom Irving, but in contrast was silent and shy, blushing at the slightest provocation, and awkward in word and act, except where engines were concerned. Frank Groves had been an art student, and kept us amused with his quick sketches of incidents and caricatures of people and his bawdy reminiscences of life at an art school. Edward Parry was his constant companion and the butt of many of his jokes. He had been studying music until the war caught up with him. He was small and frail with a perpetually lost air, except when the muse of music was criticized, when he was quick to leap to her defence.

And Ben Storney. Older than all the rest of us, without all our advantages of education and upbringing, he was an example to us all. Even under the shadow of impending action he was determined to make his promotion merely the first rung on the ladder of success. He was learning English Grammar, French, art from Frank, music from Edward, the rudiments of arithmetic from myself and mechanics from Joe. He was restless and eager, full of fun and the sly, acute wisdom of the old soldier, which meant that we often got wind before the other squadrons of extra food or kit and, more particularly, new sources of water – he had an uncanny instinct for finding hidden water-holes and unmarked wells whenever we moved to a new area.

Our worst trials at this time were the dust-storms and the khamsin. The latter was the oven-hot wind which blew from the south across the endless deserts of central Africa, eventually reaching us, after being toasted for so many miles, as a dry, searing, blistering wind of great heat. It was not like the heat of the sun, from which there was some relief in the shade or from the occasional fresh breezes. Nor was it like the damp, humid, sweltering heat of the tropics. It was a dry, burning heat, just as if an oven door had been opened and its hot blasts were being blown across the desert. It lasted normally for about three days and was heralded by a day of complete calm, rather like that before a thunderstorm, when our nerves became gradually more and more on edge.

When the khamsin ended, into the vacuum formed by the rising of the oven-hot atmosphere it had created rushed the winds from the west, carrying with them all the loose sand and dust which had been stirred up by the wheels and tracks of a thousand lorries and tanks. For about three days we would be enveloped in a fog of sand, a tangible fog which clogged the eyes and nostrils, entered the most closely sealed boxes and cases, covered the tables and chairs and beds, and mixed with our food and water. We gasped for air and water, and stumbled from tank to truck and truck to mess tent in a blizzard of sand, which meant that we had to set a compass course to reach vehicles which were only a few hundred yards away.

Flies were, at this time, only a minor tribulation. Separated from the rest of the Army as we were by about thirty miles of open desert, we were not so afflicted as other units nearer the coastal areas. And when the flies became too bad in one place there was always room to move elsewhere.

So the days passed in training and preparation. There were lighter moments when we had shooting competitions and sports, when we had tortoise races and scorpion tournaments and our life became quite civilized, with the usual amenities produced by NAAFI, when the railhead reached Tobruk.

3

Comparisons and Fears

IN early May a German staff officer was captured, from whom enough facts were eventually extracted to show that an attack was planned for the end of the month. As a result we were all warned that from 20 May until 1 June we would all stand-to an hour before dawn and an hour before dusk. Meanwhile plans were pushed ahead to meet this attack.

Day after day I and the other two tank squadron leaders went with Kinnaird to inspect and reconnoitre interminable ridges and crests on which, at given code words, we would take up battle positions to meet the enemy. So many were the alternatives that we soon had no room to mark them on our maps and could only list them on long sheets of paper, each position being shown by its map reference and the name of some famous general of the past.

Gradually the confidence which had begun to grow up in our new equipment, in the evidence and knowledge of our previous successes, and in the new commanders, began to evaporate. There seemed to be no determination to fight the battle to our plan, but always an anxiety to find a place where we could hurriedly position ourselves to meet an enemy thrust. And to us on the southern flank there was the even more inexplicable fact that nearly all the positions we looked at were opposite the centre of the line between Gazala and Bir Hakeim.

We had about four infantry divisions, two armoured divisions and two tank brigades, equipped with Matildas and their successors, the Valentine. Two of the infantry divisions – the 1st South African and the 50th Northumbrian Division – were in the line, the South Africans on the coast and the 50th just south of them. To their south, after a considerable gap protected only by widespread minefields, the Free French Brigade held an isolated position at Bir Hakeim. Immediately behind the two divisions in the north were the two tank brigades, and behind them, with their motor brigade at Knightsbridge, was 1st Armoured Division. Both its armoured brigades – the 2nd and 22nd – were just south of Knightsbridge. Behind this division, in Tobruk, was the 2nd South African Division and a part of the 5th Indian Division, the other part of the latter being a long way south at Gubi.

In the very wide gap between Gubi and the French at Bir Hakeim was 7th Armoured Division, protecting the open left flank, with a motor brigade just south of Bir Hakeim and another motor brigade patrolling west of the line in no-man's-land but ready to take up a position at Retma, south-east of Hakeim. North-east of the French, and separated from them and the motor brigade near them, we were disposed with our regiment and one other forward, just to our south, and the third regiment and brigade headquarters some way behind near Divisional Headquarters.

With the lesson of Rommel's two previous spring assaults from Agheila and his dash to the wire of the previous winter clear in our minds, we felt sure that this open flank would be the line on which he would attack. He was always intent on achieving surprise, and a slow-motion, bludgeoning attack through the centre of our line would be unlikely to surprise us. Nor had we, faced with an enemy line on the frontier the previous winter, tried to knock a hole through the middle. Perhaps we were prejudiced into believing that ours was the important flank. Events were to prove that we were not wrong! And if the Germans did come round the flank, we were very badly disposed – dispersed, in fact – to be able to deal with them effectively. However, other views prevailed, and we could only hope rather despondently that they were right.

Other news which was passed to us at this time did no more to encourage us, although that was the obvious intention. Kinnaird had fairly frequent conferences with the squadron leaders and certain other key officers in the regiment, and at one of these he handed round a document saying:

'Have a look at that. It's a tally of the two opposing teams prepared by Army or someone. It shows the totals of tanks which we and the enemy are supposed to have now. I have no idea how accurate it is.'

The table read:

British				Enemy	
Honeys	45	} 112		Mark III (H)	215
Crusaders	180		} 282	Mark III (J)	20 } 275
Grants	170			Mark IV	40
Matildas	135	} 225		Italian M 13	205
Valentines	90				
	620				480

Kinnaird waited until we had all seen it and then went on:

'You see I have made some pencil marks against the totals – I will explain them. We know to our cost that the Honeys and Crusaders are no match for the Mark IIIs, and so I have counted their value as half their true total – that means, as you see, that in the battles which we can expect to be fighting our equivalent total is about 280 and the Germans 275. So let's have no illusions about the battle. I knew these figures were sent to convince us that as we have so many more tanks we can't lose; but that's the mistake Army have been making all along – it's not totals only that count. Now I have left out all the Matildas and Valentines on our side and the Italian M13s on the enemy's. They practically offset each other in numbers and we are unlikely to see either in any big tank battle – the M13s because they are of little value, and the Matildas and Valentines because they are so slow and in any case

252

are practically locked up in the infantry areas to give them close support – they may join in, but we can't possibly count on them at this stage.'

He paused, and we all pondered on what he had said. This seemed awfully like another example of the fatal optimism of the previous winter, the sign of which was the daily cry of 'The enemy has only sixty tanks left'. We knew that all 275 German tanks would fight as a solid mass against which we could triumph only if we fought with more cohesion than our dispositions then implied.

We knew, too, that the German tanks would fight in very close concert with their anti-tank guns, a closeness which we had by no means achieved and which in any case would have been far less effective, as we had only a few anti-tank guns which could compare with the German 50-mm. and none at all with their 88s.

Kinnaird interrupted our thoughts again:

'I have another piece of paper here which I am not going to pass round, as it is such arrant nonsense. It gives figures which are meant to show the performance of the various tank and anti-tank guns. It is so inaccurate that it is useless. I'll tell you what I mean – now let me see – ah yes – here it is. At a range of a thousand yards it shows that the German 50-mm. tank gun goes through about 4 mm. less armour than our two-pounders. Now we know that that is nonsense: it almost certainly goes through 10 mm. more at that range. Again, at the same range it shows the 37-mm. of the Honeys and Grants going through 14 – yes, 14 mm., more than the 50-mm. – whereas it probably goes through the same thickness as the two-pounder – that is, 10 mm. less. I just don't understand how figures as inaccurate as these can be allowed to get round, but no doubt someone thinks we are complaining without reason about the inferiority of our guns, except for the 75s in the Grants. Well, there you are, for what they're worth – they're meant to encourage you, but I shouldn't have any illusions but that the battle is going to be a hard one.'

Late in the afternoon of 26 May, while we were all sitting in the shade of the mess shelter, Kinnaird suddenly appeared outside in his staff car and leaning out of the window shouted, 'Tac R report says that the Jerries have started. They were seen moving due east in a solid mass. Make sure everything is O.K. – we are bound to be in it sometime to-morrow.'

He drove off in a cloud of dust to visit the other squadrons, leaving us sitting in silence for a few moments while we all grasped the fact that after all the weeks of waiting we would soon be in battle.

In silence, too, we filed out of the shelter until Edward Parry, intense, nervous but supremely honest, turned to Ben Storney, saying:

'My God! Ben, I'm frightened. Do I look it? Are you? You don't look it.'

'Of course I'm frightened,' Ben answered bluntly. 'Anyone who's never frightened ought to have their 'ead examined. I'm always frightened before the battle starts, but when it does, then I seem to be all right – extra all right, if you see what I mean.'

'Well, it's nice to know you are afraid too, Ben. I thought you'd seen so much action you wouldn't be afraid any more. The worst part is being afraid that I will seem and look afraid – but if everyone's frightened, then I don't mind admitting it.'

'There's nothing to be ashamed of in admitting you're afraid, Ted. Don't be frightened of fear, we're all – terrified. Me 'eart thumps, me bowels turn to water, me mouth goes dry, me knees feel weak – I feel awful; but I'll get over it, and afterwards, I don't know 'ow to describe it, I feel that I can cope with anything – it seems to give me extra strength and I feel all keyed up and awake.'

'Yes, I've noticed that before,' Tom Irving, serious for once, added thoughtfully. 'If I'm going to do something which terrifies me, then I seem to have some extra stimulus which makes me do well – but if I'm not afraid, then I seldom do so well. If I'm on the verge of panic before I go in to bat I nearly always make a lot of runs.'

'But I'm afraid for the people who will have to look after themselves if I'm killed,' Joe Carless, usually so silent and incoherent, suddenly said. 'I'm scared stiff about the battle, but I don't mind showing it now, after what Ben says. But my main fear is what's to happen to my wife and kids if I'm killed. I expect the fear of the battle will act as a stimulus, but the fear of the possible consequences depresses and worries me.'

'I don't know about your stim – what-you-call-it, Joe,' Ben

answered, 'but if you worry enough you'll be afraid, and if you're afraid you'll get some extra punch which will make you fight well and probably get away with it. Come on now; we can't spend all day chatting. We'll 'ave to tell the crews that battle's about to commence.'

Fear of appearing to be afraid was always the worst worry, devitalizing and depressing, making men feel that they were different from others, and therefore less capable of meeting danger or difficulty. A year before Ben would probably not have been prepared to admit his fear, but now he knew that everyone, except the most insensitive, felt fear and that the symptoms of fear of which he was aware each time were not felt by him alone. Frequently it was those who did not fear fear who were the first to crack under the stress and strain of battle; and those who went into battle having been on the verge of overwhelming fear found that they were in a state of extraordinary physical well-being and felt an acute spiritual exaltation; they became aware of unsuspected powers of endurance and capacity.

But fear was like a drug or dope: it had the power to release men from the shackles of their normal limitations. With the awareness that there was no need to be afraid or ashamed of fear, it became a necessary spur to courage. For without it there was no real courage: that curious exaltation, high-hearted and slightly light-headed but superbly clear-headed. But, like a drug or dope, there could be too much fear. The stimulus applied too long in the end tried the mental and physical powers too much, and men who were brave and enduring became craven and weak. The resistance to the sapping quality of fear differed with each individual, as did the reaction to it, courage. As the saying was, 'Fear rightly used is the father of courage'. And the most important step in fostering courage was to make each man aware that fear was felt by each and every one and that it was nothing of which to be ashamed.

We dispersed to our various tasks, thankful to have something to do to keep our minds off the impending battle. Our nerves were a bit jaded in any case, as the day had been the first of calm, clear weather after a period of khamsin and dust-storm.

We stood-to at last light and learned then that the enemy advance had come to a standstill about twenty miles west of the centre point of our line – giving no sign as yet of the intended direction of their further moves.

We ate our supper in solemn silence – even Tom Irving was unable to raise a vestige of humour or of his boisterous laugh. Afterwards we went to bed – in my case to lie awake for some time thinking of the impending battle, wondering at our chances, trying to remember whether I had forgotten to see to any vital detail and finally, and rather belatedly, regretting that I had not written home more often.

4

Sudden Disaster

TOWARDS dawn, while it was still dark, I was woken by the guard and told that the whole regiment was to stand-to. I packed the belongings I would need on my tank in my small haversack, checked my map and pencils and binoculars, and told Hawkin, my batman-driver, to pack my bedding and to take my car to join the rest of the supply lorries as soon as it was light.

In the cold, damp dawn I walked over to my tank. The crew were already awake, had dismantled the bivouac and packed their bedding and were sitting in their various positions waiting for me. I climbed into the turret. Wrapped in an overcoat, scarf and bala-clava, I sat huddled in the cupola waiting for the dawn and watching, with mounting curiosity and anxiety, the incessant display of parachute flares in the direction of Bir Hakeim. At any moment we expected to be ordered to move, for if the enemy was indeed turning the southern flank, the best battle position on which we could engage him was on a prominent ridge south of Hakeim and the motor brigade's position there.

But the hours passed with no orders and no clear information. When it was at last light enough to see clearly I walked over to Kinnaird's tank and found him leaning against the front sand-shields smoking a cigarette.

'What's the news?' I asked.

'I haven't a clue, Tony,' he answered. 'There's no doubt that quite a large force have come south – their move was reported throughout the night by the armoured cars who know the exact enemy positions. But apparently either Division or Corps, or

Army perhaps, cannot make up their minds whether this is the main attack or only a diversion before the proper attack on the line. They'll have to make up their minds pretty soon, but meanwhile we are to sit tight and do nothing.'

We talked on for a few minutes, being joined by Williams and Richards with the same question as I had asked. Eventually I walked back to my squadron and gave what little news there was to the troop leaders, and then lay down by the side of my tank and dozed fitfully.

At six o'clock I went over again to Kinnaird, who still had no definite news or orders. While I waited with a small group of the other anxious inquirers, he checked again with Brigade and then said:

'Still nothing, so I think we'd better all have breakfast.'

By now we were all beginning to wonder whether our anxieties about the southern flank had been without reason and to think that perhaps the main attack had already gone in on the minefield and that we would hear details in due course. Revived by the thought that the enemy had embarked on what appeared to be a hazardous plan and reassured by the absence of a hectic, scrambling first-light battle, we set about our breakfast with a will. The mess was well stocked with delicacies, and we sat down to an appetising meal, while each crew prepared the food which suited their particular tastes.

By 7.30 a.m. we had all eaten well and were contemplating whether there was time to wash and shave. All round the leaguer I could see the crews tidying up the last vestige of breakfast and stowing the kit. One or two men were taking their spades for a walk. Tom was belching loudly in satisfaction over his breakfast and was discussing with Ben Storney his favourite breakfast menus. We all gave a hand to dismantle the mess shelter, and it was while I was encased in the folds of tarpaulin that I heard a shout from my tank, where Chandler was listening in on the wireless.

'Mount, start-up and be ready to move as soon as possible.'

There was a wild scramble. I arrived panting and hot at my tank after running the intervening 200 yards in what must have been record time. While I scrambled into the turret, pulling off my overcoat as I did so, Chandler held up the head-phones so that

I could hear the first reports from Williams' light squadron, who had been warned first and were already out west of us.

' ... The enemy are still some way off, and we can't make out exactly what they consist of, but there's a hell of a lot of them. I am moving another figures one thousand yards forward to get better observation. Off.'

There was silence for a time. I checked that all the squadron were ready to move and then waited for Kinnaird's hand signal to advance, as I knew he would not use the wireless in case the light squadron had any further news to report. As we moved off, Williams came on the air again and we listened in silent awe.

'DINA calling. There are at least figures two hundred tanks – I say again two hundred tanks – making straight for us now. I am about figures two thousand yards ahead of your position and the enemy are about another figures one thousand five hundred yards from us and moving fast. There's nothing I can do here – what do you want me to do? Over.'

Kinnaird answered immediately, 'Hullo, DINA. Don't get embroiled there – we are just moving up to a ridge on which we will take up a battle position, so there's nothing useful you can do in front of us; move now to your right and watch our flank there, as we have no neighbours for some distance to the north. Off to you. Hullo, JUMA, hullo, HAMO,' he went on. 'We will form battle line on this ridge figures three zero zero yards in front of us. JUMA [which was my squadron on the left] will try to make contact with the people on our left. No one will fire until I give the order. Off.'

We had been in this particular leaguer area for some time and knew the ground fairly well. We were all aware that beyond the ridge we were now approaching the ground sloped away gradually to the smooth expanse of a saltpan about two miles away to the west. It was not a perfect position, as there was only room for one regiment, but at least we would have some advantage over the enemy.

As we moved slowly up to the crest we must have all wondered what we would see on the other side. Already beyond about 1,500 yards the ground was covered with a shimmering haze, so that to the naked eye nothing was very clear. When we had halted and I looked through my binoculars my heart sank to the depths of my stomach and I felt breathless and weak at the knees.

Williams had not exaggerated. Before us, spread out in a wide fan covering a frontage of over 5,000 yards, I could see the squat black shapes of at least 200 tanks, their height and shape distorted in the haze and by the fact that the crews were still sitting on top of the turrets. They were moving in a north-easterly direction, slightly obliquely to the way that our ridge faced, so that the enemy's right flank were already considerably closer to the left of my squadron than their other flank was to our right, where the light squadron had now moved back and were extending the battle line of the two Grant squadrons to the north.

Remembering Kinnaird's orders, I at length dragged my eyes from the horribly awe-inspiring sight to my front and turned to look for the other regiment on our left, to see if I could make contact with them. I imagined that they would have moved at the same time as we did, and searched for them in position extending our left flank. But there was no sign of them there, and turning farther towards the south-east I was aghast to see them still in their leaguer area. Not a tank had moved. Some had still got their bivouacs fitted to the sides. Men were wandering about calmly and slowly, as if there was no need for haste at all. I signalled Kinnaird.

'JUMA calling. The people on my left have made no move at all and do not seem to be ready to move either. Over.'

'Hullo, JUMA. I can't think what they are doing. I will give them a call on the rear link and see what they say. Off.'

There was silence while we all watched the advancing enemy. Occasionally I glanced again to my left, desperately hoping to see some signs of urgency, as time was getting very short and the enemy right flank was closing rapidly on to the unsuspecting leaguer.

Eventually, as if it were in a film which had suddenly been speeded up, I saw the whole leaguer break into galvanic action. But already it was too late. Ominous black puffs of smoke marked were shells were bursting; men, who at one moment were dashing madly to man a tank, in the next moment fell to the ground and were still; tanks, in the action of turning to face the enemy, came suddenly to a stop and in some cases started to belch smoke almost simultaneously. And we could now hear the sounds of battle – the crump of shell-fire, the crack of shot, the chatter of machine-guns.

I told Kinnaird. 'JUMA calling. People on our left have been overrun. I don't think a single tank has escaped. The enemy have not had one casualty, and are moving straight on towards us. Over.'

'Hullo, JUMA,' he answered. 'I was afraid of that. For some reason they had made no preparations to move. You will have to keep a sharp look-out to your left now, as there is no one else on that flank at present. Off.'

Still we had not fired a shot. Whether it was due to our immobility or our silence, the German advance, after they had overrun the leaguer, gradually slowed down. When they were only 800 yards away from the left flank of my squadron their speed was reduced to walking pace, but still they came on. And still Kinnaird did not give the order to fire. It had the extraordinary effect on the Germans that they, too, were, in the main, silent, so that it was in almost complete quiet that the range between us was slowly closed, that on my flank being the shortest because of the oblique angle of the enemy's approach.

At length I deemed it was time that we retaliated or we would be overrun by the weight of numbers opposite us before we had had time to destroy sufficient of them to halt their advance. I called Kinnaird:

'JUMA calling. The enemy are now not more than figures four hundred yards from my left flank. May we open fire? Over.'

Kinnaird answered instantly, 'Hullo, all stations. Fire now – I say again, fire now. Off.'

In readiness for this moment I had made sure that both the 37 and 75 gunners had picked a particular tank as their targets and had kept pace with the German advance by making the necessary adjustments on the range-scales. The guns were already loaded and each loader was standing by with another round. All I had to say was 'Fire', and both guns roared immediately.

After that it was each tank for itself. There was no manoeuvre required; we were to stand and fight it out, and all my attention was required to control the fire of the two guns. To be able to check the fall of shot, I fired them alternately.

'75: Mark III to your immediate front which has that white splash on the turret – four hundred and fifty yards. Aim for the base of the turret. Fire.' A pause while I watched the line of flight, and then: 'Low – it hit the ground just in front. It's still moving, though. Same range and same sight – reload and wait.'

Then '37: Mark III which is stationary in front of us: there – that one that has just fired – four hundred yards. Fire. .... Good shot! – hit on the hull front. Reload and wait.'

'75: Fire. .... Hit! Good shot! Reload and fire again.'

I heard the loader dragging the round from the bin and then the clang of the breech as it closed; then a shout from Rogers, 'Firing now', and the tank rocked back slightly with the recoil and I could see the trace of the shot in the air and followed it until it hit again.

'75: Good shot! I think that one is knocked out. Relay on the tank immediately to the right of that one. Reload and wait.'

'37: Fire. .... Hit again. Doesn't seem to be doing much good, but fire again. No, wait – machine-gun. Traverse right on to the tank that the 75 has just knocked out – there. Engage the crew baling out – that's it,' I said as I heard the chatter of the gun and saw the bullets spraying the ground round the tank.

And so it went on until at last we could see that we had brought the enemy to a definite stop, and indeed here and there one or two were withdrawing slowly out of the battle leaving behind a satisfactory quota of silent or burning tanks.

Chandler interrupted me from time to time to keep me informed of the news on the wireless: 'Two B says his commander and 37 gunner are killed but they are still engaging with 75.' – 'Four says that he has a fire in the turret and is withdrawing slightly to deal with it – he will be back in figures five.' And once he tapped me on the shoulder and pointed to my left, where a tank was in flames. As we watched, it blew up with such a roar and concussion as we had not known before. I tried to discover whose tank it was and decided with a sickening feeling of anguish that it was Ben Storney's. After all his triumphs and luck of the previous winter to go like that in the flash of an eye!

At intervals I could feel the thud of a hit against the armour and the dust would engulf us inside the turret so that we could barely see each other. But we suffered no apparent damage until Rogers, the 75 gunner, shouted back, 'Periscope smashed – have to change it, sir.'

261

'O.K.,' I answered; 'but for God's sake be quick.'

Meanwhile I went on engaging with the 37 until a further hit jammed the turret and we were unable to traverse at a moment when there were no enemy tanks directly in the line of sight. With both guns temporarily out of action, I had time to look round me and see how my squadron had fared.

To my left Ben Storney's tank was still smoking and on fire. Beyond him one of his other tanks – the one which had had the commander and 27 gunner killed – was still firing intermittently with its 75. Next to me, the third tank of his troop appeared to be undamaged.

But beyond these three tanks on our left flank only one of the tanks of Edward Parry's troop appeared to have survived. Though I watched for some minutes I could see no sign of life from any but the outer tank, whose guns were firing spasmodically. I tried calling them on the air and at last got an answer from the sergeant commanding this tank: 'One Beer answering. We're doin' all we can, but I'm runnin' pretty short of ammo and my driver's 'ad it. We've cleared up the mess but we shan't last much longer – Jerries are working round to my left flank now that they've dealt with that other lot.'

I drew Kinnaird's attention to this precarious situation and was reassured by his information that the 25-pounder battery would be moving into position there in the near future – as they did only a few minutes later. They were one of the batteries of the artillery regiment of the Brigade. They must have given the Germans a nasty surprise, for they advanced no farther on that flank.

On my right the situation was somewhat better at this stage. Tom Irving was still engaging with both guns. Beyond him I could see that two of the six tanks of Joe Carless' and Frank Groves' troops were on fire, though neither had as yet exploded.

Beyond them, Kinnaird's headquarters' tanks were right up in the firing line, exchanging shot for shot with the enemy. Farther I could not see in the smoke and haze which shrouded the whole field of battle, though I knew from Richards' recent reports that his squadron was in much the same shape as mine.

Rogers fixed the new and only remaining spare periscope we carried and we continued firing with the 75. Occasionally as an enemy tank crossed the line of sight we were able to engage with the 37, though this, too, had had its periscope damaged and Larkin had replaced it with the spare.

It was at about this time that Williams, still on the right flank with his light squadron, which could do little in the gun battle, reported:

'DINA calling. A fairly considerable proportion of the enemy tanks seem to be detaching themselves and moving off to the north. At a guess I would say that we are left with one of the Panzer Divs and the other is moving off somewhere. I have seen no sign as yet of any of the Italians. Over.'

Kinnaird's answer gave us some inkling of the wider picture of the battle.

'Hullo, DINA. I think you're right – that's some satisfaction, though Lord knows we're left with enough to deal with here. I am told that there are fairly considerable enemy forces behind us, too, though they are probably nothing more than 90th Light Division. My immediate superiors say that theirs have been overrun and captured. Off.'

This was certainly startling news. For Divisional Headquarters to be surprised and overrun something serious must indeed have happened, considering all the various sources from which they should have been given warning. Somehow our battle assumed an even grimmer aspect now that we knew that the chaos was much more widespread than we had begun to suspect.

There was a yell from Rogers which interrupted my gloomy thoughts, 'Norton's been 'it, sir. Shot wrecked 'is front hatch and 'e's been 'it in the 'ead. Can't do nuffink for 'im, sir. 'Fraid 'e's dead.'

'All right,' I shouted back. 'Leave him and go on firing.' It was all we could do, but we were vividly aware of the gaping hole in the front of the hull through which any shot could now come.

Rogers' next shout was no better news, 'Gun-mounting jammed, sir – can't move any ways – and me periscope's bust. Shall I just go on firing on spec, sir, an' 'ope we 'its somefing?'

'O.K., do that,' I shouted back, and now gave all my attention to the 37.

We were in no better luck with this, however, as its periscope, too, was shattered a few minutes later and I could only tell Larkin to go on firing in the hope, as with the 75, that a stray shot would do some damage. At least it would make the Germans think that we were still effective and deter them from pushing home their attack.

But we were not very successful with even this hopeless stratagem for very long. A minute or two later another shot chipped the edge of the aperture where the driver's hatch had been and broke into fragments, one of which entered the side of Rogers' head, killing him instantly. With a cool courage which I had not before suspected of him, Harden pushed aside the dead bodies of Norton and Rogers and then continued to load and fire the gun himself.

The next disaster was that a shot struck the upper surface of the mounting of the 37 gun, the force of the impact shearing the bolts which held the mounting to the inside of the turret so that the gun and recoil system complete slid slowly to the turret floor, leaving a gap facing the enemy even bigger than that in the front hull. In the next instant another shot crashed through this gaping hole, killing Chandler and wrecking the wireless set behind him.

There was now no hiding the fact that we were seriously crippled, so I shouted down to Harden:

'Can you drive?' and surprisingly the answer came back:

'Yes, sir. I know what to do, but I don't know 'ow well I can do it.'

'All right,' I answered. 'Just start up, put it in reverse and we'll go out like that.'

While we waited for Harden, Larkin and I struggled round the mass of the collapsed gun and found places on the floor of the turret. Even so we were not very much safer, as we were then in line with the wrecked driver's hatch. It was with infinite relief that I heard the engine come to life, and a moment later we began to move slowly down the slope behind us. After a hundred yards or so we were completely hidden from the enemy, but continued in this fashion until we had covered the half-mile which brought us to the small group of vehicles where I found Henderson tending the wounded.

He walked over to me as I stopped, wiping his bloodstained hands, and said, 'Thank God you're all right, Tony. Edward Parry's crew have just brought in his tank and we've just buried him. I hear Ben Storney was blown up. Sergeant White and

Corporal Hoskins have both been killed. How are we doing? Can we hold them, do you think?'

'I don't know, Doc,' I answered. 'I wish I knew how we got into this mess. We knew this attack was coming, and yet we've been caught just as unprepared as if it was a complete surprise.'

While we were talking another tank arrived. From it I saw the crew carry out the body of Tom Irving, who had been hit in the head. They had come back as they were completely out of ammunition. While they refilled with a new load, I and the operator cleaned the blood from the turret and I transferred my belongings from my own tank. By this time Harden and Larkin, with the help of other willing hands, had dug the shallow graves for Norton, Chandler and Rogers. I helped them put the bodies in and watched while the earth was shovelled over them. I left as they were fixing crude crosses to some stone-filled petrol tins.

'Good-bye, you two,' I said to Harden and Larkin. 'I've taken over Captain Irving's tank, so you had better take that one back to the fitters and see if you can get it to workshops.'

'O.K., sir,' said Harden; 'but can't we come with you to the new tank – no, I suppose not,' he added as he saw me shake my head. 'Well, we'll look after this one, sir. It didn't do us too bad, did it? Some of the lads have counted the hits on it, and they reckon there's thirty-two.'

I waved to them as I climbed on to my new tank and then turned to fix the head-phones and arrange my map as we moved off.

When I arrived back in the battle line the firing had died down somewhat, so I had a chance to check what remained of my squadron.

All three tanks of Edward Parry's troop were knocked out, two still in position but silent and derelict looking, so I could not tell how many of the crews had survived and could get no answer on the wireless. One tank of Ben Storney's troop was still in action, his own still smouldering and that of his Sergeant silent and derelict. So much for my left. Counting my own crippled tank, one survivor out of seven.

On my right the situation was somewhat better. Of the seven that had started in the morning I was in Tom's relatively undamaged tank. There were two tanks missing from Frank Groves' troop – his own and that of his troop sergeant – and I had no idea what had happened to them. Joe Carless was still in action with one other tank of his troop, his third one being in position but blackened and smouldering. Four out of seven. And in the squadron five survivors of the fourteen Grants that had joined battle not two hours earlier.

Farther to my right I could see Kinnaird's two tanks, and beyond him, Richards' squadron appeared to be as depleted as mine, and Richards himself I knew to be wounded, as I had seen him brought in to the doctor while I was there.

5

Despairs and Frustrations

I SAW that the German tanks in front of us were still as numerous as ever, a solid, threatening line. Behind these were a number of tanks still smoking and smouldering and others which we had apparently damaged in some way – the total was between twenty and thirty. It was a small figure compared to our own losses; a regiment completely wiped out – a loss of about fifty tanks – and our own regiment sorely depleted – some twenty tanks destroyed or seriously damaged. At least we had managed to hold the German advance, though we were now in a precarious position, short of ammunition and seriously reduced in numbers. At length we were forced to withdraw to refill. While doing so we were attacked by some of the German tanks, which had followed up our move. These Williams' light tanks were able to hold off just long enough to enable us to get away.

After joining with the other regiment, who had not yet fired a shot, we moved north-east through scattered and wandering columns of lost supply vehicles and, here and there, small groups of shattered and burning lorries until we reached El Adem. Here, in the early afternoon, we re-formed and received a few reinforcements. I took command of all the remaining tanks of Richards' squadron and these, with the reinforcements, brought me very nearly up to strength again. So the regiment now consisted of the light squadron and only one heavy squadron.

In the evening, rested, fed and replenished, we moved west

against the scattered columns of the German 90th Light Division, which, during the day, had so disrupted the supply columns and headquarters, and had even reached the main dumps of all supplies north of El Adem. In the fading light we inflicted a number of casualties and drove them headlong west until our advance was at length halted by darkness. We had managed to avenge, if only to a very small extent, our disasters and tragedies of the morning, and we moved into harbour with spirits somewhat revived.

On the following day we were able to continue our success, gradually driving the enemy farther and farther west until he had joined forces with his other divisions and we were at length halted by a co-ordinated line of anti-tank guns. We had cleared the battlefield east of a line running north and south through Knightsbridge and had again had sufficient minor successes to revive our morale.

As in the previous summer battles, we found that the long hours of daylight meant that we had only a short time each night for all the many duties of repair, replenishment, reorganization and sleep. We stood-to each day at about four o'clock and we were lucky to be in leaguer at night by ten. At midday, it was true, the haze of heat so blinded each side that active battle was almost impossible, but we were not always allowed to rest at this time and were frequently on the move. The heat and our mounting exhaustion depressed and weakened us, so that there was little if any time devoted to chat or gossip either in leaguer at night or in the peaceful periods during the day.

On 29 May another khamsin started, doubly unpleasant compared with any we had previously experienced, as the oven-hot wind now gathered up all the loose sand, cut up by the tracks and wheels of the recent battles, so that we were scorched, blinded and choked at one and the same time. All morning we stayed in open leaguer, just west of El Adem, vainly trying to get cool, to avoid the fine dust and to quench our thirst. In the afternoon, however, we were ordered west and placed under command of 1st Armoured Division to join in the tank battle which had been fought intermittently throughout the day to the north-west of Knightsbridge.

We struggled through the blinding sand, making the best pace we could, but continually being so smothered in a fog of dust that progress became quite impossible and we could only halt and wait for a clearer patch. Navigation by sun compass was impossible, so we were forced to rely on our prismatic compasses and to endure further delays, as the navigators had to make frequent halts to climb down to check their bearings, since any reading taken on or near the tank was bound to be inaccurate.

Late in the evening we eventually reached the fringe of the battle area and Kinnaird warned, 'Watch out for anti-tank guns.' But for once it was we who surprised them – probably they never imagined that we would be moving with a khamsin blowing.

To my front I saw Joe Carless halt his troop, and a moment later the crash of his 75 firing was borne on the wind to me, muffled by the swirling blanket of sand and whirled past me by the still fairly high wind. But there could be no doubting the elation in his voice when he reported:

' ... Have knocked out an anti-tank gun and crew,' and a moment later, ' ... Have knocked out another and set one enemy vehicle on fire. Over.'

I acknowledged only, but Kinnaird was quick to appreciate the situation and at once asked Joe:

'Can you see any other guns on your front? Are any guns firing at you now? Can you see any men anywhere? or vehicles? If not, we may have managed to knock a hole in his line. If so we must act quickly. Let me know what you think as soon as you can. Over.'

There was a small pause and then Joe replied:

'No, I can see no signs of anything. I think we have knocked out the only guns on this bit of the front. Over.'

'O.K. Off to you,' Kinnaird replied, and then to me: 'What do you think? If we have caught them napping we must move quickly. Over.'

I could see little of the ground to my front and certainly not far enough ahead to decide whether we had made a breach. But by now I knew that Joe would not have given other than a carefully considered opinion and had no hesitation in backing his view.

'I can't see from here, but I think we should risk it,' I answered, watching Kinnaird, who had moved his tank up close to mine, as

I did so, and then added, when I saw him raise his hands for the advance to continue, 'Off to you. Hullo, all stations JUMA. Advance now. Off.'

With our vision still limited by the swirling sand, we moved forward again, past the two guns which Joe had knocked out and over a small ridge behind them. There we found ourselves running down into a large, saucer-shaped valley. Over the crest to our left we saw five or six vehicles approaching towing anti-tank guns, and over the crest to our right about the same number disappearing. There was no time to stop and engage. Waving the two left troops forward to meet the oncoming vehicles, I myself turned right with the other two troops in an effort to catch the disappearing enemy. Short of the crest we had knocked out or run over four, but the small delay entailed in dealing with them had allowed two others to escape, and when we breasted the ridge they were already in firing positions. At that extremely short range their first two shots hit and penetrated two tanks at once and a further one immediately afterwards before the rest of us could bring our fire to bear and destroy them.

The short, sharp battle was fought in complete wireless silence – there was no time for talk – and we rallied and soon afterwards moved into leaguer, well satisfied with our work despite the loss of three tanks and two men killed. Again Joe Carless had escaped, and I made a mental effort and resolution not to allow his survival to prey on my mind and conscience as that of Peters and Drummond had done the previous winter. But it needed great effort.

The next day and the two following we did little that could influence the battle. Kinnaird went early to Brigade for orders and gave them to us on his return.

'Apparently,' he said, looking ill-tempered and frustrated, 'the enemy have started to withdraw west up against our minefields. As that is the case he is to be harassed only by the guns, while we and the rest of the armour scout the battlefield outside his defences and mop up what we can find.'

We could all sense his disgust and bewilderment at these orders and felt entirely in accord with his views, particularly after our brief success of the previous evening.

So for three days we wandered vaguely about the battlefield.

We went south to the area of our first battle, where many tanks had been reported, and, sure enough, found some forty derelicts on the scene of our fight. We destroyed or captured a number of wandering enemy trucks and took a few score of prisoners. But we felt that we were doing little for the main course of the battle in rounding up these waifs and strays.

At length we moved north again and leaguered for the night in country which I had not seen since our first watch on the Tobruk perimeter almost eighteen months earlier. We were about six miles north-west of Knightsbridge, and before going to bed wondered what was in store for us.

During the next morning two depressing events occurred. By eleven o'clock we were enveloped again in the full discomfort of a khamsin laden with dust. Hot, weary, and choking, we were in no mood, after the pointless frustrations of the previous days, to receive the news, at about midday, that one of the brigades of the 50th Division had been entirely surrounded and eventually beaten into submission, together with the headquarters of one of the heavy tank brigades and a complete regiment of Matildas.

We knew instinctively that this was a major turning point in the battle. Instead of the enemy being trapped against our mine-fields, surrounded on all sides, and cut off from all his supplies but for the most precarious routes running north from Bir Hakeim, he had now joined up with his forces on the west of our minefields and had opened up a short and direct route to bring forward all he wanted. While we had been sent on a wild-goose chase, frittering away valuable time and energy, the whole face of the battle had changed. Up to this time, after the first amazing successes of his surprise attack, the enemy had been hemmed in and might have been hammered with all the weight of our forces. But now he had every chance to turn the tables on us. It was a sobering and disturbing thought which kept us companion for the rest of the day while we struggled against the trials and discomforts of the weather – a nagging, aching doubt about the functioning and competence of our commanders. It was the same old story being repeated again and again: brigades and units isolated all over the battlefield, left to the attentions of the enemy, who fought as a combined body.

By evening the dust-storm had died down sufficiently to allow us to see some distance to the south and we were, at last, ordered to move to engage the enemy. The Brigade was still only two regiments strong, and we had not been supplied with sufficient tanks to make up our other heavy squadron. In the event it was decided therefore that we would protect the left flank of the other regiment, who were still fairly well up to strength.

Though the storm had cleared, the air was still laden with fine particles of sand and dust, on which the evening sun shone and glistened so that it was difficult to distinguish any detail, though the prominent features of the landscape were easily visible.

We moved from our day positions across a fairly flat, rock-strewn plateau and then dipped down to the floor of a wide valley, running east and west, across the line of our advance. Beyond the high ground to our immediate front we could expect to see the main body of the enemy lying in the protective folds of the ring of ridges – the area within which was already coming to be known as the 'Cauldron'.

When we were no more than half-way across the floor of the valley we suddenly became aware that the regiment on our right had swung due west in a wild scurry of movement and dust. A moment later Kinnaird spoke on the wireless.

'Hullo, all stations LOMA. Halt now where we are. The people on our right are being attacked by figures five zero tanks which are moving down the floor of the valley from the west. We are to protect their left flank and will keep watch on the ridge to our front. Off.'

For a time we sat in silent watch, vividly aware of the tumult of the firing to our right and wondering how it was going. The battle was too far away for us to see through the dust-laden air. It was a bewildering scene. Behind us we could hear the bangs of our own artillery as they engaged targets which were invisible to us from the floor of the valley. From our right, with growing frequency, shells and shot fell among us, the overs from the battle there. In the prevailing hubbub of noise it was some time before we realised that four 88-mm. guns had come into action in positions on the ridge in front of us. Either the dust had hidden us from them when we moved down the forward slope or they had been moved into position in concert with the tank attack on our right. They were busily shelling the groups of transport

271

behind us, and we only knew of their existence because of the terrifying recognizable sequence of the noises of their shells – so high was their muzzle velocity that we heard first the crack of the shot passing overhead, followed quickly by the crash of the detonation behind us, and only then the deeper, duller explosion from the gun. We could not see their positions nor could they see us, or they would without doubt have engaged. I was selfishly thanking my lucky stars when Kinnaird ordered me:

' ... There are four of those guns which must be put out of action. You and I and those two just in front of you will engage. I do not want any of the others to move until we know how the battle goes on our right. We will reverse slowly up the hill behind us and engage as soon as we can see the positions of those guns. Off.'

We moved into position as fast as we could. The 88s had already caused considerable damage and confusion on the ridge behind us, and if left unmolested they were likely to take a hand in the tank battle also.

We were in luck, though. The ridge up which we reversed was some feet lower than that to our front. The 88s were able to engage the guns and vehicles behind us only at the maximum angle of depression of the barrels. When we were almost at the top of the slope up which we were reversing we could clearly see the 88 positions, and started at once to range on them. Through my binoculars I saw the crew of the gun I had picked as my target dive for cover as my first shell landed on the slope in front of them. But a moment later they were back at their positions, and the next shot which passed over my head was not accompanied by an explosion, so I knew they were firing solid shot at me. A hit by an 88 even at a range of about 3,000 yards would almost certainly have been fatal, so it was with the utmost urgency that we tried to register a hit.

But our problem was not an easy one. Though I could see the 88 clearly enough, the ground behind it fell away so sharply that my shell-bursts beyond it were lost to view, even if I had been able to distinguish them at that range and in the prevailing visibility. So it was impossible to engage by the normal practice of bracketing – alternate shots in front and behind, halving the distance between each burst until eventually a hit was registered. I resorted to the more laborious and lengthy process of creeping up on the

88 with each round, avoiding any big increase in range which resulted in the shell going over the 88 and disappearing in the low ground beyond.

I was happy that I was keeping the gun from firing at any other target and complacently thinking that I had all the time I wanted to destroy it, when I noticed that after each round that was fired the crew dashed to the front of the gun and shovelled away vigorously at the ground below each wheel of the carriage so as to lower further the angle of the barrel. I noticed, too, that the crack of the shots was considerably closer above my head. I was reluctant to move, as it would have entailed starting afresh the whole process of ranging, but I knew that, as a last resort, I could move slightly down the slope if the 88 managed eventually to depress to an unhealthy angle.

Nevertheless I now felt that there was a considerably greater degree of urgency to my task, especially so when three Grant tanks, newly arrived in the battle area and coming forward to join us, came to the crest behind me and were promptly knocked out by the 88s on the further ridge.

Each shot of my creeping approach fell closer to the target, but the accidents of the ground made the calculation of each increase of range a complicated task. To start with, on the lower, flatter slope at the foot of the ridge each increase of elevation of the gun produced a definite and similar increase in the range of the fall of each shot. As the angle of the slope increased, however, the same increases in elevation produced apparently smaller differences in range, until we reached beyond the crest itself, when the first round appeared to go double the distance previously attained by the same increase of elevation.

All the time the crack of the shots above my head was getting closer and closer – it was impossible, however, to gauge how close, or whether it was in fact exactly overhead. I was torn between a pressing desire to move to avoid the almost certain death as a result of this, and a compelling reluctance to change my position and so to alter all the adjustments of the ranging we had so far done.

Grimly the gunner and I went on with our task. The air had cleared to a great extent and we could now clearly see the flash and puff of smoke as the 88 fired each time. And each time my

273

heart leapt to my mouth. For all I knew, the shovelling between each round might just have made all the difference.

Kinnaird had had no better luck, and I clearly heard the note of exasperation in his voice when he interrupted both his and my shooting to say:

' ... People on the right have had fairly heavy casualties and are starting to withdraw. They will be passing through us and up on to the area behind. We've got to get these guns. Off.'

My next shot fell beyond the 88, and the one after, halving the bracket of the range, just in front. I knew that the alterations that my gunner could make on the elevating wheel were now so small that it was useless my trying to tell him how far short we were and could only say, 'Up a fraction – careful now.' We were in the hands of fate – each slight variation of weight of explosive charge in each shell or the slight play in the gears of the elevating mechanism might just make all the difference between a hit and a miss. The next shot fell plus again and the next still plus. Despite the closeness of the shell-bursts, the crew of the 88 were still shovelling between shots, and I wondered with mounting desperation who would win the duel. But my gunner had the answer. He had noticed that the play of the gears was less when depressing the gun, and by going beyond and then coming back with each round, he had largely eliminated one of the two inaccuracies. The next shot hit the 88 fairly and squarely – there was no doubt about it. After the flash of the explosion of our shell, another large and loud detonation followed which blew the barrel to pieces. A train of explosions ensued as the ammunition stacked round the gun caught fire and exploded.

So embroiled had I been with my own duel that I had not noticed that one of the two tanks of my squadron, which had fallen back with Kinnaird and me, was on fire. I switched to engage the remaining 88s, but with a sigh of relief saw that they had ceased firing and their crews were busily hitching them to the towing trucks – honour was satisfied apparently, at one all, and they could not as yet see the other regiment withdrawing down the valley. We redoubled the rate of fire, and one lucky round hit the truck towing one of the 88s just as it began to disappear over the crest. We plastered this cripple until the truck was well on fire and the gun had been tipped on its side.

Meanwhile the withdrawal of the other regiment continued unmolested as, in the now failing light of the evening, the enemy gave up the chase, since he could not distinguish our positions in the lengthening shadows of the valley bottom.

We passed through our sister regiment on our way back to leaguer and noticed that they were now reduced to the same strength as ourselves – they had lost about a squadron of Grants, though they claimed to have inflicted the same number of casualties on the enemy. But we knew by now that that was not enough to redress the balance of the enemy's superiority in performance and our own lamentable and inexplicable inability to bring him to battle with a numerical superiority to our advantage.

6

Disaster Again

THEN for two days we did nothing, and after that for almost a month we had an unrelieved succession of disasters and disappointments. Day after day when we felt we should have been harrying the enemy we were left uncommitted. And when on each occasion we were ordered into battle it was with so little warning or preparation that we began to expect disasters and to suspect that the plans were incompletely worked out and co-ordinated. More and more we began to feel that it was useless to enjoy an over-all superiority in numbers if the enemy were to be allowed to smash our units and formations one by one, by always being superior in numbers at the vital point. We knew we could beat him if only we were given the chance – we had beaten him the previous winter, though then we had had equipment which was even more inferior to that of the enemy.

The heat, the incessant dust-storms, the stress and strain and the prospect of imminent death were taking their toll on our resistance. If we had only been able to feel that we were being led with some plan and decision our bewildered hopelessness would have vanished. As it was, there was apparently no rhyme or reason in most of what we were told to do. On days when we could have been left entirely at rest to recuperate and reorganize we were ordered to maintain a fruitless vigil against an enemy who was often invisible from the positions to which we were sent. Four hours of sleep, at the most, each night was all we got, and after a time this became more than the human frame could stand, since there was no rest nor relief in the burning daytime hours, when we were always expected to be alert.

On 5 June Kinnaird heard from Brigade that a determined attack by two infantry brigades had gone in at dawn that morning in the area south of Knightsbridge in a westerly direction, aimed at the centre of the enemy positions in the Cauldron. This attack was to be followed up by an armoured brigade while a tank brigade attacked due south just west of us.

All day we waited for news of the progress of the attack. Kinnaird went three times to Brigade, and returned each time with reports which were entirely contradictory: they spoke of good progress in one moment and heavy casualties in the next.

Suddenly, in the late afternoon, Kinnaird ordered:

' . . . We are to move now to engage figures one hundred enemy tanks which are attacking the people on our right.'

We moved due south for four miles and came in on the left flank of the Tank Brigade. In concert with them we withdrew slowly north again, leaving behind about fifty Valentines and Matildas which had been knocked out in the day's battle. That night in leaguer we heard that the Armoured Brigade which had taken part in the southern attack had lost about the same number of tanks, and that two complete brigades of infantry, together with four regiments of guns, had also been either destroyed or captured.

At dawn next day we moved north of Knightsbridge and then south-east and south until we were on the edge of the scene of the previous day's battle. Here we were able to rescue some of the stragglers, pitifully few from the thousands who had moved forward at dawn of the previous day.

So ended this brief and sudden disaster. We lost about 110 tanks from the two brigades involved, and felt even more frustrated about the daily growing tally of instances where not only were we asked to do more than we could ever be capable of, but where opportunities to inflict defeat and even destruction on the enemy were unaccountably allowed to slip.

Another period of pointless activity followed – pointless

because we were continually engaged in fruitless probing of the fringes of the enemy positions without ever being concentrated sufficiently to make a decisive move. For four days we ceaselessly patrolled the desert south of Knightsbridge, never meeting the main weight of the enemy armour, which we knew, from our contacts with the patrols near Bir Hakeim, was already investing the isolated French defences, which eventually fell on 10 June. Bewildered even more by this further sign of the inexplicable inertia of all our actions, we waited with growing bitterness and despondency for the next move.

We had not long to wait. Next evening we were confronted with a Panzer division moving north towards us. We had turned to face south, since the entire southern half of our original defences had now fallen and our line had been re-deployed eastwards from the area north of the Cauldron. We did no more than make contact that night before darkness overtook us and we moved north some miles and into leaguer.

Our orders the next morning were to break through the Panzer Division and 90th Light, which was farther to the east, to regain the open desert to the south, so that we would then be able to act offensively against the flank of any enemy advance northwards.

As the sun topped the eastern horizon we moved cautiously south through dispersed trails of morning mist which reduced our visibility at intervals to less than 500 yards. The light squadron of each of the two regiments moved about 500 yards to the flanks of the two remaining Grant squadrons, mine being on the right. I moved my own headquarters behind the centre of my squadron, and a few hundred yards to my right was Kinnaird in a position from which he could control both his squadrons.

As we knew in our heart of hearts would happen, our first intimation of the enemy was the fire of his cleverly camouflaged anti-tank guns to our right. Three of the tanks of my squadron and two light tanks went up in flames before we could reverse to positions where the ground gave us some protection. Kinnaird at once ordered:

'Hullo, all stations KANO. We will not try to advance any farther until the mist clears and we can locate and destroy these guns. Off.'

But no sooner had the mist dispersed than it was followed by

277

the heavy heat-haze of mid-morning, so that we were no more capable of locating the enemy than before. Before the mist finally dispersed, however, the German anti-tank gunners took advantage of the movement of its swirling folds, which temporarily hid the view opposite the gap between the two regiments, to move forward four of their guns. When the mist rolled back again, the tank on my left flank was destroyed and the regiment on my left had lost two of their Grants.

Throughout the midday hours, as usual, the visibility was so bad that neither side could move. At three o'clock, as the haze decreased, we saw the enemy tanks moving towards us from the south.

'Hullo, all stations KANO,' Kinnaird ordered. 'Stand fast here and engage. We are still to break through to the south if we can, so we must not withdraw. Off.'

There seemed to be more hesitation than usual about the moves of the German tanks, but nevertheless they kept us fully engaged. So long as we kept up a continual rate of fire they halted or even withdrew, but once we stopped they came on again. Casualties occurred on each side, but we managed to score the advantage; I could see five of their tanks on fire for the loss of only one each from my own and the other Grant squadron.

Kinnaird, with his two tanks, had joined our firing line, but I now heard him call the light squadron:

'Hullo, BOXO; KANO calling. Can you make out what is causing that cloud of dust to our right flank? It looks to me as if it's this side of Knightsbridge, so I don't think it is shell-fire. Over.'

'BOXO answering,' I heard. 'No, I can't. That one has only just started, but if you look left of it you will see another smaller one which seems to be a good deal closer. Have we any friends in that direction? Over.'

'KANO answering,' Kinnaird said. 'I had not noticed that there were two distinct clouds. The northern one may well be people like us, as I know that one lot are east of us and the other lot were north. Wait. I will see if I can find out. Off.'

I took this to mean that 2nd Armoured Brigade was east of us and 22nd Armoured Brigade, or what was left of it after its very hard battle of the 5th, was in position, where we had seen it a few days earlier, north of the Knightsbridge box.

Meanwhile we continued to devote our attention to the Germans in front, not over-anxious, at least as far as I was concerned, about the news from our right flank until the light squadron reported again:

'BOXO calling. The southern dust-cloud is made by a number of wheeled vehicles which I can now see at a range of figures two five zero zero yards. I cannot yet make out who they are. Over.'

'KANO answering. I have been trying to find out what is happening, but my own superiors say that there is a hell of a muddle, and they are not at all clear at the moment who their superiors are. Wait. Off.'

At once it occurred to me that Divisional Headquarters had been captured again, as on the first morning, and my heart sank with the memories of the chaos that had then ensued. But Kinnaird had not said they had been captured, and so I dared to hope that it was not so. But obviously the situation on the right flank was nothing to be complacent about, as the next message showed:

'BOXO calling. I still can't make out who these people are. They have moved much closer to us and appear to be putting out anti-tank guns. I can't make out whether these guns are facing this way or not. Over.'

Kinnaird, whose interest was obviously centred now on this flank, answered at once:

'KANO answering. I can still get no information. Send someone out to see what those people are doing. Over.'

'BOXO answering. O.K. Off to you. BOXO Two, go out and see what you can make of that lot. Go carefully, as we don't know whether they are friends or not. Off.'

Despite the enemy to my front, who were still as active as ever, I was gradually feeling more and more apprehensive about the right. It was obviously causing Kinnaird some worry, and by now we were never confident that some nasty situation would not develop without warning.

BOXO called again. 'That northern dust-cloud seems to be getting very much closer, but I still can't see what it is that is causing it. Shall I send someone out?' and when Kinnaird agreed, he continued, 'BOXO Three. Move out until you can see what it is to our north-west.'

For some five minutes there was silence on the net and then,

'BOXO Two calling. There are a lot of British vehicles among this lot, and there seems to be no unfriendly behaviour as yet. I am going farther forward. Off.'

And from the northern troop a few minutes later, 'BOXO Three, I can see the vehicles making the dust, and I think they are tanks – which seems probable judging by the size of the cloud. I cannot see what type of tank, so I'm going farther forward. Off.'

Again for a time we could hear only the thrumming of the wireless sets, interspersed at intervals by the crump of enemy shells or the crack of one of our own tanks firing. Then, in a quick, breathless hurry:

'BOXO Two calling KANO. These are Italians. I have been fired on by the anti-tank guns. More are being put into position, and behind them heavy guns are being moved up. Over.'

'KANO answering,' said Kinnaird. 'O.K. Do not go any farther forward, and come back if you are likely to be shot up there. Off to you. KANO calling BOXO Three. What news from you? Don't go too far, as I have a nasty feeling that that lot is the other Panzer Division moving down on us. Over.'

'BOXO Three for KANO,' came the immediate reply. 'These are German tanks all right. I can see them quite clearly. They have opened up on me and are coming in fast. Over.'

'KANO for BOXO Three. Rejoin us now. Off to you. Hullo, all stations KANO. We are in great danger of being shot at by two Panzer Divs. I have reported the position, but we cannot expect any help for some time. We shall just have to fight as best we can as we withdraw northwards. Off.'

The next twenty minutes were the most unpleasant and kaleidoscopic of my life. Incidents were so many and so varied that it was impossible to register each as it occurred or take any coherent action. As the northern Panzer Division drove into the attack, the Italians opened fire with a large variety of heavy guns and the Panzer Division to our south came to life and moved forward.

All round me I could see the fall of many shells and the strike of innumerable shots. The already darkening sky to the west was further shrouded by clouds of smoke from the shell-bursts and by the dust-cloud which, blown by the evening westerly breeze, preceded the advancing enemy tanks.

We had no chance. My own tank was soon completely crippled, though we all managed to get out unhurt. Kinnaird's, too, I could see had been knocked out, though I could not see where he or his crew was. All round me our tanks were crippled or burning, and as I ran from each shallow hollow to the next I was joined by more and more of the men of my squadron. All we could do was to hurry north on foot, trying desperately to put as much distance as possible between us and the enemy, so that in the few minutes left of daylight we would not be overrun and captured.

Two tanks of my own squadron and five of the light escaped the first holocaust of fire and, driving north in the gathering gloom, weaved their way about the battlefield picking up those like myself who were walking.

Festooned over these seven tanks like the fruit of an over-ripe tree, we made north for the escarpment leading down to the peri-meter of Tobruk. Behind us we could see the enemy tanks closing up on us and firing as they came. The tank I was on jerked sud-denly and came to a grinding halt. We all flung ourselves to the ground, and a few moments later found ourselves looking down the barrels of the guns of two German tanks, halted some ten yards away.

Slowly we raised our hands above our heads and, shepherded by a tense-faced, dust-covered, fair-headed German, we were herded in an untidy mob, numbering about twenty, back the way we had come.

In the gathering gloom the Germans did no more than make a cursory search for officers. I was able to avoid notice as I wore no badges of rank on my shirt, and so was marched away with the rest, towards where we could see the German tanks already form-ing up to move into leaguer. The German, sub-machine gun in hand, walked on one flank, continually urging us on with shouted commands which none of us understood. It was interesting to see that he and the other men of the crews of the two tanks were worn and obviously tired to the point of exhaustion. We pointed this out to each other as we marched, until we were silenced by a menacing movement of the gun which bade us to be quiet.

I had placed myself in the middle of the bunch so as to avoid being at all conspicuous. As we walked I failed to notice that the men in front of me had moved away to each side of the direct path to avoid a large trench. Before I saw it, I had fallen to the bottom of this trench, my surprised oaths muffled by the weight of two further men falling on top of me, their oaths less violent than mine as they fell on the soft cushion that I made for them. With commendable quick-wittedness they lay where they had fallen. When they at last moved off me and I climbed out of the trench, I saw the body of prisoners already 200 yards away, the German guard marching stolidly on the flank, still unaware that we had escaped.

All night we walked northwards towards Tobruk and at dawn, by chance, came to the area where the remnants of all three armoured brigades were re-forming. We found that Kinnaird had been put in command of all that remained of the two regiments of our brigade which had survived the battle of 27 May, when the third regiment had been almost entirely overrun – a composite regiment of fifteen tanks was all that was left! Of the other two brigades fifty tanks remained. All found we were slightly over the proper strength of one regiment.

Shortly before midday we moved west, north of the Knights-bridge box, and spent the rest of the day trying to repulse the attacks of the German tanks towards the coast road – attacks which, if they had succeeded, would have cut off the retreat of the two divisions still in the line. With scratch, mainly untrained crews, all dog-tired with exertion and lack of sleep, in tanks which had either not been adequately prepared for battle or were almost entirely battle-worn, we were unable to give a good account of ourselves. Although we held the enemy advance, we lost another twenty tanks in the process – two from our so-called regiment – mainly from the attentions of the German anti-tank guns, among them the 88s, which worked in perfect collaboration with their tanks.

7

Tobruk Captured

THANKFULLY we withdrew to leaguer – thinking all the way of the rest and food we would get at last after a thirty-six-hour day! But first we had to survive the discomforts and annoyances of the journey back – the stopping and starting, the muffling clouds of dust, the stifling fumes of fuel, the exertion of climbing down from the tank each time there was a halt to find out what had caused it, the labour of climbing on again afterwards. We seemed to have gone for miles when, during a halt which was more prolonged than any previously, I walked to the head of the column and found Kinnaird.

For some time I had seen him only briefly in leaguer – each night there had been far too much to do in reorganizing crews and preparing tanks for me to be able to stay for long in the inviting friendliness of his car. We had spoken only of tanks destroyed, crews killed or wounded, new tanks which were due and the allocation of new men. Now, for a time, we were able to stand and talk.

'Hullo, Tony,' he said, after the faint glow of his cigarette as he drew on it had lit my face. 'Come to see what's happened? I thought you'd be along soon. We're moving back to the frontier area to refit. We move through Tobruk to-night. I've sent someone to find the lane through the minefields. No sleep for you, I'm afraid.'

'Blast!' I said, too tired and dispirited to elaborate any more on my feelings. To have hoped so desperately for sleep and rest and to have my hopes so abruptly shattered was almost all I could bear. All my feelings of desperation and bitterness welled up uncontrollably. 'Refit for what?' I blurted. 'To be chucked in again into some shambles of a battle so that those who survive can refit again afterwards? When are we going to get a decent chance?'

'Enough of that, Tony,' Kinnaird answered. 'I know you've had a bloody time recently, but don't give in now. We've got to make an effort to keep going. The Jerries are probably getting just as tired. You hop into my car and sleep. I'll send one of the spare crews back to your tank.'

But I had not reached the stage of desperation where I could see myself facing my crew the next morning if I had slept all night when they had not. I thanked Kinnaird for his kindness and went back to my tank. Now I knew what was happening I was less anxious at each halt, and dozed fitfully when we were not moving.

All through the night we fumbled our way through the minefields, pushed our way through the congested streets of the town, and eventually found ourselves on the open road beyond – heading for Bardia. In Tobruk I had had to leave if not the comfort, at least the rest I could get in the turret, to help sort out the innumerable tangled traffic jams. The whole army seemed to be on the move. The garrison was re-deploying within the fortress and new units were joining it, among them the defenders of Knightsbridge, the rock round which the tides of the recent battles had surged and eddied. We were disturbed by the thought that at long last they, too, were displaced, but we were too busy to think much more about it.

At dawn we were still moving steadily east along the coastal road, and two hours later we turned south to the area of Gambut, where we settled down to refit and re-form. Our rest was disturbed by the constant sound of our own aircraft landing on and taking off from the nearby airfields. We had been completely unmolested by the German air force during the battle, and had been profoundly thankful that it had been so. We were now somewhat bewildered by the scale of our air effort, of which we had been ignorant previously, and wondered why it was that some at least had not been used to hit the enemy while he was bottled up in the Cauldron. Another of the mysteries of those inexplicable days!

For two days we slept and ate and worked. Kinnaird was completely tireless. In that time he built up his composite regiment again to two weak Grant squadrons and a squadron of Honeys. My own squadron, for instance, had three troops of three tanks and my own Grant. The other two regiments of the Brigade were at about the same strength – but we were a mixed and inconglomerate force. Some of the tanks were lacking vital items of equipment; some of the crews knew nothing of the tanks they manned; most of the tank commanders and nearly all the troop commanders were new to battle. Strive as we did to get some semblance of order and cohesion, we could not possibly make of ourselves more than a scratch force.

Two hours before midday of the 16th we were warned that the enemy armour was again nearby, had moved east to the area of Sidi Rezegh – even the name of the place caused some apprehension among those of us who had known it before. We moved south up the escarpment and then west towards El Adem. East of Sidi Rezegh we met the anti-tank screen we knew by now so well.

Our partly trained crews had their first chance to indulge in target practice, but by the time the light failed we had made little impression.

We moved out again at dawn, and took up a good position on the southern escarpment overlooking Sidi Rezegh, where we could see the German tanks massed behind the protection of their guns. Here we were in a dominant position – if the Germans wanted to advance east or against Tobruk they had first to deal with us – and at last on ground of our choosing.

It was with exasperated bewilderment therefore that we heard our orders in the early afternoon to move on to the aerodrome and then west against the German armour. The Brigadier, so Kinnaird was told, had gone to remonstrate about the order, but meanwhile, we were to advance. Leaving one regiment to move west along the top of the escarpment, the other two regiments, ourselves on the left, moved down the gradual incline to the aerodrome and then swung slightly left to face west.

By now we were being engaged by the German 88s and already, to my right front, I could see two Grants on fire and a Crusader tank smoking heavily. From then on the battle developed almost exactly as we had dreaded to expect. Gradually the Grants were picked off by the concentrated fire of the 88s and the German tanks until they were reduced to half the original strength. As before, the two Panzer Divisions were working in complete harmony, so that while we engaged the enemy to our front, we were suddenly assaulted by the other division on our left flank. Our own third regiment, on the escarpment failed to appear and with difficulty we started to withdraw. As always Kinnaird was in the forefront of the battle and his sane, calm voice on the air averted what might well have been another rout like that of the 12th.

As darkness overtook the battle, the German tanks gave up the chase, leaving us free to go unmolested, as they had already driven us from the field that we had controlled so completely earlier.

It was another night of endless driving, enveloped in sand and petrol fumes, another defeat on which to ponder bitterly and wonder whether we would ever be launched into a battle with some hope of success and an even chance to avoid disaster.

Even Kinnaird allowed himself one bitter comment on the day,

'We've had the Benghazi Handicap, the Msus Stakes, the Gazala Gallop and now the Rezegh Race. I wonder what it will be next?'

But more than that he would not say, and when we rallied near the Frontier wire the next day, he went round all the crews joking with them and offering encouragement. I thought of the lines that Milton wrote, and understood at last his wording:

> *Courage never to submit or yield;*
> *And what is else, not to be overcome.*

Not only did Kinnaird refuse to give up but, which was entirely different, he would not give in. Courage took many forms – each person reacted differently to fear, which was the cause of courage. And as with fear, courage was easily catching – a hint of either would spread like a bush-fire, the influence of either was magical in its swiftness. Some acts of courage were apparently so commonplace that they were difficult to detect. Kinnaird's courage that morning, which showed itself in his being able to behave so naturally after so many disasters, was one example. Courage was not necessarily or only shown by those who performed positive acts of noticeable bravery. There was as much courage, and often much more, shown by those who had not the influence of the high exaltation of fear to stimulate them temporarily in a dangerous or difficult situation. I thought that, though I had seen Kinnaird perform many acts of positive bravery, this manifestation of calm ordinariness was perhaps his greatest effort. I began to understand the cool courage of the men and women under the Blitz, the sailors in imminent danger of death for days and weeks on end, the airmen of the bombers which went out night after night, and last, but by no means least, the infantrymen in their trenches.

On 21 June we heard that Tobruk had fallen. Sick at heart and weary, we accepted this as merely the logical culmination of the disasters we had already suffered. In the papers we got, days out of date, we saw that the correspondents were already magnifying Rommel, and daily we heard his praises sung on the wireless. But we knew, with an angry, bitter certainty, that the emphasis should have been on the muddling inadequacy of our own efforts rather than on the competence of Rommel, except that he had developed an intuitive knowledge of our failings and was prepared to risk all on boldness.

On the 23rd we started to move back to the area of Mersa Matruh, where we were in position in the desert some thirty miles inland by the morning of the 25th. In the late afternoon of the following day the German armour crossed the Matruh to Siwa track, five miles to our west, and then halted for the night. At dawn they advanced again. We and 22nd Armoured Brigade held the advance of a depleted 15th Panzer Division, this time completely separated from the 21st Panzer Division by the steep slopes of the escarpment. At its foot, 21st Panzer, in full view of the New Zealand Division, who watched with quiet confidence from positions on the high ground, moved east through the gap between them and the Matruh garrison.

By now, wary of being caught unprepared because of lack of information from above, Kinnaird had arranged wireless sets to listen on the nets of each of our formations involved, so we knew of the progress of the battle. At last it seemed that we had a chance to administer some of the medicine of which we were suffering from an overdose! All afternoon Kinnaird kept saying: ' ... Don't waste ammunition on these people in front. We must be ready to move to engage the other Panzer Division.' Or later, ' ... You will withdraw now, one at a time, to reload with ammunition. We must not run short.' All the time he repeated to us what he knew of the enemy movements from his intercepts, and told us that one regiment of 22nd Armoured Brigade had already been ordered back.

And then, at about five o'clock, when we were on edge with expectation and a fierce determination to avenge all the defeats we had suffered, we were ordered to withdraw! The disgust in Kinnaird's voice was quite plain to us all when he passed the order on. We had no difficulty in disengaging from 15th Panzer, who seemed to be most reluctant to follow up. By nightfall we had moved about forty miles east and were due south of the subsidiary escarpment which ringed the next positions at Fuka. Kinnaird's only comment was: 'And now we've had the Matruh Marathon!'

Here for two days we did nothing. We were, indeed, so far south that it was as if we were involved in a separate war, except that we saw no signs of the enemy, who we knew, from Kinnaird's intercept system, were already into Fuka, where they had overrun the small columns left to delay them.

On the 30th, in the folds of a blinding dust-storm, we moved slowly east again. We had no idea where the enemy had got to, and peered anxiously through the shrouding screens of sand, hoping to catch the first glimpse of the enemy so that we could take action in time. We were moving as the leading regiment of the Brigade, intent on finding our way through the sandier, more difficult area near the coast. I was between Kinnaird and the leading squadron, acting as a link between the navigator and the forward screen. We were none of us over-anxious about the area to our front, as far as the enemy were concerned, being fairly certain that the first reports would be either from the flanks or from the screen we had left out behind. There were occasional wireless messages, dealing with the bearing of our direction or the state of the ground, but mainly we heard the steady thrumming of the set and the occasional cracks and crackles of the atmospherics.

Until suddenly, 'Hullo, MONA; DULO calling. Halt now – I say again – halt now. To my front, at a range of about figures one five zero zero yards, I can occasionally glimpse through the sand what looks like the whole of the Afrika Korps moving across my front from north to south. Over.'

Kinnaird acknowledged, ordered us to halt, drove forward pas me to the farthest patrol of the light squadron and we heard no more for a few minutes. Then he said, 'Hullo all stations, MONA. We will advance again now. Keep your eyes skinned for any stragglers. We do not want to get involved in a running fight in this visibility. Off.'

By nightfall we were still short of the positions we knew had now been occupied round the station at El Alamein. We leaguered and spent a restless night, with the guards doubled and each man at rest only, since few slept, fully clothed and ready in an instant to climb back into our tanks.

At dawn, our view still severely limited by the swirling sand, we moved on again, every nerve and sense alert for the first signs of what the news bulletins were calling the 'Alamein line'.

Again, to our astonishment, we very nearly bumped unwittingly into the full Afrika Korps. This time the rear patrols of the right-flank regiment reported that the enemy were bearing down on them coming from the south, where we had seen them go only the previous evening. We increased speed, and at length found that we were passing south of the defended box at El Alamein station. With difficulty we managed to persuade the South Africans, who were manning it, that we were not enemy, but only after some of our lorries had been hit, the flames of which acted as beacons, attracting part of an enemy attack which had already been launched against the western face of the box.

At length we broke free and drove on, only to find that we were hopelessly and helplessly embedded in an area of soft sand about ten miles farther on. All day we struggled to extricate ourselves, thankful at last to be behind the forward areas of a line which we believed to be strongly fortified, anxious lest we should become entangled in the battle, which we could hear raging just behind us, before we were clear of the meshes of the sand, hopeful that, after so many tribulations, we could now turn and throw the enemy back.

For a fortnight, day in and day out, sometimes north of it, sometimes south, occasionally on the summit of its crest, we contested the vital ground of the Ruweisat Ridge against what remained of the Panzer Divisions and 90th Light. The battle ebbed and eddied on the bare slopes of the rocky ridge, at times one side gaining the advantage, at times the other – every yard of ground daily bitterly contested, both sides determined to control what, except in battle, would have been a barely noticeable fold on the ground.

Though we heard of preparations of further defence lines being made farther east in the Delta and Nile areas, and knew that others, at least at the back of their minds, were still considering the prospects of further withdrawal, we felt that we could now hold the enemy attacks. Each day we sensed that there was more cohesion and determination to our actions. Each small area of ground assumed an importance which sweeps of country twice their size had never acquired during a fully mobile operation.

At the western end of the Ruweisat Ridge there was a small valley over which so many battles had been fought, and for possession of which each side strove so desperately that its floor was littered with the bodies of the dead, neither side prepared to grant the truce to enable them to be buried.

Whatever we did, wherever we went during these first two

weeks of July, we were followed by the sickly sweet, pungent, musty odour of decomposing bodies, and hounded by the flies, which grew in size each day, gorged by their beastly feasting on the dead, coming to renew their appetites or satisfy the curious cravings of their palates by nibbling at our fresher diet. So gross were they that they refused to be disturbed from where they had settled, and we had to cover carefully each morsel as we moved it to our mouths, or we took a bite of flies as well.

One day we carried out a raid into the enemy positions, the success of which lifted our spirits as nothing had done to date. We moved suddenly west along the ridge when the German armour was employed elsewhere, encircled most of the Italian Brescia and Pavia divisions, killing and wounding many at the same time, and eventually withdrew with a heartening tally of prisoners.

But what revived us more than anything else was our move south, away from the stench and flies of 'Stink Valley', to the broader, cleaner areas nearer the Qattara Depression.

During the last half of July both sides gradually extended their positions to the south until the respective lines ran from the sea-coast to the cliffs hemming the Depression, leaving only a narrow gap on the southern flank round which any encircling move could be made – a gap too narrow and too closely patrolled to allow any wide outflanking move which could be delivered with surprise.

Two further attacks were launched against the centre of the enemy front by our infantry, supported by Valentines. But they failed to break through the daily harder crust of the enemy positions. We had missed our chance to repulse the enemy, but he had equally failed to clear the path to Alexandria.

In the relative peace and quiet after the storm of battle we settled down to renew the tattered fabric of the regiment. The men of the other units left us to return to their own, we assumed our proper identity again and gradually built up our strength in trained men and tanks.

8

Alam Halfa – the Tide Stemmed

EARLY in August the front was visited by the Prime Minister. Though he did not come anywhere near our part of the front, we heard tales of his progress from others nearer the coast and wondered what was afoot. Baffled by the monotonous sequence of our disasters, our pride bruised, our confidence battered, we were all sensitive about our defeats and a little hurt by a feeling that perhaps our worth was in dispute and that we were being inspected to determine our efficiency. We wondered whether those at home fully understood why we had twice had to come back from Agheila; what effort and sacrifice had gone into the winning of the battles of the winter of 1941; our bitterness that somehow the fog and bewilderment of war had prevented us giving of the best of which we knew we were capable in the battles only recently over.

In the middle of the month the commander of the Army was changed and soon afterwards Kinnaird went off to attend a conference called for all commanding officers. I would never have believed that so great a change was possible in so short a time when I saw him on his return. He was alert as I had not seen him for weeks, if not months. He was cheerful and full of confidence.

'Now at last we know where we stand,' he said. 'The Army commander has said – and these are his words – "there will be no withdrawals, absolutely none – none whatever – none". We stand here and fight. The enemy are apparently preparing to attack again, but there seems to be no doubt that he will come round the south flank. As the Army Commander said, "Rommel is a very able commander, but he has his weaknesses. He has a tendency to repeat his tactics. He has rather a one-track mind." '

With a will we set to to prepare the positions on which we were to give battle. South of the Ruweisat Ridge and a few miles east of it there was the ridge of Alam el Halfa. If the Germans came round the southern flank they would first have to seize this ridge before they could go any farther east.

'It's like the Gazala battles over again,' Kinnaird said, 'except that this time we shall be sitting in the path of the Panzer Divisions not by ourselves but with the whole Brigade around us, and just to our east another armoured brigade, and behind them a complete infantry division.'

There was no chance of a recurrence of the disaster of our isolated battle of the morning of 27 May. In carefully prepared, in some cases elaborately dug positions, we disposed ourselves on the western end of the Alam el Halfa Ridge with the other regiments of the Brigade on each side of us, so close that we could give them the support of our fire and *vice versa*. Behind us, when I went back to Alexandria one day for a change of clothing and a bath, I found the massed batteries of our guns. In Alexandria I heard from those who had recently come up along the desert road from Cairo that it was flanked by new aerodromes on which the bombers and fighters were never still.

New divisions had arrived from England too. The 44th Division was occupying the Ridge to our east. We ourselves came under the command of a new division, the 10th Armoured. We heard, too, that the 51st Highland Division had arrived in the Delta.

All these preparations, the news that even better tanks – the Shermans which we were soon to see – were on the way, the rest and the brief chance to return to Cairo and Alexandria, now normal again after the scares of a month earlier when the entire population seemed anxious to evacuate in the face of the enemy advance – all these restored our spirits and confidence. But none of them so much as the knowledge that we were now controlled by a strong hand and that there was no vacillation or indefiniteness in our plans.

During the evening of 30 August the Air Force first detected signs of the southwards move of the enemy mobile forces. We went to bed that night with none of the qualms we had felt before the start of the enemy's previous offensive, and I was woken from a heavy sleep by Foden, one of my new troop commanders, saying:

'Come and look at this, sir; I thought you wouldn't want to miss it.'

Almost I was rude to him for having destroyed my slumbers, but when I had put on my greatcoat and had climbed out of my bivouac and stood looking to the west where he pointed, I was glad that he had done so. Twenty miles away, where we knew our minefields ran, the sky was brilliantly lit by parachute flares, and even at that distance we could occasionally make out the dull glow of the bursts of the bombs. Reassured and deeply satisfied that the enemy was getting all he deserved, I went back to bed and slept soundly till dawn.

My confidence was a little shaken when, soon after first light, we were shrouded in the folds of yet another sandstorm. Hidden by the screens of sand, the enemy moves during the morning were not seen from the air and we had little idea of their exact positions until about midday, when the patrols of the light squadron some way to our south reported:

' ... Can just make out the enemy about figures two zero zero zero yards to our front. They seem to be having some difficulty getting through the sand of the Ragil depression, but once through are coming on quite fast. We are withdrawing but keeping contact with them.'

Later they reported, ' ... The enemy has now halted and is refuelling.'

Late in the afternoon from our dug-in positions on the ridge we started to catch occasional glimpses, through the swirling eddies of sand, of our own light tanks and beyond them the menacing, squat shapes of the German armour.

By nightfall they had driven in our light screen and we could see them at long range in the gradually improving visibility as the sandstorm died down. All night the Air Force bombed and machine-gunned the enemy leaguers, giving them no rest or respite to refuel. The noise of the aircraft circling their targets and the incessant din of the bombing disturbed our sleep too, but we were well content.

At dawn we could see the mass of the German divisions lying dispersed and stationary to our south, pounded at regular intervals by waves of closely-packed formations of bombers, and by our own longer-range artillery. We were all alert to repulse any move by the enemy, but even though there was no sign that this was threatened we sat in our turrets, our eyes glued to the spectacle of the punishment the enemy were receiving.

So intent was I on the scene that I failed to notice Kinnaird climb up on to my tank and only became aware of his presence when he tapped me on the shoulder. I turned to see him standing

293

on the engine-covers behind the turret, grinning broadly and pointing to yet another wave of bombers just passing overhead.

'This is the stuff the doctor ordered, isn't it, Tony?' he said. 'If we'd only done this two months ago when we had them bottled up in the Cauldron, we might still be at Gazala.' He looked pensive for a moment and then added, 'I don't mean only this air effort. Look how closely we are working together with the other armoured brigade too. And at last we seem to be one jump ahead of the enemy each time – another brigade has now been moved up behind us to our right because it's expected that the enemy will attack there next. I can't keep my eyes off them now that they are getting all they damned well deserve. Perhaps this will change their minds that war is a game. Well, I must be off. I can't keep still, I'm enjoying this so much.'

Soon after he left, the Germans attacked us again, with little enthusiasm and so little determination that they withdrew when we had knocked out about ten of their tanks, though they had also had some few successes against us. One tank of my squadron was holed and the tank commander killed. Away to my left I could see three more of our tanks on fire.

Behind the leading waves of enemy tanks their reserves, their transport, their guns were being pounded again by the bombers. The wind of the previous day had died down to a light westerly breeze which carried the smoke and dust of the explosions of bombs and shells in a high wall across the desert to the east. The black clouds of a satisfying number of fuel and ammunition fires were blown away too, at times shrouding the glaring light of the sun.

In the afternoon the German tanks attacked once more. Again they were driven back, their withdrawal harried by swarms of fighter bombers.

All through that night and the following day, in perfect weather and clear skies, the enemy columns were bombed, machine-gunned and shelled. From our positions we could see innumerable fires and wondered what other vehicles had been destroyed without being set alight. That day the enemy did not attack at all and we relaxed the tension of our vigilance, certain that he had been defeated soundly and excited by the evidence of the strength of our new-found cohesion.

After yet another night of ceaseless bombing the enemy was seen to be withdrawing during the afternoon of 3 September. Though we had not believed it possible, the intensity of the bombing was increased even further. Threatened no longer by the enemy tanks, we climbed out on to the hulls and turrets of our tanks and from there watched, as if we were at a race meeting, the processions of bombers flying out and returning.

By now we were sobered and thoughtful at the clear evidence of our superiority. We were, too, a little sorry for the crews of the German tanks which had suffered so long such a merciless pounding. There was a surprising degree of fellow-feeling in our attitude to their sufferings. With one or two small exceptions the Germans had fought cleanly and fairly. We respected, sometimes even admired, the excellence of the tactics of individual tanks and anti-tank guns. We knew that they were hard and determined fighters who expected no quarter and gave none in return. But in the course of the battles we had come to know their habits, their identities and the details of their equipment. The desert would not have been the same without them. Not that we liked them nor felt any remorse that they were receiving all they deserved. Our feelings were much the same as those of the hunter of big game – we could respect and admire the finer qualities of our enemy, but we knew that if we did not get him first he would get us.

We were now in no doubt that when the time came we could beat the enemy. For a few days we were disappointed that we had not been allowed to follow up the withdrawing enemy columns, but we soon heard of further preparations, not yet complete, for another offensive, and consoled ourselves that this, when it came, might at long last, if it were planned with enough care, drive the enemy once and for all beyond the fateful bottleneck of Agheila. We dared to look beyond again to Tripoli; so long the goal of all our hopes and ambitions.

Meanwhile leave, food and rest were uppermost in our minds.

PART SIX

1943: A DAY'S MARCH
NEARER HOME

―――――

1

Posted to Brigade Headquarters

THROUGHOUT September and October the massive preparations
continued. Everywhere we went in the desert and in the areas just
behind the front we saw the evidence of the forces being trained
and positioned for the attack. The memory of our failures and
disasters began to fade before the bright prospect of the victories
which we felt lay ahead. We shed our battle-weariness and
instead grew daily more eager and determined to be in whatever
battle might occur so that we should not miss the triumphs nor
fail to taste the revenge we so earnestly wished for.

In September I had a week's leave in Cairo. Even after so many
months away, the peace and relaxation of leave could not entirely
banish the tense awareness of impending events, and it was almost
with relief that I returned to the regiment, prepared to give all my
attention to the matters in hand.

A day or so later Kinnaird sent for me and said, 'I don't know
what you will think of this, Tony. You have been posted to
Brigade Headquarters to take over as Brigade Major. You are to
leave at once – to-day, I mean – so you had better go and pack
your kit and I'll tell them you'll be over this afternoon.'

I was too astounded to say much, and left to do as Kinnaird
had said without fully realizing all that this would mean to me.
Only as I collected my belongings and said farewell to the officers
and men of my squadron did I begin to comprehend that I was
going to a life which would be as new to me as the one to which
I had been introduced three years before almost to the day when
I had first joined a regiment in the desert. I suddenly felt as lost
and bewildered as I had ever felt before in my life – when I had

first gone to school, or to Sandhurst, or when I had first joined my regiment in England. All the well-known landmarks would be gone, the responsibility would be greater, the work new and baffling, the other officers and men strangers – the Brigadier a vague figure whom I had seldom seen except on his visits to the regiment.

My last farewell was to Kinnaird. I found him sitting in the back of his staff car writing letters. 'Come in, Tony,' he said, looking up and clearing away a few papers from the seat beside him. 'Don't look so depressed. You'll find you'll settle down pretty quickly, and I think you'll like all the people there.'

'I hope so,' I answered, rather doubtfully; 'but what do I do? I haven't a clue what my job will be and I have no training in what the staff does.'

'Don't you let that worry you,' he answered reassuringly. 'Just remember that there are three things which are most important. First, you must serve the Brigadier – help him in every way you can think of. He's a very busy man and will rely on you to have facts and figures and details available about anything and everything to do with the Brigade. Second, you must make sure that his wishes, his orders or his instructions are passed on to all the people who need to know: the other members of the staff; other staffs, at Division and flanking or nearby brigades; the units under command. And third and equally important – and remember this or I'll be on your tail – you must serve the units under command: give them all the help you can, pass on their requests, frame your orders with their difficulties in mind, fight for their rights if they are ever in question. I won't go on and on any more. Remember those things and I don't think you'll go far wrong. Come and see me if you want any help, and anyway come and see us whenever you want to.'

Cheered and enlightened by his remarks I drove away to my new job with my anxieties partly allayed. It was, at first, a bewildering life. Compared to life in a regiment in battle perhaps the most noticeable difference was that I had to think so much farther ahead – either that or rely on my native wit and what experience I had gained to enable me to think and talk myself quickly out of any new problem. Occasionally that was the inevitable and only way in which to deal with things but whenever possible, and more and more as I got to know the job, I tried my hardest to foresee the difficulties which might arise well in advance so that I had my solution at least partly worked out in readiness.

During the early part of October we were all busy putting the finishing touches to the plans for the great battle to come. We were still on the southern flank of the Alamein positions, where we were to take a not very conspicuous part in the impending operations. In essence we were to be ready to advance west, where lanes had been cleared through the enemy minefields, to engage the 21st Panzer Division, which had been located opposite us, and so prevent it from moving north to join in the battles there.

Early in the second week of October the Brigadier was wounded during one of his frequent journeys to the front. Colonel Hodderson, the Brigade second-in-command, had only recently joined the Brigade, and was as yet too new to the desert and the details of the impending attack for it to be more than a remote possibility that he would get command. Nevertheless he was a valuable and inspiring companion. A big man, tall and broad but thin waisted and with the long, flexible legs of the born horseman; about forty-four or five, reddish-brown hair with no touch of grey, piercing blue eyes below shaggy eyebrows and a firm, straight mouth. He was a gay and resolute person to have about; whatever he was lacking in knowledge of the desert or the operations, there was a wealth of experience behind him of almost everything else.

At about midday of the following day, when we were sitting in the command vehicle, Hodderson said, 'Come on, Tony, we'd better get down to all this work, as the new Brigadier, whoever he is, doesn't seem anxious to arrive.' There was a bustle outside, and Kinnaird poked his head inside the door.

'Any room for another one in here?' he asked.

'Yes, come on in, Peter,' Hodderson answered. 'We are trying to get on with the work until the new Brigadier arrives. Perhaps you can give us a hand?'

'I hope so,' Kinnaird answered, 'as I am the new Brigadier.'

For a moment I did not fully realize the import of his words, and it was Hodderson who exploded in loud and genuine delight.

'My God! Peter, that's good news. Welcome to the Headquarters – we'll leave this work and go and celebrate. Tony – you come, too, as I know how pleased you must be.'

Apart from the Brigadier, Hodderson and myself, there were a number of other officers on the headquarters staff. Between us we tried to meet all the demands of serving the Brigadier, imparting his orders and helping the units under command. During the times when we were static our lives centred on ACV 1, while the administrative staff worked in ACV 2. Round these two square, large, armoured, box-like vehicles the work of the headquarters revolved.

Inside ACV 1, surrounded by maps and lists of codes and code-names, we worked at a small table, our movements cramped by the limited confines, our days marked by the incessant hum and crackle of the wireless sets, one linking us to the units, the other to Division, or the demanding ringing of the telephone bell.

In battle the Brigadier commanded from a tank, in which I travelled also, responsible for keeping in touch with Division and telling them of the minute-to-minute progress of the battle. A mile or so behind us followed ACV 1, those in it recording the details of the battle and ready to take over when, at the end of the day, we moved into leaguer and had to use somewhere more convenient than the cramped interior of the tank to cope with the many complications of an armoured brigade in action.

Though our lives were less fraught with danger than those of the men in the tanks and infantry sections, the hours we worked each day were as long as those to which I had been accustomed, but for much longer periods at a time. This was inevitable. The reports of results, of prisoners captured, of enemy tanks destroyed, the information about our own tanks lost, of men killed and wounded, which the units prepared as soon as they got into leaguer, reached us some two hours later. These we had to check, sort and collate and pass on to Division.

Only when this work was done and the orders for the morrow issued could we at last hand over watch on the wireless sets to the duty officer – usually one of the liaison officers attached to the staff – until dawn again signalled the start of another day of battle and we stood to meet any emergency, and then sleepily washed and breakfasted in the dim light of the early day.

In the centre of the web of the pattern of the battle positions of the Brigade I was always conscious of what was happening on the extremities. As I dragged myself from my bed, I could imagine over a hundred tank crews crawling from their bivouacs; as I ate my breakfast, I could see in the mirror of memories the crews with whom I had brewed tea and cooked unsavoury meals day after day in the years that had passed; as I climbed into the Brigadier's tank, I could imagine the actions and reactions of the crews of the tanks on the outer fringes of our formation as they prepared to meet the enemy and give battle, as we had done so often in the past. In the wide expanses of the desert it was difficult, if not impossible, for the commanders and staffs of the Headquarters to lose touch with the men in the firing line, to forget their trials and tribulations. Sometimes, on the march, we could see the outlines of the farthest tank in front of us as it nosed its way carefully to the crest of a ridge, searching for the enemy. Often on these occasions I caught Kinnaird's eye and we exchanged an unspoken comment on the memories that this simple scene stirred of actions in which we had taken part.

2

El Alamein and Beyond

At 2140 hours in the evening of 23 October, the great artillery fire plan which preceded the battle of El Alamein started. Over a thousand guns opened fire, so that even the bright moonlight was dimmed by the flashes of the explosions. Spread over so wide a frontage, it was not the noise of the gun-fire that was so impressive as the constant illumination of the flashes. We stood in a silent, awe-struck group at Brigade before we climbed into our tanks to take our part in the night's operations.

We moved west behind the rumbling, dusty columns of our own regiments, towards where we could see the gun-fire landing on the enemy positions. Ahead of us the infantry had already passed through the first minefield and were fighting to establish themselves in the western field.

We moved behind the leading regiment into the narrow lanes swept by the engineers, the limits marked by wavering lines of white tape and the flickering lights of coloured lamps. The battle was still raging furiously about a mile to our front, the progress slowed by scattered mines which took their toll of the tanks and vehicles which, having passed through the swept lanes in the known minefields, tried to fan out to right and left in support of the infantry.

Beside the heavy fire of our own guns the night sky was lit by the tracer of enemy machine-guns and the occasional brighter streak of the shot of an as-yet-undiscovered anti-tank gun. When well into the lanes our progress came to a definite halt, and we were left stranded, unable to move sideways, forwards or backwards and surrounded by the burning hulks of tanks and vehicles which had either been blown up on the mines or destroyed by the enemy guns. Their flickering fires lit the scene with an eerie glow, showing up every detail of the long lines of motionless vehicles and lighting us, we felt, as sitting targets for the surviving enemy guns.

At dawn our position was made worse by the fire of guns on crests farther west, to whom we had been invisible at night. All day we stayed in full view of the enemy while the infantry and engineers tried their utmost to clear a path for us. They were, however, unable to find and sweep the innumerable scattered mines which, just as we seemed each time to be able to press forward again, took further toll of our strength and brought us again to a halt.

On the 25th, our threatened advance having held 21st Panzer in the south for a vital period, we were withdrawn, and two days later moved north behind the rear areas of the desperate infantry battles, to a position where we could be ready to exploit instantly any gap that was made in the enemy lines.

Here for six days we watched and waited for our chance, while the slow and bloody fighting to penetrate the intricacies of the heavily defended enemy positions slowly pushed farther and farther west. Gradually we began to sense that the ever-swaying fortunes of the battle were swinging in our favour. Areas over which we had fought in the early days of our arrival in the Alamein defences, and which had since been held by the enemy, were captured again.

At the end of the month we knew that we were in sight of the break-out which we were so anxiously awaiting. This was a new role. In our earlier battles it was we, in the Armoured Division, who had made the first moves to advance into enemy-held territory, to pass behind the flanks of his positions, to threaten his rear areas. Now, when the ends of the line rested on the sea in the north and the impassable country just north of the Qattara Depression in the south, there were no flanks, and we had to wait for the hole to be blown in the enemy line by the dogged, slogging, bitter battles of the infantry, behind whom the patient, methodical engineers cleared the vital passages through the minefields, which were to be our exits to the wide spaces of the open desert beyond, where we could once again assume our usual role of chasing and harrying the enemy.

To the battles which were to blow the final gaps was given the code name 'Supercharge'. This had the correct ring of vigour and determination which we all felt at this stage. Though the fighting had been extremely heavy and the casualties in the infantry divisions severe, there was an air of determined confidence throughout the battlefield area. As spectators in the first and most bloody period of the battle, we were determined to justify the high endeavour of the infantry by grasping any fleeting chance that might occur for us to fight our way through to the open door beyond the rearmost enemy lines.

In the early hours of 2 November, Supercharge began. Behind a creeping barrage of artillery fire a successful advance was made to the west. During that day and 3 November the Germans threw in the full weight of their armour, but by the next morning the way was clear and we moved out south-west in pursuit of an enemy who, where he could, was in full retreat.

As the sun rose, it was marvellous to see again the Brigade spread out in open battle formation, with the plumes of sand billowing in the wake of each tank and vehicle as we moved in a wide arc to cut off and encircle the enemy columns on the coast.

In the afternoon of 6 November, when we were closing on the enemy columns in the area of Mersa Matruh, we were delayed by such rain that the desert was turned into a bog and all movement was brought to a standstill, except on the metalled surface of the coast road, where the enemy continued to make good his escape.

Despite our acute disappointment we were encouraged by the evidence of the enemy defeat. Everywhere we went we could see the losses of a disintegrating army – tanks, lorries and guns in their hundreds; aircraft; stores and equipment; prisoners and dead.

When the rain ceased and the water drained away, leaving the desert hard again for the progress of our tracks and wheels, we took up the unrelenting, triumphant chase which was to finish six months later, after only brief periods of rest and pause, in the final destruction of the enemy on the shores of the bay of Tunis, some 2,000 miles away.

By 11 November we had covered nearly 250 miles, crossing the frontier, as we had done so often before, near Maddalena, and were on the outskirts of Bardia. By the 13th we had gone another 100 miles and were again near Acroma. Turning south round the flank of the minefields at Bir Hakeim, we were at Msus – 550 miles from the break-out at Alamein – on the 17th. A week later we were 100 miles still farther on – between Agedabia and Agheila.

Here at last we paused and I took stock of all that had happened to us in the hectic fortnight since the chase had started. The intensity of the operations, the rapidity of the moves, the daily, almost hourly, changing needs of the Brigade, had given me an insight into the nature of my duties which no course of instruction, however long and detailed, could have achieved in the time.

In the few weeks since he had assumed command, Kinnaird had acquired, with an ease and assurance which surprised even me who had known him so long, an adeptness in the exercise of his command which ensured the success and efficiency of all our operations. No longer had he to think of only three squadrons of tanks, a battery of guns and a company of infantry. His command now extended over three regiments of tanks, and usually a squadron of armoured cars; a complete regiment of guns and a battalion of infantry, and, behind them, the field hospital, the supply echelons, the workshops.

His own particular contribution to the success of our battles was his insistence that his force fought as a single, cohesive entity. He transferred the tactics of the close control of his three squadrons, which he had learnt from bitter experience, to the actions of the Brigade. Each regiment fought as part of a closely knit pattern of forces.

Our battles, after Alamein, were small in comparison to those of the previous two years. The German tank force was so depleted that never again did we engage in the furious onslaught

303

of opposing masses of tanks which had occurred so frequently in all our previous battles. Too often now the enemy rearguards, anxious to live to fight another day, escaped farther and farther west before we could come fully to grips with them. Our leading squadrons still had their brushes with enemy anti-tank guns and small forces of tanks, but these had gone before a way could be found round their single flank, since the other rested on the sea, by a force large enough to deal the mortal blow.

For over a fortnight we paused before the German positions at Agheila, from which, twice previously, they had emerged to drive us east again, back across the miles we had won with such loss of life and equipment.

There was little chance for conversation in the days of the advance, which started before dawn and kept us fully occupied until two or more hours after the sun had set. It was with relief that we halted now, though we were harassed by the German Air Force and hag-ridden by the memory of the threat that these same white, innocent-looking dunes had held on two earlier occasions.

But gradually our confidence became stronger and Kinnaird pointed out the major difference. 'It'll be all right this time, Tony. For once, now that we have got here, instead of being weakened by the demands of other theatres, we are becoming daily stronger and stronger – and the enemy is now finding other things to occupy his attention.'

We were heartened and encouraged by the fact that other forces were at last in Africa too – had landed, in fact, at the end of the first week of November, when we were once again in sight of the Egyptian frontier, and were now hammering at the gates of Tunis. Perhaps, despite the knowledge that this added strength would inevitably be decisive, we were just a little anxious lest they should wrest from us the spoils of all the battles we had fought, would seize Tunis and enter Tripoli before us – Tripoli, the capture of which had for so long seemed to us the ultimate goal which we would be asked to reach, after which, as in some vague, too-pleasant dream, there would be endless vistas of peace.

To our relief, both because Agheila had so many bitter memories and because we were anxious to be on our way again towards Tripoli, we moved forward on 14 December. The enemy rearguards moved west again, though we managed to catch a few, and while the armoured cars continued the chase, we halted near Merduma to wait for supplies to catch up. Christmas, the first in three years which we had been able to celebrate with some of the traditional fare and out of the range of the sound of guns, we spent in a pleasant valley by the sea and heard that Sirte, 130 miles farther west, had fallen to the armoured cars.

We were all in high spirits for the occasion. The DAQMG was the leader of revels, a part he assumed naturally but also because he had been instrumental in the delivery and share-out of the food and drink, without which we would have been lost.

Late in the evening Kinnaird and I walked slowly along the moonlit beach, with the white phosphorescence of the waves lapping a few feet from us. We walked in silence until Kinnaird said, 'Why do men fight wars? When can we hope for an age of peace? Somehow when we were fighting for our very lives there seemed some object in the war. Now that the tide has turned, each day of war, each mile we move depresses me somehow.'

I didn't answer, but I knew what he meant. Some of the tension had gone out of our lives and we were left with the drudgery of war.

3

Tripoli at Last

JANUARY and a new year, and we could see before us the near image of the capture of Tripoli. Storms had lashed the harbour at Benghazi so that our supplies were delayed by the damage to the port, and without fuel, food and ammunition we could go no farther. The armoured cars had pressed on another fifty miles and were in contact with a new enemy position at Buerat.

At length, on 15 January, we moved forward with the New Zealand Division on our left and the 51st Highland Division on the coast. Before the Wadi Zem Zem we were engaged by 15th Panzer Division again, but after a short battle they withdrew. 'I suppose we would do the same,' Kinnaird remarked, 'but these interruptions seem futile and pointless.'

It was not what he meant exactly. Before Alamein we had become accustomed to the daily toll in casualties that each battle exacted. Now, after so few battles, we all resented the loss of life that resistance by the enemy implied. Where before we had been actuated by a determination not to be defeated, now we often felt a cold fury at the continual loss of life, which made our reaction to enemy resistance, already more efficient after so much practice, more relentless and unfeelingly severe.

Early on the morning of 23rd we entered Tripoli, and by dark were already many miles to the west. Some days later the Prime Minister visited the city and said in a few words all that we felt ourselves and all that we hoped others felt about us.

'You are entitled to dwell on these things with the satisfaction which men, in all modesty, feel when a great work has been finally done.

'You have rendered a high service to your country and the common cause.

'In the words of the old hymn, you have "nightly pitched your moving tents a day's march nearer home".

'The achievements of the Eighth Army will gleam and glow in the annals of history.'

We had come 1,200 miles in three months to the day – we had captured the last great city of the Italian African empire. Behind us we had left, strewn over the wastes of a thousand miles of desert, the graves of our friends and companions. Near Tripoli we came to more cultivated lands, where green groves of trees here and there dotted the arid sameness of the desert. We had known only a few themes to our lives – sand and the burning sun, alternate defeat and victory, death and wounds. After so long the new themes were a surprise and shock – victory without much fear of defeat, green trees and cities. We had come a long, long way.

4

Mareth and into Tunisia

FEBRUARY – we closed up to the Mareth line, the last enemy barrier between us and the Allied armies to the north. On a cold, misty morning we moved north round Medenine and isolated the twin features of the Tadjera hills, the outposts to Mareth. Here on 6 March, Rommel, whose gambles had so frequently before been successful, tried one last throw against us. But now we were too expert, too closely co-ordinated to be disturbed by the wild flurry of his blows. After a day of dramatic incidents, seen as if on the screen of a cinema where every move the enemy made was noted, reported by the observers on the hills and marked up on the maps of our command vehicles below, he withdrew, leaving fifty tanks behind him.

It was a most unusual battle for us. All day Kinnaird and I sat in the ACV as the reports came in from all parts of the front. I listened and marked the enemy moves on the map, and Kinnaird sat for most of the time silent, with his chin cupped in his hands. I did not know what thoughts were passing through his mind. For myself, when I had a moment to spare I could not help comparing this day with many in the past. After two and a half years of deadly struggle against an enemy who always seemed to have the power to come back, it was a new feeling to be utterly confident of the outcome of so vicious a battle. In character it was almost exactly the same as our successful defensive battle at Alam Halfa, against Rommel's final attack at Alamein. We waited, making no move, for the enemy to attack our fixed defences. But, whereas the previous year, after so long a series of faults and disasters in the weary withdrawal to Alamein, we had not dared to hope that the tide had really turned and that we could in fact defeat the German tanks, now we were completely confident.

As the day passed we began to be sure, with an absolute certainty, that never again would we feel the sting of disaster, never again would the enemy be able to turn defeat to triumph. On that day we really began to know that the Germans had begun to crack. Throughout their long, skilfully conducted withdrawal it had not been very obvious, but now it showed in a number of things – some small, some big. It showed in the sterility of the German tactics – the same methods which, though they had succeeded often enough when we were out-gunned, out-armoured and unco-ordinated, had proved ineffective at Alam Halfa. It showed in the hesitation of the advance of their tanks, now cautious and indecisive, a pale shadow of what they had been in the past. It showed in the failure of the German artillery and infantry to take any part in the battle. And finally it showed most clearly and convincingly in their failure to withdraw or destroy some of their tanks which were only slightly damaged, but which they allowed to fall into our hands.

Kinnaird broke his silence towards evening when the battle was clearly won. 'That's that, Tony. However long the war goes on for now, I don't believe we'll ever again have the trouble we first had with their Panzers. Come on, let's go and drink to the swiftest, shortest, surest victory I've ever seen.'

There was now a lull until the end of the month while the preparations continued for the break-out beyond the Mareth line. With our new-found, solid confidence it was a lull that was filled with no worry nor foreboding. The infantry divisions and our own infantry brigade were holding the line, so we were at last absolved from any responsibility and could really rest. The cold, misty days of late winter were giving way to the first warm, bright days of spring – a spring which brought at last more than hopes of ease and victory, brought with it a promise of the end of the war, whenever it might be.

It was a lull that we all needed. For the first time for months, if not years, I saw Kinnaird relaxed. 'This is doing me good, Tony. I'm fed to the teeth with war. Let's forget about it if we can.'

But we could not altogether, nor did Kinnaird really turn his mind to other subjects when he had the opportunity. He was weary of the unending tension, the constant need for alertness, the quick resourcefulness to deal with the ever-changing, constantly varying conditions in which we fought. He wanted quiet to sort out his ideas, to tabulate his experience of the past and relate them to the changed nature of the country and of the enemy.

For the desert, which had been so much a part of the pattern of our lives, had been left behind now to all intents and purposes. We now had to adapt ourselves to the closer, more rugged features of Tunisia, to change our methods to suit a land where we could no longer let each vehicle pick its own route on the broad expanses of sand which offered few obstacles. There were many new complications to be mastered.

But I found that so far from being in any way a handicap, our previous experience of war in open spaces was a distinct advantage. Having seen what the next man or vehicle, the neighbouring unit or formation was doing when we could observe every action, it was not so difficult to imagine what it might be doing when we got into country where we could not see more than a few hundred yards in any direction.

Now that the future was no longer darkened by seemingly endless years of war, I could also look into myself and see what the war had done for me. For three and a half years I had given little thought to the future, thankful only that I had survived each day, regretting momentarily the loss of close friends and companions, but hardened to the acceptance of the tragedy. Through it all I had gained a degree of self-confidence which I could not have acquired in any other way. I had had responsibilities thrust upon me which before the war I would never have dreamt of. I had seen and felt such fear as I never wished to know again, but had learnt, in part at least, how it could strengthen and how weaken one's resolution.

On the night of 20 March the battle of Mareth began. While the 50th Division attacked the northern end of the line, close to the sea, across the Wadi Zigzaou, a strong force moved south on a wide turning movement to bring them in on the enemy's rear in the neighbourhood of Gabes, thirty miles behind the front lines. We were to be spectators only until we could break out through the positions captured by 50th Division.

The frontal attack was unsuccessful, but the flank move, after surmounting appalling physical conditions, succeeded in reaching Gabes, just failing to cut off the enemy defenders of the main Mareth line.

So by the end of March we were faced by the next obstacle to our progress – the Wadi Akarit, which ran from the coast, just north of Gabes, westwards to join with an area of lakes and marshes, some fifteen miles away. North of the Wadi was a line of steep-sided hills which completely dominated all the area to the south.

5

The Chase Again

APRIL – and by the end of the first week we were out beyond the Wadi, making north as fast as we could go through the olive groves – 1,500 miles from Alamein. There had been a dogged, determined fight by the infantry to wrest from the enemy this last line, which they bitterly contested, since its loss meant that they had nowhere else to stop us until the hills about Enfidaville, 200 miles farther north, on the very doorstep of Tunis.

As the country of southern Tunisia was a marked change to that of the desert, so was the country through which we now moved as distinctly different again. Behind us we had left the wild regions of our journey and were, at last, into areas which smacked of civilization. Roads and houses, farms, carefully cultivated fields – all the signs of a civilization in which we had grown up and which we had missed, except in the Nile Delta, for so long.

At Agareb we trapped the tail of one of the Panzer divisions desperately trying to escape across our front to the coastal roads on which they could move north to escape us. Caught on an open stretch of road between the converging fire of two armoured regiments, the casualties they suffered were severe. The next day as we drove past the road, south of which we had leaguered for the night, I was appalled to see once again the extent of the carnage of a battlefield. The same scenes of dismembered bodies, more gruesome now, since they had been denuded during the night by swarms of thieving Arabs, burnt-out trucks and destroyed equipment. Over all, even so early in the day, the pervading bitter-sweet, sickly stench of decomposing flesh.

By the 14th we were face to face with the enemy defences in the hills north of Enfidaville. We had come 1,700 miles from Alamein, but were faced now with an area which was, in the main, quite unsuitable for tanks – it was a formidable barrier to any move farther north. We were entirely overlooked by positions in the hills, so that when we stirred from the shelter of the large cactus plantations in which we hid our tanks and vehicles we were shelled by their long-range guns. We all became more and more convinced that we could make no move farther, that our part in the campaign was at last at an end and that we should have to watch the Allied forces to the north defeat the enemy left in North Africa and capture Tunis.

Reluctantly we accustomed ourselves to this disappointment, content at least that we had behind us the capture of Tripoli and half Tunisia. We knew that the divisions which had landed in North Africa had fought a bitter campaign in the winter mud of the northern hills and were prepared to concede, in our own minds at least, that it might be appropriate if to them should fall the triumph of the capture of Tunis. Appropriate if we were unable to take a part, but we regretted deeply that we could not crown the achievements of our advance over so many miles by the final prize of Tunis and the destruction or capture of all the enemy armies which remained on African soil.

6

Over the Mountains

MAY – and we were half-way over the mountains which separated us from the 1st Army, facing the gates of Tunis. The call had been dramatic in its scope and suddenness. At midday the previous day we were facing still the enemy positions at Enfidaville – resigned to seeing the campaign concluded by others, impotent in face of the natural strength of the physical barrier that held our further advance. By nightfall the tanks were already loaded on to transporters, and as darkness closed in we moved off on a march of 170 miles with the beckoning prospect of being in at the kill. Over wild, unmarked tracks, in places almost disappearing among a mass of tangled rocks and undergrowth, in wireless silence so that our move would not be detected, we drove until we reached the first signs of the new Army which we were to join.

In two days we were together again, in an area 120 miles west of Tunis. Here we were issued with new tanks and new vehicles to fill the gaps in the ranks of the sand-covered, battered columns of our units. We were given, too, a generous share of the delicacies of their canteens – food and drink which we had not tasted for three long years, whisky, English chocolate and beer, English cigarettes. Only when we saw them did we realize how atrocious had been the supplies on which we had existed so long – Egyptian beer, 'V' cigarettes, chocolate tasting of straw.

We began to note and silently judge the Army among whom we had so abruptly arrived. They were smarter than we were, their equipment and uniforms new and glistening with paint and polish. Their methods were different too. They relied to a great extent on written orders, whereas we had become accustomed to settling all but the smallest details by conference and discussion, swiftly convened and quickly over, the decisions just as complete and binding.

Perhaps it was most like the meeting between a mature, seasoned veteran and a young, brilliant, eager amateur. We had learnt too much from bitter experience to put much faith in the books and manuals; our new companions had thought and trained for so long that they were steeped in the exact theory of the conduct of operations. They had fought a hard, bitter war for each yard of their advance and were not so ready as we had to be for moves of more scope and speed.

Gradually we began to know each other and some of the rough edges of our mutual suspicion wore away under the surge of the imminence of our next enormous task. We became less conscious of, and boasted less of the length of our advance; we were less aware of the difference of our garb and the colouring of our equipment, still splashed with the dappled yellow and grey which had served to hide us among the ridges of the desert. We began to feel less guilty of our peculiar manners, our peculiar and barbaric phrases – all the hundred and one differences of manner, language, outlook which had grown from so long an isolation from home and been nurtured by the multiple character of the nations and races which formed our Army.

'They look like novices, but they've done a good job,' was a typical, somewhat patronizing remark. It was difficult for each side not to be patronizing – their 'Of course you won't find it the same in the mountains,' was no less offensive than our, 'After three years we ought to be able to do something.'

Hungry for news of England, of their reactions to our many defeats, which still rankled with a secret guilt in our minds; eager to know from mouths which could not be censored of the views and conditions of our various parts of the homeland; homesick and desperately anxious to get home – we must have appeared to those of the 1st Army a peculiar mixture of aggressive confidence and baffling diffidence.

Disputes and disagreements, slow anger and swift resentment gave place to gratitude and a feeling of mutual esteem, gratitude that one had helped to man the precarious defences of an embattled island, and the other had kept alive the spark of resistance on land against all the efforts of the Twin Tyrannies to seize an outlet to lands and oceans which would give them almost limitless chances of invasion.

7

The Crowning Triumph

THREE o'clock in the morning of 6 May. From our temporary resting places of the night in the rocky canyons of the roads leading through the mountains to the plains of Tunis we heard the first dull rumble of the opening barrage of the guns – a rumble which reverberated and re-echoed against the rocky sides, growing in noise as each new thunder joined the echoes of the last.

By midday we were out again into open country beyond the lines of the stolid infantry of the 4th Indian Division, our companions in the victories at Nibeiwa and the Tummars all those many months earlier on a battlefield nearly 2,000 miles away. It was good to see the grinning faces of the Ghurkas as we passed them in the fields of swaying corn and paused to give them a drink from our water-cans.

That night we leaguered on a hillside from which the outskirts of Tunis were only just out of sight. Around us on three sides the armoured regiments were also at rest, in their individual leaguers, each not more than a mile from us. Behind us the lorry-borne infantry of the Division moved into positions to cover our next day's advance – a sensible precaution, lest we met unexpected defeat and were forced to fall back on to defences already established.

But in our minds there was no doubt that victory was at last in our grasp: a victory so complete that it would rank among the most memorable of all history – the end of a campaign by the total elimination of the enemy.

Kinnaird commanded the Brigade that day, as in all the days of mobile battle, from his tank. That night we had no command vehicle in which to assemble, as it had been left too far behind. We each felt the tension of the moment so much that we were unable to go to bed. The wireless traffic with the regiments had been completed very early – they, too, no doubt were feeling the same sense of the magnitude of impending events and had cut short the nightly chatter about supplies and losses and reinforcements, knowing that another day would bring this part of the war to an end for us and that all their efforts would be wasted.

We stood in a silent group at Kinnaird's tank, sipping the drinks which had miraculously appeared from somewhere. There was Kinnaird and I, the commanders of the regiment of guns and the motor battalion, the squadron commander of the armoured cars. At sunset it had come on to rain in a thin, misty drizzle, so we were huddled into our coats. Our feelings were beyond expression. They were composed partly of a sense of triumph, in part of excitement and exhilaration at the prospect of the imminent success, in part of thankfulness that we had been spared to be present on this day, and in part of sadness at the memory of all those whom we would have wished to be alive to savour with us the deep contentment we felt about a job at last completed. For my part I thought of Egerton, who had been my companion on that first journey to join a desert squadron, and of Chesham, killed on the airfield at Sidi Rezegh; I thought of Peters, who had died attempting to save Drummond, and of Bolton, whose fate remained unknown, and of Seagrim, whose death I had watched. All these men and others were in my thoughts: some had lived long enough for me to call them friends, others had gone to death so soon after joining that they had left no impression on my mind. And somewhere, too, there lurked a feeling of relief that, for a period at least, we should see no more of war – a feeling of utter weariness after a tension so long prolonged; a feeling even of anti-climax after the months and years of longing for just this moment.

At length the others departed to their beds and Kinnaird and I were left alone, leaning against the front sand-shields of his tank as we had leaned so often before, not saying anything, each pre-occupied with our own full thoughts, idly listening to the thin swish of the rain against the trees and grass around us.

We were at last at the end of a period of our lives that would forever be woven into the pattern of our beings. And not only us. There were thousands like us, who would in all the days to come be suddenly reminded at odd moments by some small incident or word of something that we had seen or heard across the thousands of miles of our campaigns, across the months and years of our endurance.

Next morning the clamour and the shouting of the hysterical crowds in Tunis stirred us again to excitement and exhilaration. As we had found nowhere else on the long journey, here at last were all the outward and visible signs of victory—surging crowds, cheers, tears and laughter; old men and women silent in thankfulness; young men and girls, noisy, demonstrative and shouting.

We swung north through the suburbs of the city, as before relentlessly on the heels of the enemy. But it was soon to be over. Reluctant to fall into the hands of those whom they did not know, the 15th Panzer Division turned and gave themselves up to us. We watched the long lines of dejected men, tired and dirty, walk past us down the road to the cages where we were collecting all prisoners.

'Look at them, Tony,' Kinnaird said; 'these are the men who we've fought and hated all this time – they don't look very different from us, do they? And they fought well – too well, damn them! But what a waste! I wonder how many of them we will have killed and captured when this is all over. And what have the survivors to look forward to?'

Even in the flush of a triumph so complete, in a moment of pride that we of the desert, the Desert Rats, had come so far and won so much, our overwhelming feeling was of the futility of it all.

But we would remember these years that the locusts had eaten, despite the sorrow that the exertions and sacrifices were ever made necessary. We would remember them with pride in the victory that now at last was won. We would remember the battle for all its seemingly endless hopes and despairs – for its duration and the relentless fury of our fights – for the friends we had found and the friends we had lost – for the trials, the perils, the terrors, the fears that we endured – for the many evidences of man's unconquerable spirit.

'Well, that's that,' said Kinnaird, 'thank God. I wonder what's next?'

THE END

Some other Penguin war books
are described on the
following pages

ONE OF OUR SUBMARINES

Edward Young

1000

Commander Young joined up as a Sub-Lieutenant in the Royal Naval Volunteer Reserve in April 1940, and four months later entered the submarine service, the first R.N.V.R. officer ever to do so. After three years almost continuous war patrols in all weathers, from Norway to the Mediterranean, and after escaping from a sunken submarine, he became the first 'wavy-striper' to command an operational submarine. This is his story. It was placed by the *Sunday Times* 'in the very highest rank of books about the war'.

The main part of the narrative describes the author's time in command; and besides being an account of H.M. Submarine *Storm*'s wartime operations, it is at the same time the story of a very amateur sailor learning an unusual job.

'Here, in unaffected terms, so openly written that at the end of the book it seems that the author has barely passed muster as a submarine captain, is as near the whole truth about conditions in a British submarine as one is likely to get.' – *The Times Literary Supplement*

THE CRUEL SEA

Nicholas Monsarrat

1121

When this book was first published in England in 1951, it was instantly recognized as a great war saga, and as one of the most exciting sea stories ever written. 'Nothing can stop its becoming a front-rank best seller, and it is absolutely right that it should be,' said *John O'London's Weekly*, and this reviewer judged correctly. Its sales were enormous; it was made into a film; and published in a special version for children. This is what some of the other London critics said about it:

'The best novel I have read since the war.' – John Connell in the *Evening News*

'One of the best novels that have yet been written about sailors at war.' – *Spectator*

'Awe, relief, gratitude and admiration are the feelings with which one closes his book.' – *Listener*

' . . . the finest story of the last war.' – *London Star*

'A sea saga like this comes only once in a generation.' – *Daily Dispatch*